On the Meaning of Adam Lambert

By Juneau and Xena

BadBoys Garage

PREFACE

This book is a compilation of web posts written by two women who found each other through Allegra Huston's essay on the wowOwow web site, "What Is It About Adam Lambert?" In that brief column, Huston confessed her infatuation with the 27-year-old, openly gay singer who rocketed to fame as the runner-up in American Idol's eighth season. She writes: ". . . there's something about him that keeps me—and half the women I know—replaying old "American Idol" episodes on DVR and gazing at photographs of his blue-penciled eyes." Huston's essay unloosed a torrent of comments from readers, particularly from women Baby Boomers mesmerized by Adam Lambert's virtuosic, borderline-over-the-top renderings of iconic songs from their youth.

We signed on to the site under the names of "Xena Princess Warrior" and "Juneau Underwood," and soon became the most prolific posters. Over the course of several months and more than eight thousand postings, we became close friends, sharing intimate details about our lives and giving expression to unfiltered feelings. In the sheltering anonymity of the Web, we formed bonds with many other women from all over the world. We cheered one another on as we shook up our lives, took on new challenges, confronted issues in our relationships, shared the excitement and experience of seeing Adam perform in the American Idols tour, and dealt with triumph and loss in our own lives. The women became as addicted to this community as they were to the rising young rock star.

This is a collection of Xena and Juneau's correspondence. We would love to have included the many other contributors to the site, but due to the challenges of keeping the book to a manageable size, and the difficulties of obtaining permission from other writers whose true identities we are not privy to, we decided to restrict this collection primarily to our own writings. We apologize in advance to all whom we had to omit.

Working with the staff of the Bad Boys Garage has been a smooth ride, yet highly revved when we needed it, sliding through the gears of burnished titanium with ease and comfort. Each one of the Bad Boys graciously attended to our needs with patience and exceeded our expectations during each mile we rode together to the finish line. You are holding a piece of art, the top of the line, formed by highly skilled craftsmen. Thanks to their wisdom, creativity, and guidance, our words have roared to life. If we ever find ourselves foolishly believing we have written another book, we hope Bad Boys Garage would join us for another ride through the countryside—destination unknown.

To our Muse, Adam—this book is our homage and expression of gratitude for releasing our hearts and souls to the love, beauty, and joy in our lives and for inspiring our minds to imagine. Merci.

qui audet adipiscitur

To the wonderful women, the Glambertinas, our deepest, heartfelt thanks for your creativity, inspiration, and friendship. Your support, encouragement, and laughter at our jokes and verbal cavorting made the process of writing a sheer joy. You are forever our Muses.

Special thanks to "Cleo" and "Xena II" for their photographic skills, to "Glorious" for her devoted research to produce the Adam Timeline and favorite quotes, and to "E" for giving us permission to quote extensively from her postings.

Above all, we offer our undying gratitude and love to our splendidly patient and tolerant husbands and daughters, for their love and support through this experience, even if they may have been mystified and aghast at times by the depth of our obsessions. We dedicate this book to you.

What makes the engine go?
Desire, desire, desire.
The longing for the dance
stirs in the buried life.
. . . Touch me,
remind me who I am.

(Stanley Kunitz, "Touch Me")

Chapter I Engine of Desire

The first reader comment is posted at 1:46 AM on the day Allegra Huston's essay goes live. The comments start to pour in, one almost every ten to fifteen minutes. Here is a sampling:

"Thank God it's not just me! . . . I'm a 40+ married mother of three and can't get enough . . . my husband claims I'm one Adam Lambert sighting away from a restraining order. . . ."

"I, too, am a member of the Adam-obsessed. When I told my grown daughter that I had found his brother Neil's blog so I could glean insider info, she said, 'Mother, enough!'"

"He's gay? Who frickin cares . . . I like men too!"

"Last night my nine-year-old son grabbed my iPhone from me and yelled to my husband: "Mommy is still watching Adam Lambert. . . ."

"Adam makes me feel young—like I want to reconsider my career choice of attorney and instead be a rock star. . . ."

". . . he's like an aphrodisiac . . . I can't wait to get my hands on my husband (we've been married 22 years). . . . My god! Our sex life has never been better!"

"I need help, but I really don't want to stop."

"His attitude and his graciousness are just sooo appealing and sexy . . . I never do this, but here I am. I am 43, old enough to be his mother."

June 2/09 Article by Allegra Huston is published: What is it About Adam Lambert? http://www.wowowow.com/entertainment/allegra-huston-adam-lambert-american-idol-304646

June 3/09 Sixteen pages of comments following Allegra Huston's article

"We're never too old (I turned 77 on Wednesday) to enjoy a spark!!!!!!!! I'm glad I've lived long enough to see this kind of talent and actions revived."

"How dare you give all us lesbians away? Our Adam Lambert fascination is confidential information. . . ."

"Sexy? Adam Lambert? You bet. Right up there with Keith <smile>."

"There is so much Love, kindness, and creativity in that young man that he could share it for years and never run out."

"Refreshingly, the intensely aphrodisiac nature of Adam's energy not lost on this fifty-five-year-old lesbian mom with three sons his age. Sexuality is, indeed, fluid."

"He communicates so completely it takes my breath away. I think those things transcend sexuality, and draw us to him as a person, not just an object. But, he is really cute."

"OMG—I had thought I was going insane—the constantly thinking of Adam, the stalking on the Web . . . now I find I am amongst kindred spirits. . . ."

"I was just wondering what had happened to all the great men singers and then Adam comes along—thank you Universe!"

"And so many women have suppressed their inner radiance to cope with this world. He is awakening it in us again!"

". . . my Book Club literally LAUGHED at me when I revealed my obsession with Adam—I will never forgive them, with their highbrow snickering!!"

". . . about 18 years after the death of Freddy Mercury, we finally have a brilliantly talented young gay man who is starting his recording career out of the closet."

"I feel completely unsettled by my attraction. It feels so, so right and so, so wrong at the same time."

"Adam Lambert is a bad influence . . . I can see right now that our GNP and productivity rates are going to plummet, 'cause I, along with a large percentage of this group, am spending most of my waking hours scouring the internet for sightings and snippets about OUR IDOL."

"Oh my, I've got Adamitis bad. I am actually crying as I read these posts."

"It's kind of like watching porn. You can't really have what's on the screen, so the one who's right there gets the benefits."

"I plan on tossing my massive panties onto the stage. I just hope Adam doesn't mistake them for a parachute and dive into the audience."

"Yesterday I mailed a small gift to our boy, Adam. It's the first time I have ever sent anything, even a letter to a celebrity but it was such a blast!! . . . I then had a vision of being found dead in the car with the box addressed to Adam in my lap. What would the headlines read? '54 year old Doctor and obsessed Adam Lambert fan dies of excitement writing his name. . . .'"

"I am a 53 year old white male—happily married for over 14 years and up until a week ago I was 100% sure that I was 100% heterosexual. Hell—I am hetero—but what is going on? I've read all of the posts and am suffering from the same addiction. I can't get enough of Adam."

"Don't worry about it! We're all going to hell in a hand basket because of this wonderful piece of alien stardust called Adam!!!"

"My husband is almost as big a fan of Adam's as I am—in awe of his voice, and thinks he's beautiful too. "That doesn't make me gay, does it?" he asks jokingly. "Honey, everybody's gay for Adam," I reply."

By the following day, more than 200 comments had been posted when Juneau fires off her first post:

Interview with Eber Lambert http://www.sandiegoreader.com/news/2009/jun/03/blurt1/

Adam's detractors complain that he is all artifact, but I think those of us who have worked hard for what we've achieved appreciate the unrelenting work and desire that go into his effortless-seeming performances. I applaud him for re-inventing himself, for transforming himself from the sandy-haired, freckle-faced artsy character in high school into a global rock and sex god. You can follow his journey (it's all on YouTube).

I identify with his explorations from high school "music guy" geekdom through the purpler fringes of the gay club scene, the musical theater world and finally to the platform of American Idol, which he has used so courageously and masterfully to launch himself onto the world stage. I don't feel he has become something artificial and un-genuine. I feel he has discovered and unleashed who he really is. And who he is multifaceted, like all of us. He's the sweet boy next door AND he's the rock god. He's a smart, disciplined operator AND an artist who truly pours out his heart for the world to see.

The blog posters are endearingly incoherent, the streams of consciousness of people unhinged by this unanticipated surge of hormonal excitation that is being unloosed by Adam Lambert. I'm feeling the same way, and I want to understand where this is coming from. As I mentioned, I feel a tremendous sense of identification with Adam. Through him, I am reliving my own youth, and at the same time shining a light on my life now, wondering what I may have let go along the way.

I was a geek in high school, back when there was nothing redeeming about it (no vindicating "geeks rule" slogans in the popular culture). I was a restless goddess trapped inside a myopic school valedictorian, violin-playing science nerd. I started to free myself in senior year when I hooked up with a hippie artist boyfriend, and then become completely wild when I headed off to my Ivy League college. I dutifully attended lectures during the day. At night, I went out clubbing with a gorgeous gay man. We became a hot disco dancing couple and started living for the midnight to dawn world of the gay club scene. This was in the late 70s, when gay clubs were exhilaratingly and joyfully transgressive. This was before Saturday Night Live came along and took disco hetero and mainstream, and of course before AIDS. It was edgy, and I felt liberated and completed.

I now look back and realize that this period was brief, but it was a defining moment. Life moved along. I had boyfriends (and now a husband) who were not into the gay club scene, or into any dancing for that matter. I gave up other things I love: outdoor adventure, budget travel in the developing world, sky diving, scuba diving, horseback riding. I dove instead into my career and family life. I have been blessed with a wonderful husband and daughters. Nurturing them and creating a rich home life for them gives me great joy. In my career I have had opportunities to do what I love, and I feel that I am making a difference in the world. I wouldn't change a thing. But maybe I need to shake up my life a bit. That's what I'm wondering. That's why I'm watching Adam. (Plus, he makes me happy!)

An aside: I am of course eager to share Adam with my teenage girls and hold him up as a great role model. Sadly, they don't get him! I showed my eleven-year-old the Born to Be Wild video, thinking it was mainstream enough with an exciting beat that she'd like. Her reaction: "He's scary! He wears makeup!" I argue with her: "He's different. He celebrates who he is!" But no, this argument carries no weight with her. Now I realize she, and the millions who voted for Kris Allen, can't handle Adam. He teeters dangerously close to the edge of everyone's comfort zone. It's just that some of us decide to take the leap and embrace it (and become like the Adamaniacs on this blog!), and some recoil. It's too disturbing (yes, it IS!). Maybe I should have started her with "One" . . . (sigh) a mother's job is never done, never perfected. . . .

By Juneau Underwood on 06/04/2009 11:49 am

Juneau, I love your post, and your story.

I've been pondering the idea of "Change" and think what we are seeing is a real tectonic shift, or maybe a convergence of factors, like I saw in the 60s . . . things happening at the right time and place. We needed George Bush to be exactly who he was to usher in the era that would vote for the first black president—you know, he HAD to be so bad that people would actually vote for the black guy. His theme was change. Now we have this young man (on a much smaller scale, I know, but big things start small) entering the picture at a time . . . and singing the song "A change is going to come," when there is a shift in most American's thinking about Gay marriage. He is the perfect vehicle, talented, yes, but sooo comfortable in his gayness, so accepting of everyone, so sure of himself, so eloquent and non-threatening in his message. None of us doubt that he will be a huge international star, and he will not have to face the issues that Freddie Mercury or Elton John did. A change IS going to come! I'm sure of it.

Don't give up on your daughter . . . but take my advice as the mother of three grown sons, they NEED to find their own heroes, and they need to be someone other than their mothers. It's how they separate. The more you encourage Adam, the more she will run. Keep your fantasies to yourself . . . or continue to share them with us. WE totally get it!!

By E.—on 06/04/2009 12:35 pm

Hi E., I'm glad you enjoyed my post! I hope you are right about a tectonic shift. Certainly there is a reversal in the pendulum swing, and for now, we are riding the momentum. It would be wonderful if the great masses of Americans out there really are changing their views on gays. It seems grossly unfair to put this unasked-for role on Adam's shoulders, to be a figurehead for the gay rights movement. I hope he changes hearts just through his beautiful example. He has a magical ability to make people feel intimate with him. Do you find yourself having imaginary conversations with him?

I have to say I really don't understand the prejudice and violent hatred of gays. I lived in the Bay Area the year Harvey Milk was murdered, and I was horrified by what happened, but it was only when I saw the film "Milk" that I truly understood what he had represented in the movement for civil rights. I was a tourist in the gay world then, not a foot soldier. ***By Juneau Underwood on 06/04/2009 5:54 pm***

Hi S., thanks for the kind compliment! I am a writer but I've kicked myself upstairs into management, so I don't have many opportunities to write lately. I felt inspired to post on wowOwow because I feel so at home with all these smart, funny women who are dropping their panties over Adam. Look! The Adam phenom has inspired me to write again, and in fact to write for the first time about my own experiences and feelings. ***By Juneau Underwood on 06/05/2009 6:00 am***

RE: Adam's fabulousness, he knows how to deliver it, but he also knows it's a performance. Adam won me over even more (as though that were possible) in an interview where he says he knows he's also "a little ridiculous" and that he achieves his look through "smoke and mirrors." He has a great sense of humor. He'll need it when crazed grandmothers start tearing off his clothes. ***By Juneau Underwood on 06/05/2009 1:38 pm***

I think you're going to get a torrent of responses to this one, V. Re: the flick of the tongue in Ring of Fire—it's wonderfully ambiguous to me. Did he mean to do that? The shirt-lift. How about the silver zipper on his jeans, its glimmer taunting the eye from the shadows. I adore the beginning of Cryin' when he sings "I was so broken-hearted" with that half smile and tender sweet eyes. I love his *au naturel* look in One (although I prefer the Studio recording because he has the time to pace the emotional movement with a more natural ebb and flow). Beth was the ultimate for me, with his twinkling eyes (rhinestones!) and eyebrow twitch. Totally beautiful. Totally camp. I think it's the tension between gorgeousness and outrageousness that is causing my insides to churn so delightfully. ***By Juneau Underwood on 06/05/2009 7:51 pm***

You ladies crack me up! Don't short out your laptops with your drooling because I need you to keep posting! Adam's the total package, but let's talk about his voice. I listen to his recordings all day. What do you think it is about his voice that is so compelling? It's in a relatively high register for a man. It's so powerful but exquisitely controlled. It's manly and youthful. Maybe the voice evokes memories of horny teenage boys (or an ideal one, i.e., with the control)? Or maybe it's the androgynous quality of his singing.

My husband observed something interesting about the music our teenage girls listen to these days: the guys are all about sensitive ballads, while the women are doing these angry, aggressive rock tunes. Gender role reversals. But Adam spans the genres. He's all about fusion, about spanning vast reaches of experience. We're living in a time when boundaries are breaking down. He's the singer for our times. (I keep telling my girls, he's the singer of their generation, but they don't believe me. I need to shut up and let them discover him on their own. Of course, the fact that I love Adam may have made them cross him off their list forever . . . that would be a tragedy!) ***By Juneau Underwood on 06/05/2009 8:58 pm***

"I need to shut up and let them discover him on their own. Of course, the fact that I love Adam may have made them cross him off their list forever . . . that would be a tragedy!)"

Juneau, you just need to wait until he does a concert and bribe your daughters to come with you, the rest will take care of itself. Once they see him in person they will be under his spell

I am sitting here with a raging toothache, won't get to the dentist til Monday, the 2 Aleve haven't kicked in yet . . . but guess what works? Ear buds . . . nice and loud . . . with my favorite Adam song:
http://www.youtube.com/watch?v=1VQo6mCkEso

By E.—on 06/06/2009 12:13 am

Adamesthesia! We could have fun seeing how many words we can derive from "Adam." I am plotting to get our girls to a concert, but it's so hard to wait that long.

Sometimes I wonder if the AI producers were genius enough to have orchestrated the whole second-place finish. Think about it. If Adam had won, it would have been anticlimactic. Sure, people would still have been excited about him, but it would not have set off the media firestorm and fan frenzy that ensued after he "lost." It lit a bonfire under all his fans who are now out evangelizing for him. Plus, Kris needed the first place finish, and Adam got to display his graciousness and genuine joy for Kris. It's the most brilliant PR coup ever. However, I digress.

Thank you for introducing me to that Five for Fighting cover. It's lovely. I'll listen to it again (and again).

I'm so sorry to hear about your toothache! Horrible that you have to wait until Monday to have it looked at. Hope the Adamesthesia keeps working. ***By Juneau Underwood on 06/06/2009 7:40 am***

Juneau, you're going to love this . . . so we had the wedding and reception at noon, perfectly nice, on a beautiful day at a local rose garden. Then in the evening we had a party with a group of friends at the home of a gay couple we haven't seen in a while, adore them both. I had a conversation with each of them, starting with "OK, did you watch American Idol ?" . . . and with that P. & I spent 15 minutes discussing the perfection of Adam, that his partner usually never watched it but walked into the room in time to catch "Ring of Fire" and shouted "Who is that ??" and became hooked. Then I talked to S. about Adam and he showed me the hair raised on his arm, saying "OMG, see what he does to me?" I asked him "OK with your gaydar, could you tell he was gay from the beginning?" Answer: absolutely, no question, knew it in a minute. So we spent several minutes in Adamecstasy, he said he had never heard the Brigadoon song, I've promised to send him the link, we agreed we are obsessed, my husband thinks I am certifiable, and S. & P. & I said ain't life grand!!!

Gotta go, I'm sending them links to "Come to me, Bend to me," the new years songs, and the adorable 15 month old girl, Paisley, who kisses Adam on the iPhone . . . great day, and my tooth feels better!

By E.—on 06/07/2009 12:47 am

Beth is on the KISS Medley video, available on iTunes. I'm not a KISS fan, so I amazed myself when I pushed that "buy" button. Adam has opened me up to music that I had not cared for before. That's one of the many gifts he has bestowed on his listeners. Ah, and when he does sing a song that I like, he elevates it to a new level. How cool is that?

I think about where that gift comes from. It's not just his vocal instrument. It's the emotional connection, and there he is tapping into some pretty deep springs. Although we all love and admire how comfortable he is with himself today, I imagine it was a painful journey for him to get there. He grew up in the most conservative part of California, and being gay in high school is no picnic. Even with the support of loving parents, it's not easy to find your way. I'm sure I'm projecting from my own youthful experiences hanging out in gay clubs, but for many of my friends, beneath the flamboyance, fun and FY attitude, there was a lot of loneliness and pain. I hear that pain in Adam's voice. This man stretches my emotions in ways that bemuse and astonish me. I am as giddily happy as a teeny bopper to see him achieve his dream, but at the same time I am overcome with sadness and fear for him, that his celebrity will put the love he is seeking out of his reach. He is now riding a wave over which he has little control. I wish him the very, very best.

By Juneau Underwood on 06/06/2009 8:17 am

OK ladies, time to scrape ourselves off the floor and play a game. Who wants to play "If I could do X for Adam, I would. . ."? I propose starting with something relatively innocuous, like "If I could cook a meal for Adam, I would. . . ." Here goes: I hope his adventurous and sensuous personality extends to gastronomy, so of course a meal has to begin with oysters on the half shell with mignonette, followed by healthy comfort food—a light seafood chowder and really great multigrain bread fresh out of the oven—a salad of frisee, feta and slices of Asian pear (contrasting textures and flavors, bitter, salty and sweet), finished by a velvety dark chocolate fondant. (H e picked up a few pounds over the course of American Idol; he needs some delicious ways to take them off!)

By Juneau Underwood on 06/06/2009 4:37 pm

June 6/09 Adam is surrounded by paparazzi and saved by Quween http://socialitelife.celebuzz.com/archive/2009/06/06/adam_lambert_saved_by_a_quween.php

June 7/09 Adam wins Young Hollywood Artist of the year

Some of the best stories about Adam are on his hometown news outlet, the San Diego News Network. There's a very amusing interview with three opera experts who rate Adam's voice, appearance, style, etc.

There's a wonderful account of his visit to the children's musical theater company where he had his start. This quote made my throat catch: "How many of you feel a little different because you're creative and in the arts? Well, just let it go. Say 'I'm gonna be okay as a creative/artistic person and there's nothing wrong with that.' If you ever feel different, hold your head up high. We're artists. We're all crazy. And that's good-crazy!"
http://www.sdnn.com/sandiego/2009-05-11/things-to-do/adam-lambert-returns-to-musical-theater-roots#ixzzoHkGiqjhf&D

This is personal for me. My husband is a composer, and I am in absolute awe not only of his creative powers, but of his sheer bravery to lay his heart and soul bare on the stage. . . .

With our teenagers, we agonize as parents over how to nurture that creative flame or passion. ***By Juneau Underwood on 06/07/2009 8:16 am***

I admire Adam's candor about Kris. His honesty is so refreshing. Also, did you notice how with that admission, he dispelled the fear that straight men have about their own sexuality if a gay guy is interested in them? Adam had the thought, but he accepted that Kris is straight and married. He's saying hey, we can talk about this and not freak out. Love him!

By Juneau Underwood on 06/09/2009 10:55 pm

I agree the bi-curious thing is a smokescreen, Safari Girl! Those remarks about girls are just crumbs to keep his fans from turning into Furies. Thanks for pointing out the Newsweek article. But I'm not about to defect. I like my girlfriends here!! I don't know if the openness about 'shrooms and sex will provoke as much of a backlash as some of the language that I think he meant as provocative but might strike one as borderline crude and disrespectful (and I'm not talking about the F word, but terminology about women and what he has in common with Clay Aiken). There's a line between being open and honest and being just sophomoric. I hope he doesn't cross it again.

By Juneau Underwood on 06/10/2009 8:39 pm

▪

June 9/09 Signed to 19 Recordings and RCA records

▪

June 10/09 Rolling Stone with Adam Lambert on the covered is released.

Our Magnificent Obsession

We are obsessed with a beautiful, sexy, erotic, witty, sometimes peacock; other times robin, engrossing and unforgettable—nightingale. Over and over, we watch his body move and listen to his voice, so we feel his breath in our ear. We feel him next to us. Hmmm, wonder what he smells like—warm leather? When he catches us staring at him, we hope that he looks back into our eyes, the way he does at the end of Beth.

It's like brushing by the hot, but unattainable boy who is at his locker, in a crowded hallway with his back to us—as our hearts start to flutter, he looks up toward us with his heavenly blue eyes, and with a slight smile—I could faint right there!

Over and over, we listen and we watch so we can conjure up his voice and image in our heads, when we need to hear him soothing us with Beth—arousing us with Ring of Fire. Standing at the mic, using his body, eyes, voice—then with his hands, he entices us to look where he wants us to and knows we will. We memorized the videos so in our minds, we can hit "play" anytime and now he is with us all the time—we have to try to find the "pause" button every so often—when someone intrudes on our intimacy.

Adam and I are in one of those dark corners in a bar, leaning into each other, laughing at his naughty jokes and just holding hands. He sings to me in a whisper, lips to my ear.

He's flirtatious with everyone and it works, he's an extrovert who draws energy and creativity from those crowded places and then showers us with his glitter. His charisma is so powerful, it comes through the TV screen, the computer screen, still photo, film or magazine cover—such incredible power either draws in the confident and self assured among us, or frightens those who are unsure of who they are and feel threatened by his innate magnetism.

Our guy is eager to please and wants to be loved—for *who* he is—not *what* he is. His self defense is to put himself out there for everyone to see—to know as much as they can, so they can't hurt him with secrets and gossip. The only thing that could possibly shock now would be a woman who claims her baby was fathered by him!

So, to everyone out there who cares, he has stripped himself bare for you and revealed much more about himself than anyone else ever has, with candor, honesty, humour and devoid of guile. He is a blessing and a curse, since those very experiences that might make some cringe, have contributed to making him the almost ethereal creature he is now.

Adam is an aphrodisiac who can switch us on, but we can't switch him off. Used responsibly, this aphrodisiac can help us make each of our little worlds, a happier place.

Flirt a little, make eye contact more, speak enthusiastically and listen with curiosity. Put on some eyeliner and mascara when you don't have to and polish your nails! Give out more hugs and you'll get more back.

But most of all—HAVE FUN! Adam does.

By xena princess warrior on 06/11/2009 10:05 pm

Hey Xena, just wanted to express my appreciation for your post. I'm so entertained and gratified to be among so many high-powered, insightful women who are getting back in touch with their inner "14-year-olds" (well, maybe 21-year-olds? Wouldn't want my 14-year-old to be in dark corners of clubs doing 'shrooms and sucking the faces of bi-curious rock stars). The Rolling Stone article gave me pause only because there was a certain amount of posturing, driven I'm sure by insecurity about whether he has authentic rock star creds. A lot of rock stars put out an on-the-edge persona, but the most successful ones I know are at the core totally bourgeois, shrewd business people. They are unfailingly polite and careful about what they say in public.

OK, gotta take off. Have a good one!

By Juneau Underwood on 06/12/2009 8:54 am

yes folks, this is FINAAAAAAALLY ADAM!!! 9:07 PM Jun 11th from web

June 12/09 20/20 interview with Chris Connelly in which Adam states he is gay

Writing about our Magnificent Obsession has been cathartic for me. I really lost the pause button and neglected the reports I get paid to write, but where I can't use the word "aphrodisiac" no matter how hard I might try to, but government reports and data just don't have the same effect as Adam does. Maybe now, I can progress through them more quickly and get them out of the way, so I can do more "Adamdazing."

By xena princess warrior on 06/11/2009 11:37 pm

Just watched a short clip of tonight's 20/20 interview and my reaction is the same as Gloria Beth's—sadness when he talks about wanting to be in love. We have heard this emotion in so many of his songs and in the introduction to a couple of his songs at the Upright Cabaret—longing for something he can't find. I don't know how anyone could sit there and not put their arms around him.

Just love his interviews—he's adorable. Have another fantasy to share with all of you later. It's a beautiful sunny day here and driving around inspired my imagination.

He's going to need a platoon of bodyguards.

X

By xena princess warrior on 06/12/2009 3:45 pm

Thanks to Xena for her soul-baring writings (and for the kind compliments). Safari Girl, Adams Beth, J. and others, love you all! I wanted to clarify what I had written earlier. I don't think Adam is a poseur—god knows he has genuine and deep talent to burn—but under the glare of the spotlights, he's clearly exposing some of his insecurity about his attractiveness, his lovability, and rock star credentials by being brash and a bit out of control. I was so impressed earlier on by his self-possession, cordiality, and ability to rein in the temptation to be snarky (I'm sure he has a wicked and biting wit), so I'm a bit concerned by this latest turn. He should realize he doesn't have to act out in this way. Let the attitude and over-the-top sexuality be expressed on the stage. Off-stage, be professional, kind and humble in public, and keep the rest of your life private (as best one can). Successful rock stars understand that what they do on stage is a performance, an illusion. Sure, they may have colorful private lives, but the smart ones (and these guys are smart) don't get sucked into their own hype, and they learn to not say things that will alienate their fans. Adam's head must be spinning with everything that has happened in such a short time. I hope he has time to step back, take a few deep breaths and figure out the difference between honesty and obnoxiousness. (Sorry to be so direct!)

OK, enough spanking of adorable Adam for this evening. Yesterday I was at a meeting with a bunch of guys, and found myself daydreaming about which of them Adam would find cute. One of them (a slender, Kris Allen type) was wearing a wedding band and I wondered if he was married to a woman or a man (here in Massachusetts, you never know!). Is anyone else finding their mind drifting into strange territory?

By Juneau Underwood on 06/13/2009 12:08

I need to step back from my anxiety (something about the Rolling Stone interview and 20/20 undoubtedly pushed some hot buttons in me). I agree Adam is handling this all remarkably well. Most of us would have had to be carted off by this point. The obsession with his gayness is just getting so tiresome. He's handling it all with grace.

I just stumbled on this interview with Adam after he went to see Hair on Broadway. This is the Adam I love.
http://www.youtube.com/watch?v=YdkoeUG1nBs&feature=related

By Juneau Underwood on 06/13/2009 9:30 am

Juneau, your latest posting clarifies what your concerns are about Adam's candour—perhaps I should say—extreme exposure? I know what you're saying about the old rockers and talked about them with my 18-year-old yesterday, recalling that back in the '60s and '70s the adolescents tried to shield their parents from any personal info about Mick and the boys. They were worried we would be influenced by their lifestyles and as much as they didn't do tell-all interviews, the information was out there.

"Heroin? Naw, that isn't true Dad, people just make that up to make our heroes look bad." Unfortunately, Joplin, Hendrix, Morrison and even Marilyn Monroe proved us liars. Elton John's sexuality was never an issue for anyone and I don't recall any media hounding him for confirmation. David Bowie kept us guessing, Boy George was too obvious for words and George Michael was "found out" when no one really cared.

Now, tables have turned and we are worried about letting our kids know about Adam, trying to present him as we would want our children to reflect us as parents. Too late, and that goes for me and my daughter as well.

It's always we who worry, isn't it? Boomers were raised to be polite, cautious, concerned about appearance, how each public declaration might affect our future and to be duplicitous—we present whichever face is socially appropriate for the occasion. We have each developed many personae to protect others and ourselves from facing what might be difficult questions, within a certain context. My daughter is much less so, and while she will change her outfit to be appropriate, she understands that this is just the outside presentation, not a reflection of who she is.

She is so opposite to me that I spent the last almost four years, trying not to be so paralyzed with fear that she would reveal her personal thoughts on religion to her religion teacher at a Catholic high school. Turns out she will push the envelope to the breaking point, but not let it rip open. Whew! Many hours of therapy helped both of us, but that's another story.

It's our kids who will tell us to chill and not worry, just as we tried to reassure our parents that the Stones were just posturing as bad boys and that Strawberry Fields meant an orchard. If Adam goes to work every day, he will be fine. He seems to be crazy about what he does, so I think he will work hard. Nothing will surprise. The old rockers had a contrived image they were trying to maintain, but some of them couldn't manage and it killed them.

This is a new era of invasive media—gotcha journalism out to catch Britney Speers drinking, smoking and having sex while trying to maintain a clean-cut, virginal image. They want to expose hypocrisy and Adam is anything but a hypocrite. We shall see if this openness works to his benefit or to his detriment.

We women however, are still in the closet, with the door locked. Using pseudonyms and talking within a small group of similar women to protect ourselves from people we believe won't get it. Many times I have been tempted to submit an op-ed to some of the newspaper editors I know, to reveal the Adam phenomenon on this group, but I would have to ask them to allow me to use "Xena." I'm not Allegra, just a suburban wife, mother and business colleague who drives a minivan.

This discussion, which began over ten days ago, has been fascinating and I am sure would surprise anyone who tripped over it. This is unmoderated therapy—a self-help group and exactly what I was hoping to find. In fact, there are probably some women out there reading but not writing—hope we bring you reassurance that you are not alone or crazy and find some connection to us. I hope we amuse you, make you laugh, and shiver with excitement at some of the images of Adam we present—just with our words.

I really enjoyed last night's interview on 20/20, brief as it was and Adam's answers did not seem contrived at all. Flirting, shocking, teasing and smiling are as natural to him as singing and dressing-up. A sardonic smile while talking about a "lucky woman" is meant to tease a little and he'll throw in a hug and kiss too, if you're there.

On the bi-curious and bisexual topics, our children are taught all that and more, by the time they reach high school. Adam is not much older than some of them. I can't wait to see how the future unfolds for him because we have no reference point, no template.

Love, Xena

Make eye contact and don't forget the mascara today! You never know who will look back and smile. ***By xena princess warrior on 06/13/2009 9:27 am***

Closeted indeed! I think we all want and deserve a place to express ourselves in different ways. (I do have other outlets—my girls' nights out, my book club.) I don't think Adam was being contrived on 20/20. If anything, he was a bit too unfiltered. You read his "lucky woman" remark differently than I did. I thought it might come across as arrogant. I don't care about the drugs or sex (although I worry about whether Adam is using alcohol to deal with the stress—where was it that he mentioned putting Kahlua in his breakfast coffee??), and don't feel a need to shield my kids' eyes from it. They aren't Adam fans, so they aren't paying attention anyway. And how could one possibly keep this kind of stuff from them, when their favorite song on the radio is that Amy Winehouse song about being in Rehab? Re: sexuality, I've had that discussion with my older daughter about the fluidity of sexual identities and how accepting I am. "There's not enough love in the world," is what I told her. "So whatever form it takes is a blessing."

BTW, I never had to lie to my parents about the rock bands of the 60s and 70s, because I never talked about them and my parents were just out of the loop on that part of our culture. In my early 30s I went out with Mick Jagger and decided to tell my Mom. She said, "Who's that?" How deflating was that?!

Have a fun day! Funny you mention wearing mascara. Since Adam burst into my life, I have been more diligent about always looking my best. Make eye contact and, as you say, you never know who will look back and smile. ***By Juneau Underwood on 06/13/2009 11:27 am***

Dear Downunder Fan, I've been thinking some more about the Adam phenomenon. I find that I keep peeling it back like the petals on a rose. There are so many layers. And as my singer friend said, isn't this really about you? Peeling those layers back is my psychoanalysis.

Adam is a performer who sings and dances in a way that you not only want to slip inside his body and be like him, but who "fits." His vocal range, his movements are so naturally expressive. I think he appeals especially, but not exclusively, to women because his tone is so smooth and rich, his movements are sinuous and sensual in the way that women like to move.

He's soft and powerful at the same time. And then he soars way beyond the boundaries of the average. He takes you on a ride to places you never thought or dared to go. Then there are his song choices. He has taken iconic songs from our youth, and then amazingly made them even better. (Opinion is divided on this, but I've been struck by how many die-hard fans of the original versions have posted on other sites, like iTunes and YouTube, about discovering that they like Adam's version better.)

So what does this do? It yanks us out of our nostalgia for our youth and says, look, this is happening NOW. It's not all over. Amazing things are still to come!! But you have to go for it. Act now. That's why we're all standing taller, putting a bounce in our step, brushing on the eyeliner and mascara, and posting our hearts out on this blog!!

By Juneau Underwood on 06/14/2009 9:36 am

Ladies, we are becoming a little too analytical and I will admit that I am part of that, but really need to get back to having some fun for all the work we put into being Glambertinas.

So, for a Saturday evening, I will share my latest Adamantasy. I wrote this while there were about eighty kids partying in my house on Saturday night, but I've been imagining this experience for a couple of days.

Something for you to enjoy on a Sunday morning. . . .

Shopping with Adam

I'm shopping in Beverly Hills, on Rodeo Drive, dressed in a black, body-skimming linen sundress, bangles and necklace, large black framed sunglasses, sunhat, strappy black sandals and a fresh pedicure with black onyx polish—a little shine and sparkle to add depth to the colour. But, my lipstick is red—Lancôme's "Stiletto."

Just as I step out of Tiffany's, there's Adam—silk shirt, linen jacket with sleeves pushed up and tight jeans—of course! "*Princess! You look great!*" Adam moistens his lips and kisses me on both cheeks twice (European style)—arms around my waist. His movements are so smooth and graceful; he doesn't even move my hat as he bends down.

"*Do you have some time to come and see a jacket I'm looking at for the concert?*" "*Of course!*" Who could pass up shopping with Adam!? He extends his arm and I take it, feeling the texture of the exquisite linen jacket with my fingers and rub it a little, for good luck.

Moments later we're standing in a beautiful leather store that has that musky fragrance of leather, warm from men's bodies, the aroma sets off something in my mind and I shudder to get my bearings. People are fussing over Adam; he greets them with that hypnotic grin, those twinkly aquamarine eyes and hugs all around. I feel proud to be with him and stand a little straighter.

Adam slides a lipstick red jacket from a hanger and shows it to me —"*feel this*"—my hand slips across the surface and it feels like the softest skin of a baby's cheek and responds to the slightest pressure. He moves behind me and carefully slides the sleeves up over my arms, lifting the shoulders and slowly smoothing them down, brushing my hair over the collar. In the mirror, I can see him looking down at me. I feel his breath on my neck—"*you look sooo hot, I have to buy it for you.*" There's no resisting, I can barely stand and just smile.

He winks and smiles at me in the mirror, turns me around and slides his hands from my neck, across my shoulders and down my arms to my hands and asks if I love it. (The jacket or the feel of his hands touching my body?) "*Love it!*"

Adam is starving and we decide to go for lunch. I take his hand and lead him down a leafy passage so narrow; he has to put his arm around me.

The path ends at a small café where we find a secluded table. I take a seat on the banquette, expecting the beautiful darling will sit across from me, but as Adam takes off his jacket, he drapes it over the chair, then he slides in next to me. The sleeve of his black silk shirt brushes against my bare arm as he reaches over to take off my hat and glasses. I recognize the shirt as the one he's wearing on the cover of Rolling Stone, unbuttoned and with those delectable jeans we love to see, silver buckle making the jeans bunch up a little. I have to lean on the cool marble of the table to steady myself.

"*Your feet must be hot from shopping—here, let me take off your sandals.*" Now I have to remember to breathe. He bends down and lifts my foot to place it on his thigh, right where the butterfly sat on these jeans. My sandal slides off and I wiggle my toes, leaning back on the banquette as Adam gently massages my foot in his lap. Smooth, cool hands and with gentle strokes, I feel great from head to toe.

While he's massaging my ankle, then up my calf, he starts to hum and then sing "*If I can't have you,*" I sit up and he puts his hands over mine, looks right through me with his intense, blue eyes and continues "*. . . I don't want nobody baby. . . .*"

I think I passed out, but came back when the waiter showed up. Adam was busy making plans—"*how about going dancing tonight!*"

I'll be humming "Play that Funky Music" for the rest of the day.

X

By xena princess warrior on 06/14/2009 10:10 am

Thanks Safari Gal, your response made me laugh out loud. This is from me, for you. Isn't this the most fun you can have with your clothes on? Frankly, this is one of those magical, mystical Adam effects we are wondering about. I have never written anything like this in my life—just essays, editorials, speeches, submissions and reports—on business, government and politics. He's obviously inspired something in me.

But, what a great opportunity I have to go nuts, write my fantasies and amuse some terrific women, I think of as girlfriends in a secret society. There's obviously some kind of hormone—probably the sex hormone testosterone, that our bodies are producing when we look at him, listen to him or dream about him. Those Adamgasms aren't fake and he is pleased with his effect on us—must be one of his goals.

Where do I find those jeans Adam wears so I can get some for my husband? We need an Adam catalogue.

X

By xena princess warrior on 06/14/2009 11:10 am

http://twentiesworkshop.wordpress.com/2009/06/13/tetra-hot-the-integral-. . . .

J.! This is the best thing I've read about the Adamphenom. Love this: "This kind of androgyny glorifies women without diminishing men. What women thankfully cherish in their gay boy friends is that sexuality isn't a zero sum game; womanliness doesn't diminish manliness or vice versa. It just all overflows as a giant volcano of eros. Bring it on, baby." Yes!! And I love how Xena's fantasy embodies the overflowing eros, the seamless embrace of the sensuality of shopping for fine things, the foot massage, being elevated on a pedestal of fabulousness and mutual adoration. . . .

By Juneau Underwood on 06/14/2009 12:10 pm

Wow J.—I am so glad you posted this—we are not nuts for allowing the life-force alien Adam to invade our minds and our bodies. This also explains why we get it, but younger women don't—it's our experience, evolution and sensitivity that provides us with a finely tuned radar that allows us more depth of feeling—the ability to synthesize all the senses he sparks. It can't help but intensify our emotions and some nerve endings just listening to his voice or even just replaying the videos in our minds.

Our permanently elevated mood comes from the remnants of these feelings when we aren't consciously fantasizing and it probably radiates through to others—like the 20 year old boys who asked if I like younger men last night! Maybe they just wanted more cake. It seems we've been immersed in Adam's aura and now it radiates from us. Eyes are brighter, we smile without being conscious of it and I don't know about you, but I find it hard to get very angry.

Well, sometimes it pays off to be the "mature" one and I'm glad it came in the Adam package. Glad I'm not 20.

X

By xena princess warrior on 06/14/2009 1:17 pm

Dear Glambertinas, with respect to make-up—Adam uses it the way we do—when we go out at night and when he goes to an awards gala or to perform. When he does the TV interviews, he consistently wears little or no make-up and why are we worried about this anyway? Hair grows, we cut it, it grows again.

We change our faces, wardrobe and hair to suit the occasion and I think Adam's great at that. You are beginning to make me nervous the way I was as a campaign manager, about how my candidate would "perform" during a debate. After hours of prepping him for the Q&A, perfecting his speech, selecting the perfect wardrobe, making sure each hair is in place and the fancy gold watch is removed, I was nervous as hell and could not be in the room during the debate. I either remained in the hallway or didn't go at all and had someone at the back of the room on a cell phone, to tell me how things were going. This was pathetic!

Sure, I avoided the embarrassing gaffe, the nervous tic that showed up or the heckler, but I also missed the triumphs, the applause and the standing ovations.

Relax, Adam's doing great and I wouldn't mind having a candidate like him anytime. I may not always be sure if he would stick to the script, but the result would be honest and grab our attention when we double take on something like "bi-curious."

I believe Adam is revolutionizing musical entertainment and we will be thrilled with the results, over and over again. On the 20/20 interview, we catch just a glimpse of him rehearsing what I think is a David Bowie number and there he is moving his body while he sings, finding the right moves, feeling the music.

Forget the unkempt, old t-shirt and jeans look of some of the current bands and entertainers who believe sex appeal doesn't belong in their craft. Not all of them of course.

Adam is a one-off and he's not going to play it safe—not in person, not on stage and not in the recording studio. He tried that, got bored and went for the short-cut to stardom—AI. I'm not going to be his manager, just a big fan who is totally relaxed in anticipation of a photo or an interview, because I believe in him.

Enough academic stuff. I am off to figure out how Adam is going to take me dancing—I think he has something surprising, since he won't give me any details. He just smiles like the Cheshire Cat when I ask him for information.

Keep you posted on that.

X

By xena princess warrior on 06/14/2009 11:05 pm

I detect here a longing among women for men to feel more comfortable about looking good. . . . Yesterday, I was at Sephora with my daughter and spotted a man consulting a saleswoman about eyeliner. I had a great urge to go up to him and cheer him on.

By Juneau Underwood on 06/15/2009 3:49 pm

Oh J, please encourage it! Ever since office attire became all casual, all the time, I get really excited to see a man in a well-cut suit and tie, which seems to have become a "costume." Add a little eye enhancement et voilà! I probably would have said something, embarrassed him and he would have run away, so probably better to just try to make eye contact and smile encouragingly.

During my daughter's EMO years, we got used to the boys with eyeliner and hair like Adam's—they came to my house so Xena II could dye their hair, which she still does. For the prom, she put blue highlights down the middle of her boyfriend's short fauxhawk and the next night, a different boy came and she turned him into a strawberry blonde. The new generation really seems loose on who wears what and this group wears a standard "uniform" of a band t-shirt, tight-legged jeans and running shoes—boys and girls.

I think we are ready to go back to some aspects of the '80s, like the attention to detail, hair, make-up and accessories, up to but not including a live snake wrapped around the thigh. Of course we all began with impeccable grooming and I'd love it if men got back into it, plus some mascara at least.

▪ **June 15/09** Adam nominated for two Teen Choice Awards

I might have to check out the cosmetics counters around here—research!

By xena princess warrior on 06/15/2009 4:17 pm

▪ My album is gonna be siiiiiiiick 8:41 PM **June 15th** from txt

[*Re: A post about a YouTube video of Adam singing "I Just Love You"*]

He'll make a great Dad some day.

By Juneau Underwood on 06/15/2009 7:18 pm

OK, as promised, here is one of my Adam fantasies. Apologies for the long set-up! Hope you enjoy it!

I am in LA on business. On a whim, I email a friend R, a film executive in London, on the chance that he might in town. Over the years we have kept in touch by email and phone, but had not met for a long time. But now quite unexpectedly, we are going to be in the same place. We arrange to meet for dinner at my hotel on Venice Beach. After a day of meetings, I return to my room, peel out of my business clothes and soak in a tub into which I sprinkle generous handfuls of sandalwood bath salts. The hot water embraces me and I breathe in the fragrant steam with sighs of pleasure, glad to be done with work and eager to see R.

Emerging from my bath, I dress for the evening in a sheer black T with a black, rhinestone-studded bra underneath, my favorite Japanese designer body-hugging trousers made of an amazing space-age material that resembles the softest black leather but is as light as silk, and Italian open-toed leopard stiletto pumps. I choose a necklace with a pendant made of vintage Swarovski "mink" crystals of sparkling espresso and dangling Chanel earrings of rock crystal. My dark hair falls straight to just below my shoulders. I apply eyeliner and mascara, dust the corners of my eyes with gold eye shadow, and brush on deep plum lip gloss. I gaze at my image in the mirror and toss my head, making my jewelry sparkle. I feel good!

I head down to the lobby and see R waiting there for me. His eyes light up, he smiles, seizes my hand and presses it to his lips while gazing longingly into my eyes. For a long moment, we are silent, breathing hard, savoring the pain and pleasure of being in each other's presence again. "Hello gorgeous," he finally says. "It's really good to see you." He puts his arm around me and leads me towards the dining room. We speak easily, filling a couple of hours with stories, news, flirtation and laughter.

As we sip cognac after our meal, R says he has promised to meet up with some friends and invites me along. They are a famous rock band; R is in town to co-produce their new album. We taxi to a club in Hollywood. When we arrive, there is a large throng on the sidewalk, pressing against velvet ropes and trying to talk the bouncers into letting them through. A bouncer recognizes my friend, lifts the rope and waves us into the club. Inside, the club throbs with Bollywood music. The walls are draped from the high ceiling to the floor with sheer white silk, semi-concealing a series of private rooms. We head towards the glowing wall of fabric, and R lifts aside a drape and leads me inside.

There, around a table, are sitting the members of the band. The lead singer is famously gay. And with them is—Adam Lambert. The band and Adam look up when we enter the space. Their eyes take us in, devour us with their gaze. I am suddenly conscious that R and I make a handsome pair, and I tingle with unrequited passion. I look at Adam and he smiles warmly. "Hi, I'm Adam," he says, holding out his hand. I take his hand, squeeze it gently, lingeringly, and introduce myself. His eyes cast back and forth between me and R, and I realize he is attracted to R and is wondering what our relationship is. R smiles at him and then greets his friends in the band.

The lead singer gets up to give him a hug and turns to me. I've met him before in Dublin. We hug, and he whispers in my ear, "You look fabulous. Adam is looking at you." I flush with pleasure and whisper back "You can't wait to get your hands on him, you slut." He laughs and turns to Adam and says "Isn't she hot?" Adam laughs too. His eyes alight on my Swarovski necklace and he coos, "that's a gorgeous piece!" "Take a closer look," I say and lean in. He touches it and his hand grazes my collar bone. I feel the floor tilt slightly and grab the table for balance. "It has a story. Everything I own has a story. You can have it if you want," I tell him. "Anything you desire is yours." He laughs and replies "I adore it, but it looks perfect on you." I ask him how he knows the band, and he says they were at the same recording studio earlier and they had invited him out. "I'm a huge fan," he says, and he's full of wonder and delight to find himself hanging with them. "So am I," I say, and we plunge into a lively discussion about the band's music.

The club throbs with Bollywood beats, and unconsciously, I'm pulsing my body to it. "This Indian stuff is awesome," Adam says. "Do you want to dance?" "Totally," I breathe, as visions of Ring of Fire spiral through my mind. Adam grabs my hand and pulls me up to my feet. Even with my four-inch heels, he towers over me. As he stands, I see he is wearing a beautifully tailored gray satin Alexander McQueen jacket with an ACDC T-shirt under it and tight black jeans. He gyrates his hips in tight circles and undulates his shoulders in time to the beat, and I do a little belly dance-disco move, and we are laughing and joyful. The music slows to a mystical pulse, and Adam takes my hands and draws me close. His hand brushes against me, and suddenly I feel his hand stroking my bottom. What??!! His arms are around me now, and he says "this feels amazing. What is it?" I realize he is referring to my space-age designer pants. "It's Issey Miyake, some kind of miracle fabric he invented," I laugh. "You can have it too." "I may just have to rip it off your body," he teases.

And we are dancing so closely, our bodies moving together in time to the tabla drum and sitars, and I breathe in his smell, something spicy and musky. "You smell like heaven," I whisper. Adam breathes into my hair and says "You smell amazing too." I feel his lips pressing into my head. I feel my eyes becoming moist and turn my head. Out of the corner of my eye, I suddenly become aware that R and the band members are transfixed by us, consuming us with hungry eyes, and I nearly swoon from the volcanic outflow of Eros in the air. (To be continued. . . ?) ***By Juneau Underwood on 06/16/2009 12:12 am***

Get out of town with this, it's too f**#'n much fun! You had me at (of course) "Everything I own has a story" and then it just became this curtain of yes, no, maybe emotions. I loved it, can't wait for the next chapter! You never fail me J. the Alexander McQueen jacket? This Virgo loved every detail...The girls, and maybe a couple of spouses, will inhale this with their morning coffee. ***By Safari Gal on 06/16/2009 12:30 am***

J., I have other fantasies of talking about the Torah with Adam, if you can believe it. The Garden of Eden story in particular. In the mean time, I did set you up perfectly for your voyeuristic fantasy. Just edit me out of the picture! :) ***By Juneau Underwood on 06/16/2009 8:28 am***

. . . Just had to share this Stanley Kunitz poem with you all:

Touch Me

Summer is late, my heart.
Words plucked out of the air
some forty years ago
when I was wild with love
and torn almost in two
scatter like leaves this night
of whistling wind and rain.
It is my heart that's late,
it is my song that's flown.
Outdoors all afternoon
under a gunmetal sky
staking my garden down,
I kneeled to the crickets trilling
underfoot as if about
to burst from their crusty shells;
and like a child again
marveled to hear so clear
and brave a music pour
from such a small machine.
What makes the engine go?
Desire, desire, desire.
The longing for the dance
stirs in the buried life.
One season only,
and it's done.
So let the battered old willow
thrash against the windowpanes
and the house timbers creak.
Darling, do you remember
the man you married? Touch me,
remind me who I am.

By Juneau Underwood on 06/16/2009 8:45 am

Adam, how do you do what you do to us?

Why do you suppose we continue to read, think and write about this young man who not only exists in our conscious but lurks in the shadows of our minds, to surprise us when we least expect it? The song list in our brain is on a loop and never stops—do we want to stop it? I just want more of his music to add to my playlist! Are we just the chattiest ones or do you suffer from OCD—obsessive-compulsive disorder—as I do?

What will it take to satisfy our desires, which we have not even finished describing, as if we ever could? I think at some point our forum will reach a critical mass of information, enough for someone to study and analyze, then produce a paper on how this group of supposedly mature, professional women, thought we were fully engaged in life, then realized we aren't, because Adam seduced us with a look, a raised eyebrow, the voice a choir of angels couldn't match and a body with moves to rival Salome's.

But really, that's not enough for us. We could never be fully satisfied with a cute, musically gifted, androgynously decorated and graceful panther. His conduct during judging, his generosity with his fellow competitors and his genuine excitement at being on the stage moved us in other ways. Here's a gorgeous, other-worldly creature with whom we could spend an evening—well, more than an evening—and never be bored, but amused, excited and—roused.

His honesty is so naked we want to wrap him in soft velvet and silk to protect him from the dangers of being so candid. It seems that he not only survives, but thrives on the invasive questions, the gossip and the innuendo, making it work for him. We hope so anyway, because some of us have nurturing instincts so powerful, we just can't turn off our protective mechanism and will worry about him.

Those eyes! Do they ever leave your mind? When you look at a blank wall do you see them? Sometimes he looks as though he is searching for your face in the audience and when he stops and fixes you with those black-lined, expressive eyes—sharp intake of breath. . . . Adam could give lessons in "eye seduction" à la "Beth." Now, just the still shot alone can produce the same result. Sometimes we look at it, just to gaze back at him and smile, maybe whisper something to him—I'm smiling now, just thinking about it.

Then there's the opening move in "Satisfaction," looking at us from the corner of his eye while reluctantly turning his face away. "*I would rather be with you Princess, but I have to go sing for everyone else—wait here, I'll be back,*" while smiling as though we are sharing an intimate moment and no one else knows in a studio full of people.

The emotion in Adam's voice, when he sings of unrequited or lost love betrays his real experiences reflected in those words, encouraging us to yearn for him to be happy, and to find the love he craves. "Don't cry—I'll dry your tears." We reach up to touch his face with our fingers, to catch the tear on his cheek.

Raunchy Adam comes banging on the door, demanding he be let in. He's the bad boy, who wants to give us "every inch of his love," the one who wants to be our backdoor man, who delights in getting some of the naughtier words past the censor—hahah! Eyes darkly rimmed in kohl, enhance the fierceness of his look. Body dressed in leather and denim, rough and ready. He moves with masculine, almost primitive confidence, stomping boots, pelvis thrusting, his chest heaving with a take-no-prisoners attitude, using every inch of space he has. He chokes the mic, swinging it as though it were a rival for our affections. He decides we need him and will just pick us up and carry us away to—well anywhere he wants, just make it fast.

My breathing is getting a little heavy and I feel warm. I need a cigarette.

Well, maybe it's just I who hasn't finished with Adam, or maybe I don't want to.

X ***By xena princess warrior on 06/17/2009 12:30 am***

Xena settle down. He's just a person. ***By C.B. on 06/17/2009 1:54 am***

No Xena don't settle down, that's exactly what you can't do! We all depend upon it. And I for one will join you on this quest. This is a quest into ourselves. Adam is just a person, C. B., but wow what is "just a person"—if you have the eyes to see, then they are infinite mystery, and broken shard of the divine. And some of them are channeling it so strong like waterfalls. What I am exploring as I read Xena's words is my own love energy, my own freedom, the deep core in me. Xena your appreciation of Adam stirs my feelings, which fall asleep during this Government Work! (Government work oh government work). Yes, we are well-shoed professional women and yet we have wild souls, no? How we forget. I do love the contrast between our place at society's table and that part of us that wants to crawl up on the table and reach for the displayed dutiful grapes, crushing them into blood-red trickles down the web of our hand. ***By A.L. on 06/17/2009 2:32 am***

[From Downunder: And my random question for the day—is anyone listening to anything else, or it is just Adam on repeat?]

Thank you "Down." Any other music? Great question. When I'm in the car with others, I listen to old rock and R&B on the satellite radio, or CDs of Queen, Steve Miller and more old R&B/soul/Motown—James Brown and I go way back and it depends on who is with me, what I choose.

In the mid-eighties, I was in the poster business, rock posters primarily and my radio was permanently tuned to music stations so I would know who was in and who was out. In 1987, after five years of music, I switched to talk/news radio—again for my job, as I had completely changed careers. Until now.

June 17/09 People magazine—Adam is on the list of hottest bachelors for 2009

Twenty-two years later and one voice, one amazing performer has brought me back to music. To quote Kara—"shocking!" I bought an iPod shuffle for Adam's music and for the first time, iTunes.

X

By xena princess warrior on 06/17/2009 4:02 pm

Ladies, thanks for reading and especially for writing. I have to go to a local government meeting shortly—now that's boring—and it's followed by a second one in the same place. I am putting on my power suit, high heels, mascara, lipstick and I might just flirt a little with the bureaucrats I might frighten. A senior staffer told me that after someone sees him talking to me, he is grilled. For him, I'll just smile and wink.

Maybe someone will go to lunch with me between meetings—that would really cause trouble.

There's a reason I'm called a "Princess Warrior."

Love, X

By xena princess warrior on 06/17/2009 8:27 am

Xena, thank you for that beautiful piece of writing. I will re-read it and savor the frissons of pleasureful recognition. And A. L., spot on! Adam has indeed sparked a quest into ourselves, and a journey into self-affirming hedonism. . . . Does he have any idea? Let me count a few of the ways:

- I am using an iron on my hair
- I bought a pair of tight, low cut jeans (and they look and feel great!)
- I am communing with you wonderful women!
- I am starting to sketch out a book I've been incubating in my mind for several years
- I went out for my anniversary dinner wearing a see-through top. My husband loved it, my kids were scandalized. My daughter said "you look like a rocker!"
- I'm staying up until 2AM reading and re-reading this Web site . . . when I'm not surfing the web for Adam treasures. . . .

By Juneau Underwood on 06/17/2009 8:48 am

Xena, is some part of the government going to fall apart because you are distracted by the Lambert?

Downunder, thanks for the question asking whether we are listening to anything other than Adam. I confess I was an NPR junkie, but no longer. I'd rather listen to Born to be Wild. Other musicians have also been cast into the attic. Apologies to Alfred Brendel, Dylan, Mick. . . . Interestingly, post-Adam I downloaded and have been listening to The Pretenders almost as often as I listen to him. Chrissie Hynde is the rock idol I wanted to be when I was Adam's age.

This made me think about what I was doing when I was 27, and whether I've fulfilled the dreams I had at that age. At that time, I had spent a year backpacking around the world, settled to live in Japan to write a book with a boyfriend who became physically abusive. I felt trapped because I had allowed myself to become completely dependent on him financially, we were living far from family, and I had so much invested in finishing the book. I survived that experience, moved to Manhattan, and while my boyfriend was out of town, I got myself an editorial job at a magazine, moved out of our apartment, left no forwarding address, and re-started my life. I was lucky to have good friends who protected and supported me. I had a wonderful life in the city (those were the years of clubs, the art scene, dabbling in the film industry, being involved with interesting men), then met my future husband and left Manhattan.

My dreams at that time were to be a writer, and one day to get married and have children. And to have my own house (like Adam!). I've fulfilled those dreams beyond my wildest expectations. I met and married a wonderful man, a brilliant composer who weds art with cutting-edge technology, who is so funny, loving and honest. We have two gorgeous, spirited girls and have traveled the world with them. We bought an 18th-century farm house where I can indulge my love of animals and gardening. Our world is richly populated with remarkable friends—scientists, poets, musicians. Although the writing got side tracked, I discovered new, unanticipated outlets for my creativity in the Web world and being a medical entrepreneur. Now this forum has given me an opportunity to dip my toe (with an OPI Black Onyx pedicure) into a different type of writing. Thanks for being my first readers!

By Juneau Underwood on 06/17/2009 6:10 pm

A Shooting Star fell to Earth

What a supportive group! Hmmm, so instead of being a support group for Glambertinas who need help to cope with our obsession and our compulsion to know everything about Adam, all the time, we have become a supportive group. We support each other, not to recover from our addiction, but to allow it to flourish! I use the cover of "support group to avoid an intervention" to describe us.

Have we transferred some of our cheerleading from Adam to each other? How did we get so close, so fast? We're nurturing each other with positive messages and shared fantastic intimacies we can hardly discuss with others—those who haven't heard the word. "Adam is here and he sizzles—sparks fly off him and where they land, something glows, like a shooting star that falls to Earth."

Michelangelo

Michelangelo explained that he only released the sculptures inside the marble; he didn't imagine them or create them. He simply released them from their hiding place—a mountain of white, glistening, sparkling marble. With his chisels and his hammers, he chipped away until a figure of spiritual inspiration emerged. Then he polished and polished until it was ready for viewing.

Michelangelo has been on my mind lately, in connection to Adam. Adam talks about how he made American Idol work to suit his particular goal. In essence, they just got out of the way and he gave them a show and brought AI new and different audiences—us.

Adam was inside that marble all along and just needed the opportunity to be released and wow! Did he ever! What so many of us need to succeed is to have those physical and mental barriers knocked down, to be given permission to dream a life and then go for it. Thanks to Adam, we have been cracked open to the creativity we thought had atrophied from a lack of attention. With all of our senses unblocked and uninhibited, we dream, we think, we read and we write. I have never written fiction or fantasy in my life, I don't even read it—I am stunned. Where do all these words come from every night when I write the fantasies? And people actually read them??!!

Wizard of Oz

One of my favourite stories to inspire children comes near the end of the Wizard of Oz, when the travelers are in front of the Wizard and he shows them how they each possessed what they thought they were missing for a fulfilling life. He gave Scarecrow permission to be smart, Tin Man permission to feel love and emotions and the Lion to be courageous. With simple accoutrements, each life was transformed so they would fulfill their destiny. Dorothy was wearing the shoes all along. We don't need to go see the Wizard do we? We give each other permission by responding to one another's ideas and words right here.

Dearest Glambertinas,
When I write to you in the evenings, as I am doing now, the ideas come from a synthesis of what all of you have written about recently. I try to respond to your fears and concerns as well as your fantasies, because I care about you and want all of you to be happy, reassured and having fun. I have always been a "big sister"—I can't help it. I get the same sense from most of you too. On Wednesday AM Juneau wrote "And A. L., spot on! Adam has indeed sparked a quest into ourselves, and a journey into self-affirming hedonism. . . . Does he have any idea? Let me count a few of the ways:" Absolutely A. L. and J.

Some of us have been thinking about what we will do next and either began already or are planning to take action soon. I tend to reinvent myself every five to seven years and the time is up on the current Xena. Some women tire of having curly hair and switch to straight, then after a while, they get bored and switch back. I do that with careers, but I call them "inside" or "outside" jobs. After alternating one with the other, I recently decided that I want everything!—to do the inside work of research and writing and then have my name on my work and present it as well. I just haven't decided on a topic yet.

I promise, we'll get back to sex again tomorrow night. Adam and I are flying to South America where it's so hot and humid, we have to . . . and the music is so sensuous, we . . . the fruit drips with sweet juices and . . . the wine intoxicates. . . .

Maybe I should make this a DIY story and you fill in the blanks. I'm planning a surprise for him, and I don't know how it will turn out yet. So ladies, how hot will it get in Buenos Aries or Rio? I think I will dream on this tonight. Hot, humid, sensuous music, juicy fruit and wine.

I bid you happy dreams,
Love, X

By xena princess warrior on 06/17/2009 11:56 pm

It's fun and it's sexy. And if sexy scares you, don't listen to my music. http://media.www.thechaparral.com/media/storage/paper570/news/2009/05/11/Entertainment/Backstage.Pass.American.Idol.Season.8.Part.Two-3752265.shtml

I want to bring people together and get them to dance and smile and feel sexy and celebrate our similarities, not our differences.
http://adam-lambert.org/adam-lambert-the-ultimate-interview-part-4/

It's a really, really cool thing to be able to show people that you can be yourself and you should be proud of yourself and you should own who you are and what you're about and never make apologies for it.
http://www.etonline.com/news/2009/05/74683/

When people throw their underwear up onstage, it usually has me laughing. It's flattering. Its funny. http://vodpod.com/watch/1936498-adam-lambert-backstage-at-l-a-s-staples-center

It can charge you up and make you feel like a million dollars and at the same time, it can make you feel like you got run over by a train. There is so much energy coming at you all thc time. In New York, I wanted to just give everybody as much of me as I could because everyone was so supportive and showing so much love http://www3.signonsandiego.com/stories/2009/jul/16/1w16adamm201519/

Thank you to my family and friends who've kept me grounded throughout this journey. Thank you to the incredible fans who have shown me so much light and love. It was all of you who made this dream come true. I'm eternally grateful. American Idol Tour Program, 2009

My favorite song to sing was "Whole Lotta Love." I got to say "every inch of my love" on National TV.

O for a Muse of fire, that would ascend
The brightest heaven of invention. . . .

(William Shakespeare, Henry V)

Chapter 2 Muse

Xena, it's way too late and I need to get to sleep, but I wanted to thank you for your latest post. Like you, I try to shake up my life every five to ten years. If something starts to seem routine, if I feel I am coasting, it's time for a change. And then I begin to search for the thing which I desire that scares me the most. That's my guide to life. If it scares the shit out of me, that's the thing I need to do. More about that, maybe tomorrow night, unless I let my next fantasy take over. Looking forward to finding out what happens in South America. . . .

By Juneau Underwood on 06/18/2009 1:23 am

I just bought my Rolling Stone yesterday while at the drug store with my girls. I could feel my blood pressure rising and my heart pound, as though I were scoring drugs or buying a porn magazine. I held it with the cover hidden until I put it down at the cashier, and saw my 15-year-old roll her eyes. I hastily explained my unusual purchase by telling her there is an article in there about a family friend. Which conveniently was true. My sweet, still-gullible 11-year-old asked me, "Did you know Adam Lambert is on the cover?" I feigned astonishment. "Really? I hadn't noticed." My older one set the younger straight pretty fast!

I was just wondering what to get my husband for Father's Day. Will he suspect anything if I buy him Dior Homme?

By Juneau Underwood on 06/18/2009 7:18 am

I missed the Access Hollywood interview, but now that the gay "reveal" thing is behind him, he has been disclosing more about his pre-Idol life, and that it was not such a happy time in his life. My heart ached for him when he mentioned on 20/20 how he missed out on a lot of high school things like dating. His humility comes from a real place, of having been an ugly duckling (I can relate to that), so that when he finally blossomed, it's with a true sense of wonder and gratitude, not of entitlement. There's a wonderful line in M. Butterfly which I can only paraphrase here, but it drew huge laughs when I saw it on Broadway years ago: The worst thing that can happen to you is to have been a success in high school. We are all better for it if we have to work hard to get what we want. ***By Juneau Underwood on 06/18/2009 10:04 am***

The Ice Queen has Feelings

Dear friends, I need your help with something. Am I crazy? I did something dumb a few days ago—I told someone really close to me about this OCD (Obsessive-Compulsive Disorder) I am experiencing and then, I sent her a couple of the stories I had written to you. She told me I am crazy and I think she meant it, she was shocked. After this brief euphoria since AI, I crashed and crashed hard yesterday, which forced me to think about what I am doing here.

I did get a lot of work done yesterday and tried to stay away from you, but last night I checked-in and then started to write a response to one of the messages. Instead of sending it in, I decided to sleep on it, so I could have a second look this morning and maybe discard it. Usually I just fire them off to you when I finish editing. I continue to ruminate.

My confidence has been completely shaken. Where else can I go, but to seek your support and understanding? Any psychiatrists on board? Now that I have slept on this person's response to me, I think it has to be their shock at finding out I can think those "thoughts." People close to me must imagine I am the Icy Virgin Queen, or Xena, Princess Warrior, and seeing in print what I can imagine and how I can feel, must be really hard for them to fathom. To find out that a young prince has melted my heart and shone a light in a corner of my mind that had been dark for a long time, means that I let down my defenses and she, along with everyone else close to me is left unprotected, leaderless.

She has found out that I wear lacy lingerie beneath the power suit—too much information for her. What did she think—that I actually have a metal breastplate covering me? Maybe she thinks I will run away from home and leave my responsibilities to her—I do threaten to from time to time.

Men have their stimulants, including drugs, why can't we have ours and why shouldn't we explore these feelings? What do you think? I can go on and write for myself and for you and share our joy at having our senses tweaked or—I go to the doctor and get my meds checked.

Initially, did any of us have any control whatsoever over our response to hearing and watching Adam? Do we want to recreate those experiences over and over again because they make us feel good?

Yes!

Due to my current mental condition, I've had to either cancel or postpone the trip to South America.

a wounded X ***By xena princess warrior on 06/19/2009 2:13 pm***

Dear Xena, wish I could slather your wounds with honey and bandage them up. I've also thought about sharing some of this experience with close friends, but have stepped back from that brink. We are truly walking on the edge, fascinated by, and participating in something that straddles the line between euphoric and cringe-inducing. But your joy, the self-validation, and outlet you have found here are very real and precious, so don't let anyone tell you otherwise! (However, an occasional icy bath may be a healthy antidote when our addiction becomes a bit too disruptive.) You are brave to expose yourself, and I for one am thankful to have found this safe place where we can be so open and vulnerable to one another—and have such a blast doing it. You don't need meds. Write on!

Love, Juneau ***By Juneau Underwood on 06/19/2009 5:19 pm***

So, my Web peregrinations led me last night to the adamlambertsite, which featured video clips of Adam's ex, Brad Bell. Known as "Cheeks," he's an adorable fairy queen with a droll and biting sense of humor, and he has posted these hilarious performance videos of his take on a variety of issues. Quite fun! Here's his YouTube site: http://www.youtube.com/user/GoCheeksGo

While I was perusing Cheeks' YouTube site, I noticed some gay soft-core videos popping up in the margin. J., you're going to love this! I'd never been remotely curious about gay porn, as I have not found the type of men who typically perform in them to be attractive, but while on YouTube last night, I came across a Brazilian hunk who I thought was drop-dead gorgeous. (Xena, he's ripe for your South American fantasy!)

The video shows him partially (never completely) undressed, reclining and looking seductive, running his hands slowly over his body, never going where the censors would have to intervene, but man, it was HOT. Thinking about it while trying not to burn dinner, I realized that we seldom (never) see hetero men this way, being so frankly sensual and giving that come-hither, I'm-just-on-fire look. It's Adam in Ring of Fire. Now I'm consumed with excitement to explore further, although if I ever came across a really beautifully made gay porn film with actors that I found irresistible, I think I'd have a heart attack from the sheer excitement. And what would my family think when they discovered my body slumped over my laptop with the video playing, and found hundreds of gay porn downloads in my browser history. . . ?

By Juneau Underwood on 06/20/2009 12:06 am

J, you've got me trying to stifle my laugh so I don't wake up the household and get caught checking out gay porn. That would really set the Red Queen howling, wouldn't it? Better save that one for next year. BTW, the Red Queen is my younger sister—only by two years. This revelation I forced upon her has actually turned out well. Those who know I'm certifiable (12 years in therapy) and that I'm OCD can come around about this eventually.

J, I've got to have that Brazilian—he's so perfect for my fantasy, but I can't find him. Your description is not quite enough, can you help?

Sorry to be so late responding to you on this, sometimes I have to feed people or do actual, paid work.

X

By xena princess warrior on 06/21/2009 11:29 pm

Xena Exposed

Dearest MoALS, I have been otherwise occupied and have a lot of catching up to do with you, but it's a dreary Saturday morning and I don't have to be anywhere until the afternoon—for a pedicure and manicure. Currently wearing a deep midnight blue but looking at a gorgeous, rich purple. The blue has been a conversation starter—young women love it and mature women wish they had the nerve, so I offer one of my favourite justifications—What's the worst thing that can happen?

I spent Friday evening with some live opera in a small hall full of appreciative fans. The mezzo who sang a flirtatious Carmen solo, teased and played with the audience in front of her. The tiniest little body with a voice and manner that filled the room with her intoxicating performance—she truly was Carmen the promiscuous, fiery Gypsy, in layered skirts, tight bodice, and bare shoulders, surrounded by the cigarette girls and men who vied for her attention. I had tears before she sang the last note and I wanted more. "*Love is a rebellious bird that no one can tame. [. . .] He has never known law. If you don't love me I love you, if I love you watch yourself!*"

▪

". . . can't wait for people to hear what my music really sounds like." 10:37 **AM June 20th** from web

Oh, to play Carmen for a night. Could this be spun into a fantasy? I envy those who have the talent, the skill and the charisma to affect people this deeply—as Adam does. I couldn't wait to tell "Carmen" how her performance moved me, and expected to fight a crowd to reach her. Fortunately, the men ahead of me were quite short and in my pink Guess high-heeled pumps, I easily moved them aside to talk to Carmen. If only I could return an ounce of the pleasure she gave with her performance, but she was left only with my best smiles and words of appreciation.

Revealing the Warrior

Thanks to all of you Florence Nightingales for your healing thoughts and encouragement. My analysis proved absolutely true—the Red Queen had to face the fact that her slightly older protector, mentor and self assured role model—is a sexual being and an imaginative one at that—and she shares her dreams with others!!!

No wonder her reaction was a swift and hard "Off with your head!" She finally realized that Xena, whose voice can summon legions to war, is vulnerable to tender whispers and some lusty action in the smoky, humid tent after a day on the battlefield. That Xena too, needs nourishment to cross the desert tomorrow, in pursuit of the Persians. When she removes her breastplate at night, her body is liberated from the physical constraints of battle. Mind and body, work is done, so she seeks rejuvenation from among the men she commands.

Very Happy Ending

I am so glad that I took the time to think the Red Queen's response through, and then talk to her about it. I read to her the piece I wrote to you "The Queen has Feelings" and she said it described her reaction perfectly but she hadn't realized it. We haven't had this much fun in ages and stayed in a great mood as we went to the opera together.

Would I do it again? Yes. Who will be Xena's next victim?

Love and affection

X

By xena princess warrior on 06/20/2009 10:14 pm

I adore opera too. Loved your description of that Carmen. My husband is a musician so I have the privilege of being around some wonderful singers. There's something miraculous about the human singing voice. It *is* the celestial music. Adam has a voice from heaven, so unlike the mediocre artists that are being pushed out by the pop music industry.

I have to say I'm more than a little anxious about his first CD. What if it gets overproduced? What if the songs are not great? I need him to be my Muse. ***By Juneau Underwood on 06/22/2009 11:37 pm***

Xena, I applaud your courage in facing your sister. How brave to open up the wound again. It could have all gone wrong, but instead you were healed and your relationship was enriched. Just as you felt that those around you expect you to always be there in full Xena armor, I feel the intense pressure to be wife, mother, groundskeeper and boss, juggling dozens of objects (some breakable, some sharp and dangerous!), and wonder what kind of hell would break loose if I let my attention waver. . . . ***By Juneau Underwood on 06/21/2009 1:50 am***

Oh, Dearest Juneau,

I wish I could pick you up and take you for a drive in the country. We would listen to Adam sing while I tell you funny stories and we get silly with laughter. We talk about the boys we loved and the ones who love us and there were many, still are.

We stop for lunch at a little country pub where we flirt and laugh with the man behind the bar and his regulars. The waitress gets in on it, and by the time we leave, the place is in an uproar and we can hear their voices as we drive away.

We are really enjoying this because we have left our families to fend for themselves, for a change. Laundry, groceries, cooking—we have left it all behind and you just left a note—"Out for a strategy meeting with Xena."

We keep driving and now we're singing along with Adam, but some of the songs make us cry—"Come Home," "Tracks of my Tears," so we have to stop to compose ourselves and we find a roadhouse—full of blue-jeaned boys drinking beer. The place is packed and hopping, so as we approach the door, a couple of guys grab us by the hand and practically carry us to the dance floor where your partner seizes you by the waist and with his free hand, turns you away, then turns you back with a thud against his chest, his belt buckle grazes your midriff and he twirls you away again, you're getting dizzy now.

Just in time, the music slows, but our partners are still hanging on to us and insist we dance this slow dance with them. (I now have to stop and breathe for a sec.) What choice do we have? At this point we have forgotten we were sad and we're laughing again at these boys who won't let go. How old are they? Twenty-seven, twenty-eight? (oh, oh, déjà vu recollection here) No one knows we're here, why not? Let's give in and let go.

These are country boys who do physical labour all day long and their arms, their shoulders are muscled and tanned. Their fitted denim shirts show off how narrow their waists are and our eyes slide down to where they loop their thumb in behind their belt buckle. What choice do we have?

It's a lovely Shania Twain ballad, the lights are dim, and the boys are gorgeous—what's the worst thing that could happen? So we dance, closely, and after the song is over, they slide us into a wooden booth with high walls between us, and the next table. Our protestations are met with deaf ears and a little pleading. The boys are so earnest and nosey—*are you married? Do you like younger men? I think they can make a martini here if you want one.*

We are trying to be cool and behave like the sophisticated and mature women we are supposed to be. But, we just ran away from home so for now, we're party girls—we're Thelma and Louise—just a cold beer with the boys and we'll head back. Well, maybe one more beer and another dance.

Didn't we have a great time? Let's do it again.

Love and hugs

X

By xena princess warrior on 06/21/2009 10:02 pm

Xena! You've given me a fabulous daydream to brighten my day. I'm right there with you as we drive off in our beat-up pickup truck that we keep hidden under a tarp in a vacant lot down the street. I do run away from home now and again to hang with my girlfriends for a weekend, but most of us are married so going to a bar and flirting with younger men just hasn't been on the agenda.

I'll have to fill you in on the latest happening in my life, all thanks to the Lambert effect. It's a rather long and tortured tale and will take some time to write down. . . . Off to save the world now. Love and hugs back!—June

By Juneau Underwood on 06/22/2009 9:28 am

I love both the live performances and the studio versions, for different reasons. What I love about the live performances is his sense of the drama of a song and his ability to connect with the viewer. I only listen to them as DVDs. If you listen to them without the image, you realize he doesn't always hit the notes, although he does way better than most singers.

Also, for Idol, the songs are shortened from three-plus minutes to one minute, and that forces him to compress the dramatic arc to almost the breaking point. I noticed that people who didn't like his Idol performances complained that all he does is scream. Leaving aside the fact that he never screamed (he SANG; big difference), I think he left this impression because he had to climax the song in such a short time.

To extend the metaphor, these performances were quickies. I still love them for the visual pleasure (I have Ring of Fire and KISS visuals cycling through my brain constantly) and for his improvisational skill. For pure listening, I go for the Studio recordings. There, he is pitch perfect, he has the time and space for foreplay and a more sustained peak, followed by a blissful descent. I just heard the Studio recording of Feelin' Good today for the first time. Don't know how I could have missed it. It's sublime. ***By Juneau Underwood on 06/21/2009 2:03 am***

I agree about "Tracks of My Tears." The live version was stunning. And the live version of Ring of Fire was beyond brilliant, both musically and visually. That didn't feel like a quickie. It transcended time.

By Juneau Underwood on 06/21/2009 9:09 am

It occurs to me that Simon Cowell's reaction to ROF as "self-indulgent rubbish" was prompted by Simon's discomfort over erotic feelings he was experiencing when he watched the performance. I'm not suggesting Simon is a closet case. I think he's a straight guy who was thrown for a loop, couldn't process what Adam's performance was doing to him, and had to protect his masculinity by dismissing what had just happened. Do you think my hypothesis has any legs?

By Juneau Underwood on 06/21/2009 2:13 am

Adam nailed Rat Pack!! I thought we were in Vegas, watching a show there. The whole package, the suit, the shoes, the set and the song were perfect. And that surprising ending! I gave him a standing ovation.

By xena princess warrior on 06/21/2009 10:32 am

Adam was singing Tracks of my Tears when the lightning bolt hit me, I sat down to watch and have awakened here with you. I was very disappointed with the studio version. For a love ballad like this, Adam's voice needs no embellishment and the minimalist stage version was perfect and as Smokey said, tender. Stripped down to the raw emotion where nothing can hide, not a bad note, wrong facial expression, nothing. It is the closest he came during AI, to his performances at the Upright Cabaret.

I play those every day and it's where we got to know pre-AI Adam, adding another dimension to how we feel about him—affection, empathy, sympathy, tenderness. He even looks vulnerable, dressed in soft clothes and with boyish looking hair—downright cuddly. Sometimes he describes how personal a song is for him—the theme of unrequited love that he talked about just before he sang "I Can't Make You Love Me" and after "Come Home." Apparently, the words express his feelings so well, it sounds like he is writing them and he's left with tears. How could the people in the audience not run up and hug him!

"Dust in the Wind," again the temporary nature of the love in his relationships and for this song, I have a special spot in my heart, as he sang it on my birthday. We want to soothe him with reassuring words, put our arms around him and say "I love you and I won't leave you."

In one of his interviews, he talks about searching for love and it breaks our hearts that this beautiful, caring boy has been left with so much love to give, it spills over onto everyone in his aura. But, he wants someone to be in love with.

Almost all of the songs we have found Pre-AI are sad, not happily-in-love songs. The closest he gets is "*I Just Love you*" and that's about a little daughter—but we grasp these lyrics and hold on to them, because someone is saying those words to him—someone loves him.

Even in "Kiss from a Rose," the love he receives feels "strange" and it's more a lament than a song of joy at receiving love. It's barely a light in the gloom.

I think that's why we loved "Feeling Good" sooooo much. He feels good, we feel great! There are more facets to Adam than in a piece of Swarovski crystal, no wonder he sparkles and glitters.

I agree with the rest of you about listening to the studio recordings and watching the videos, that's my routine too and I have the benefit of an ear that can't really discern a bad note.

I carry Adam around in my little pink Shuffle, headphones and an external speaker. That little pink square is one of my Adam amulets. (You will see this word again shortly)

C., thank you for motivating me to write these thoughts I had been saving for a while. By the way, you don't have to read every ridiculous thing I write—there is no test at the end and no one is keeping score.

Love you

X

By xena princess warrior on 06/21/2009 10:09 am

Ditto! I have my iTunes frozen at the image of him with his eyes sparkling and the eyebrow raised. I would turn that into my screensaver if I didn't have to use my laptop for professional presentations.

By Juneau Underwood on 06/22/2009 7:10 am

I loved T.'s name for us and am proud to belong to such an esteemed group. This inspired me to design a Symposium for us, something academic and profound. Scholars need a place to share their research and test new ideas. Please feel free to add more topics.

MoALS Symposium
Members of the Adam Lambert Scholars
The Phenomenon of Adam Lambert in the Arts, Science, Spiritualism, Biology and Sociology

Topics for Papers or Discussion Groups

The Obsessed Female Fan
Are they common sufferers of OCD or is this something new for them? The results of a scientific experiment where women who were unaware of Adam Lambert in any way (they were members of a South American tribe who had never seen any modern technology), were subjected to watching each of Adam's performances, while wired to measure their physiological responses. The control group had Danny Gokey. The results will be presented here for the first time.

Talisman
The importance of a Talisman or amulet to women who seek to rekindle that "Adam is with me" feeling whenever possible.
• Some wear very dark or black polish on their nails, which they simply look upon to recall their excitement at seeing a man with black polish, singing like an angel and moving like a cobra.
• Black Eyeliner—see above
• Silver jewelry, studded leather—ditto
• An iPod or Shuffle with Adam's music, which they carry in a pocket or handbag at all times.

The Zen of Adam
A spiritual awakening among women after watching Ring of Fire or is it just lust?

Adam as Aphrodisiac
Why women start their morning with *If I Can't Have You* and stay "happy" (per Kara D.) for the rest of the day, with brief shots of photos and visits with their online support group to keep them going till night. Surreptitiously, they also listen to their iPods, but only Lambert.

Evolutionary Biology as evidenced by the profound Lambert effect on perfectly successful and together women.

Younger, less mature women and girls seem to "just like his music."

From Libido to Fulfilling their Dreams
How Adam Lambert has single handedly motivated and liberated a generation of women, unlike anything seen since the 1960's and Friedan's "The Feminine Mystique."

Existentialism in the Age of Adam
I think therefore I am—Hot!

Families Fear in the Wake of Adamania
"*Who will feed us?*" Women are searching to fill gaps in their lives they didn't know existed before Adam Lambert sang *Ring of Fire.* Their families are left to feed and clothe themselves while the Adam Besotted females spend time communicating with their on line support groups, getting manicures and pedicures and shopping for sequined undergarments. How are families coping?

Adam the Muse
Women who have never dreamed erotic fantasies or written creatively have credited Adam Lambert for their inspiration. What is it that makes Adam the Muse for a generation of women artists, musicians, writers, entrepreneurs, corporate leaders, academics, lawyers, dentists, civil servants and policy analysts?

Adam's music and visuals are encouraged.

By xena princess warrior on 06/22/2009 12:11 am

Xena, you made my morning, and it's barely 7AM! I've been working on a couple of long posts that will take another day or two to be ready. In the mean time, your Symposium provides much grist for discussion! Two minor suggestions: I think scholars may debate whether the S in MOALS actually stands for Swooners rather than Scholars. And regarding younger women, they openly want to have sex with him. There's a line around the block. But among older women, Adam is having the effect not only of making them want to have sex with him (or watch him have sex with his lover, or use him as an aphrodisiac), but of making them want to CHANGE THEIR LIVES. Have a great one!

By Juneau Underwood on 06/22/2009 7:20 am

Hey Juneau, you're on for a couple of papers for the symposium—at least. The name for our group came from T's posting and I made a mistake at that. I should have written "Meaning of Adam Lambert Scholars." Feel free to debate this at the symposium.

I can see that you will be making a submission under "Evolutionary Biology"—Thanks!

X, MoALS Symposium Coordinator

By xena princess warrior on 06/22/2009 8:50 am

Thanks J! How on earth did we find each other? It is so great to have others who get my jokes, analogies and fantasies—when I'm here, reading your postings along with the others, I feel sane, safe and appreciated. I have had major writing and correspondence binges before (the nature of manic/depressive/obsessive/compulsive people—maybe I shouldn't generalize, it could just be me). Absolutely none like this one, with so many dimensions and challenges. We inspire one another, isn't that what Adam has done for us?

I have corresponded on war, politics, science, ethics and society and developed my own set of "pen-pals" for each topic. Academics, scientists, journalists and columnists, but this is by far the most rewarding and it's fun! While we have an intellectual thread running through sometimes, this is so personal, we express feelings. Hard to do that when discussing how NATO should react to the Balkan crisis.

The bonus is, we did not have to search very far and here we are! One of the rewards of course is the almost instant feedback we get, as though we are having a long conversation, a polite one, where we don't interrupt one another.

My daughter loves to tell me that we aren't doing this "right." How closed minded is that for an 18 year old? I told her we have no rules and we write the way we want to and it is working for us. "*You're not supposed to write letters, Mom.*" But I like to write essays and letters and I love to read whatever any of you wants to write.

I know I draw my creativity and energy from this warm group and it is sooo stimulating.

Thanks, X

By xena princess warrior on 06/22/2009 12:46 pm

Hi C., I second Xena's advice. Writing is a process that lets you find out what you are thinking. That's one of the wonderful things about this little cyber sisterhood. I find that when I write, I bring clarity to my experiences and feelings. Sometimes I'm off base on the first pass, but writing lets you go back and examine, critique and dig deeper for the truth. It's a craft that takes time to learn, so don't feel bad about feeling "out of it." We are enjoying having you as a reader and having you share your thoughts with us.

By Juneau Underwood on 06/22/2009 9:34 am

Cleopatra, not like you to be hiding in the reeds, you must be up to something. He probably never told you, but I knew your great-great- . . . Granddad, Ptolemy I, a great leader, fighter and with the gift of diplomacy. We fought side-by-side in Alexander's army across the eastern frontier to secure the world for the Macedonians. It was an eclectic bunch Alexander assembled, and when he appointed your dad as Pharaoh, we were thrilled! And here you are, the most powerful woman in the world! We are truly honoured. Not many realize that while a beautiful actress from New Zealand played me in a TV series, I am actually Macedonian and not so beautiful. Welcome Cleo.

X

By xena princess warrior on 06/22/2009 10:25 pm

Sisters, I'm going to confess something that happened to me this Father's Day. This is one of those tales that begins with a soul-flattening humiliation out of which one emerges redeemed.

The morning was a whirlwind of busyness, wresting my girls from their computers to help make brunch for their Dad and grandfather, wrapping gifts, gathering flowers in the garden for the table (will anyone notice? I grumble to myself) clean-up afterwards, and then as everyone heads off in separate directions to do their thing, I hole up in my office to read a fan letter I wrote to Adam.

I've never once thought about doing such a thing in my life, but here I am now pouring out my feelings to my Avatar Adam. I printed it the night before on a brand-new HP I bought just so I can have laser quality. I'm so excited about putting it into the mail. Will he laugh, be moved, be impressed? Or will he be mortified? No matter, I tell myself. Whatever happens will happen. This is the truth.

I hope of course that he will email me and tell me how much he loved it. But I tell myself to be prepared to hear nothing. He may never even see it because he now has a staff of people protecting him and filtering what gets through to him. Whatever, I tell myself. The important thing is that I acted. And I am writing again. But I still want him to read it.

I scrutinize the black-and-white portrait I included. It is a close-up shot of my face as I lie on my side, smiling into the camera. Do I look warm, joyful and alive? Or just weird? Do I look beautiful? I hope he finds me attractive enough—not in a romantic way (well, I wouldn't reject that), but as a face he wouldn't mind getting to know more about.

In the midst of my reverie, there's a knock on my office door. It's my eleven-year-old daughter. "Mom!" she says. "I have to talk to you." Sure, what is it? "Mom! What is THIS?" She holds out a piece of paper and she is giggling uncomfortably. I take it from her. It's my letter to Adam. I feel the blood rise to my cheeks. "Where did this come from?" I fold it into a tiny rectangle and toss it in the trash. My daughter says she found it in her printer tray.

My mind races back to yesterday, when I rewrote my letter and printed it out. I must have accidentally sent a copy over the wifi to her printer. Argghh!! I cannot believe it. "It's for a writing project I'm doing with some women," I bluster.

"Mom! You're not going to send this to Adam Lambert, are you?"

No, as I told you, it's for a writing project.

"I don't know if I can ever look you in the face again. You wrote 'Thank you my bright angel. . . .'! You're in love with him."

No it's not a love letter. It's a thank you letter. Big difference. You can go now. I have to work.

My daughter leaves, and I collapse in my chair. Did I manage to play it cool? No. I can't believe my secret is out. I'll pretend this never happened. I try to focus on work emails, but my heart is pounding. Maybe she will forget? No way. I have to deal with this. And my indignation is rising. Why should I feel I need to hide this behind a pathetic web of lies?

I go out of my office, and ask my daughter up to my bedroom, sit down on the rug with her, look her in the eye and tell her I will level with her. "I'm going to tell you the truth, but you have to respect my feelings about this."

I tell her about the wowOwow group, and how much fun I've been having. "It's not about Adam," I say. "Well, we're fans, but there's something about him that has just gotten us talking and thinking about our lives. It's important to me. I spend all my energy and time taking care of everyone else. You girls don't even let me listen to my own music in the car. You laugh at me. I need this."

By now I'm tearing up and my daughter is looking stunned. "So you can't go tell your sister or your friends."

She then delivers the thunderclap: "Dad read it too." Good God!! My mortification is total. Shit. Shit. Shit. OK, I'm done. I skulk off to my office and start surfing my iTunes, seeking solace in the velvety embrace of Adam's voice, and firing off emails in between so I don't feel completely useless.

Towards evening, there's another knock on the door. My husband comes in and we talk for some minutes about our evening plan to take the girls out to see a movie. There's a long pause. Then he says, "I read your letter to Adam." I sigh, smile weakly, and tell him about my wowOwow community.

He's not going to mock me, but he looks sad. He's shaken to realize the consuming scope and depth of my secret life. "I knew something was going on." Those late nights at my laptop. . . .

A lot of halting conversation ensues about how we are so consumed by work and family logistics; our life often seems like an unending To Do list. We are an awesome machine together, doing the work of ten ordinary mortals, an incredible team solving every kind of problem life has thrown in our paths.

▪ just a quick shout-out to fans: ya'll are the best! thank you for all ur positive energy and support no matter what. id be nuttin w/o you 4:41 PM **June 23rd** from mobile web

But I also remember how when we first met he had read Spenser's Epithalamion out loud to me on an afternoon when time stood still. Bought abundant bouquets for no reason. We dreamt up opera librettos, traveled for the sake of adventure. Less of that these days. And although he is a remarkable man, so brilliant, creative and wise, the writer of beautiful songs, I am not sure he is my Muse. Maybe Adam is filling that role.

"You're writing again." He's not upset. He's grateful. To Adam. "In the end, we have only each other. . ." We dissolve into each other's arms. Through my tears, I sob, "See, this is the Lambert effect." And he laughs, "Way to go, Adam Lambert!"

By Juneau Underwood on 06/23/2009 11:13 am

Oh, J, what a ride you took me on, the proverbial emotional roller coaster. I was hot, cold, paralyzed with fear for you and left spent. Do you suppose it was a Freudian slip to have left the letter where it would be found, so you could share this hidden compartment of your life with the people you love? So glad it worked out so well!

Love and hugs to a brave samurai,

X

By xena princess warrior on 06/23/2009 2:50 pm

Thank you Xena and Cat for reading and being so supportive. You never know. My Confession could have been greeted with stunned embarrassed silence. I can't believe I am sharing such intimate and painful secrets with you. I have been thinking about something Adam said in one of his interviews, about not hiding who you are. That one made me catch my breath. I try to live with integrity, and I am constitutionally incapable of lying, but it's all too easy to conceal parts of yourself, the parts that hurt. You have given me strength with your understanding and support. As for the possibility of a Freudian slip, who knows? Whatever hand of destiny or psychology was at work, I am proud that I was able to own it. And it was profoundly therapeutic to write about it.

Love you all, beautiful felines, women warriors.

By Juneau Underwood on 06/23/2009 6:13 pm

Juneau, thank you for being so open with us. Your story moved me to tears, and I was on the edge of my seat reading it. It was an important moment for you and your family, and it's amazing that Adam sparked your thinking and communication in a profound way.

E.! I am so glad to see you back. I've been reading since the very first postings, thanks to my Google News Alert—Adam Lambert. You were one of my inspirations and I finally thought I would burst if I didn't start writing—making my contribution to the collective that was feeding me for nothing. Unfortunately, I haven't stopped and even have a couple of pieces backed up.

Juneau—you sneaky samurai—thank you for giving us the chance to meet E.

Best regards, and we better see you again E.,

X

By xena princess warrior on 06/24/2009 12:59 am

Dear sisters! I am full of gratitude for your responses to my Confession—grateful to know that I was able to grasp the emotional core of what I had just gone through and string together words sufficient to share that voyage with you. You gave me encouragement, and you made me feel safe. You are my Muses, alongside Adam. If we do set up our own site (although this one works well for now), I suggest we call it AdamMuse.

C.! I don't believe for an instant that you don't have feelings. What can be difficult for many people, and I count myself among them, is to become conscious of what you are feeling, and then to understand what those feelings really mean. It certainly did not come naturally to me. It took a lot of time, experience (bad ones) and a lot of work. We erect so many defenses to protect ourselves from our feelings. Yet the work is so worthwhile. At the risk of trotting out an over-used expression, the unexamined life is not worth living. Socrates was right. We all have the potential to see, feel and express so much more than we do in our daily lives. How do we recognize that gift in ourselves? How do we nurture it?

G., here is an excerpt from my letter to Adam. I hope y'all don't mind, but I wanted to tell him about what has been going on here. Don't know if he'll ever visit the site, but I thought he might like to know what he has inspired:

"This is not your average fan site. The contributors can actually string together words into coherent sentences and thoughts. And what thoughts! There are, as one would expect, outpourings of love, admiration and gratitude for you as a performer, along with ruminations on why you are having such an effect. These in turn have unleashed a torrent of personal confessions, analyses, life stories from the commonplace to the kinky, and fantasies. Some people you know make cameo appearances. Their writings began to form an amazing collection, a veritable epistolary novel for the Cyber Age, capturing the lives and creative yearnings of a generation. I thought you might appreciate seeing what you have inspired. I hope you find it fascinating, amusing and touching. Some of it may make you squirm. Just don't let this go to your head, honey. If that happens, please share this web site with your wonderful brother so he can puncture our collective delusions. Remember, this is not about you. It's about Us.

What I'm writing now is about living spiritually in the 21st century. Truth comes to me from science. The Zen of my samurai ancestors informs my aesthetic. My historic and literary foundations lie in Judaism, which I study in order to guide my half-Jewish children to connect in a deep and truthful way to their heritage. The writers of the Torah had acute insight into the human condition, and when the archeological layers are stripped away, they speak to my own quest to live fully and seek transcendent experiences in the every day, whether I am placing food before my family, committing thought to digital bits, or stepping out into the night to experience the height of the heavens. Thank you, bright angel, for opening a new gate in my universe."

Have a wonderful day, lovely ones!

By Juneau Underwood on 06/24/2009 8:45 am

Here's a little bauble that I hope will amuse you:

Adamesthesia

I had minor surgery yesterday morning to remove a bump on my inner thigh (benign, thankfully). After years of being annoyed by it, I decided it was time to get rid of it. I arrived for surgery armed with my iPod to get me through the anxiety. I don't trust my overactive imagination.

As soon as I settle on the surgical bed, I pop the earbuds in, turn on my iPod, adjust the volume, and close my eyes. My Adamesthesia. My Adamvalium. The driving beat of "Black or White" fills my head.

I can feel my skin being scrubbed and pin pricks of lidocaine being injected. I visualize Adam in the B or W video, so fierce, prancing like a tomcat around the stage. I marvel at his perfect rhythmic timing. More lidocaine.

The nurse is massaging my shoulder to distract me, but we have moved on to "Born to be Wild." I hope I don't start involuntarily shaking to the beat while the surgeon is trying to make an incision. He's moving delicately with the scalpel, or so I imagine, as I don't feel any force or tugging. But he's cutting. Glad I can't hear it. I am thrilling to Adam singing "Take the world in a love embrace," savoring the sexy way in which he articulates the word "embrace."

Maybe this is too much adrenaline for surgery. Things slow a bit as we move on to "Cryin.'" I visualize Adam's sweet face (his dark spiky hair reminds me of a Tibetan mastiff puppy) coupled with his rock god swagger as he throttles the mic.

Are we done cutting? The plangent keyboard opening of "Feelin' Good" comes on. I settle into the groove of Adam's angel voice and ride along, barely feeling the blood dripping down my leg and the pressure being applied to stop it. A little tug this way and that. Is he starting to stitch?

I soar as Adam's voice climbs. I'm in awe of how he shapes that climbing melody line, holds that high note, rises higher still, and then gently, with exquisite tenderness and care, sets us down on the earth again. Still stitching.

Now I hear the haunting guitar melody (love you Edge) for "One." Should I hold up an earbud to share with the nurse? We are One, no? The tug and fro as the stitches are put in. Now I am adrift on the slow, melancholy flow of "Mad World," enjoying the luxury of time to lie still and listen. I hope the surgery lasts a while longer.

As Adam's ending high note fades out, I feel the nurse's latex-gloved hand dabbing gauze over the incision. Cleaning up. Bandage being

▪

June 25/09 Photoshoot with Robert Sebree

▪

RIP MJ 4:25 PM **June 25th** from web

applied. The mystical drums and sinuous notes of "Ring of Fire" are now creeping into my awareness. Good timing. I seize hold of its energy to get myself up and dance back into the world.

By Juneau Underwood on 06/25/2009 12:29 am

Juneau! I was just getting tired when I hit "preview" to edit what I was working on—when Adamesthesia popped up and I just can't stop smiling, my cheeks hurt and if I laugh out loud, someone's going to wake up—like the dog.

I'm so glad that you will be fine once the wound in your leg heals, but that's just physical, your mind is perfectly sound as far as I can see.

I wish I could describe Adam's singing as well as you do, but your words definitely do it for me. I hear the music and Adam's voice the same way you do, but can't express it.

I have to go to the dentist soon and I have hygienist Nurse Ratchet who talks nonstop—I'm going to give her the Adamasthesia treatment.

Now take two shots of whatever you like—for medical purposes I like a lovely, smoky single malt or a warm, sweet liqueur like Grand Marnier—and call me in the morning.

Love

Dr. X

By xena princess warrior on 06/25/2009 1:25 am

My Tribute to Adam's "Feeling Good"

Dearest MoALS and Glambertinas, thank God you're here, or I don't know what I would do to clear my head these days.

Over the past twenty years or so, I have spent about twelve in talk therapy with three different male psychiatrists and on meds. From my standpoint, I was there because society didn't know what to do with me, so I had to learn to fit in. However, I really believed that everybody else needed the therapy and I was just fine.

Well, it turns out both statements are true.

Happiness has been temporary and fleeting—of course the milestones have been there, but they don't last that long. When in the emotional dark tunnel (Churchill's "Black Dog"), one doesn't believe that happiness lies ahead, the single incentive needed to make the effort to get out of there and I had forgotten what "happy" felt like. A little flutter out of nowhere so short, you wonder if it happened and you say "*what was that? It seems a bit familiar. Happy! Wow, I forgot, but I hope I can make it happen again.*"

Here's the good news, I have been Feeling Good, positive, forgiving, accommodating and happy since May. I have had the confidence to be honest but diplomatic with people, and it has worked in my favour. Well, the diplomat in me gets a little shaky sometimes, but manages in the end because Xena can't work by sword alone.

Here's what's surprising—it came to me because of things that C has said—this group has been the best form of therapy for me and what a challenge! Today I realized that I have not taken a single one of my emergency pills since we met, I am not just happy, energized and creative, but—serene. Well, as serene as I can get, serenity having always been an elusive feeling for someone as intense as I am.

I use this expression "*You can't get the right answers if you don't ask the right questions*" and here is where the right questions are asked and answered.

I have actually taken my own advice (older sisters don't *have* to do what they advise) to put on the eyeliner, mascara, nail-polish and lipstick every day. While I am almost always friendly and open, I speak to even more people now and of course they share some words and smile back, which in turn makes me feel better.

I realized that I have been in a virtual hibernation from people, much the way shy people say they can feel lonely in a crowd, I have been somewhat closed down and not myself. No wonder I have felt anxious and depressed—I can't exist without the warmth of people in the flesh. I need the intellectual stimulation of good conversation, even a good debate is invigorating.

The range of conversation here, from analytical and academic to fanciful, arousing and entertaining to emotional and spiritual, just keeps me going and stimulated for more.

Here we have fashioned a sort of cyber cocoon of protection with words expressing feelings and creating a ring of protective arms around each other, or celebratory applause or amused laughter depending on our need. The only eye contact we have is channeled through our photos and videos of Adam looking at us and we looking back.

What a challenge—how do you hand someone a tissue for a tear when all you have are words? How do you stroke their arm when they need reassurance? How do you transmit your laughter and enjoyment?

We've done it and we are doing it. Take a bow ladies and I am sending hugs and kisses to thank you.

Love to all

X

p.s. this is just a little side-track to something I have been working on but stopped when Juneau went and mentioned Socrates to Adam and I had to write about that, and then I wanted to talk about how you have all brought me happiness, so I wrote this.

The "big" one is getting to 1,500 words, so I am trying to split it up. Forgive me for being so effusive and taking up so much space, but you left it open. I am certain to run out of ideas soon, but the last time I took off on an obsession, I wrote for seven months. My correspondents were almost all male and the atmosphere, well—it didn't smell nicely perfumed like all of you. The subject was war.

By xena princess warrior on 06/25/2009 1:15 am

Thank you Xena for sharing the story of your struggle. I feel honored by the trust you have placed in us. Surviving depression takes tremendous courage, faith and sheer perseverance. Does the darkness you have been through make your light burn that much brighter? Whatever it is, you are a beacon of wisdom and delight. Love, J

By Juneau Underwood on 06/25/2009 6:56 am

Here's Part I

An introduction of Socrates and his methods used in guiding us through our scholarly exploration of the Meaning of Adam

Juneau mentioned Socrates—my philosophical mentor and teacher, the original rational thinker, the godfather of logic. This forum is quite like those we had with the old guy in the markets in Athens.

Everyone believes it was only boys that Socrates mentored, but Xena was there too and excelled. Studying and debating with all those Greek boys—who gave her great advice on how to do her hair in an "up do" and the proper application of kohl to enhance the ferocious look so necessary to the Warrior's battle image—inspired the young Xena to maintain a youthful sexuality while fighting the Persians with Alexander the Great.

Socrates taught us that wisdom comes from the understanding that you know nothing and you should seek the truth through asking questions. We have been Socratic in our methods here, trying to understand our uncontrolled and visceral response to the beautiful Adam. We want to understand his place in the wider world as well. We know that we don't know anything, and in this forum seek to ask questions to try to reveal the truth.

I never really considered myself like somebody that people would throw their underwear at . . . my concept of myself is not that. I realize that I am doing some songs that are kinda sexual and kinda, you know, risqué. I guess it starts to make sense eventually. . . . They don't care about my preferences and what I do in my bedroom. They are reacting to what I am doing on stage which I think is the most open minded, amazing, progressive thing that they can do. http://www.youtube.com/watch?v=lysuDwGjP_Y

A couple of Socrates' wise pronouncements have influenced the way I live my life:

Once made equal to man, woman becomes his superior.

True wisdom comes to each of us when we realize how little we understand about life, ourselves, and the world around us.

And does this quotation apply to Adam?

An honest man is always a child.

Part II will follow "Now I'm Skerrred"

(Some may be uncomfortable being guided by a guy who's been dead for about 2300 years, so you might think about the detective Colombo, Socrates for the 20th century, crumpled raincoat instead of raggedy toga.)

Xena

Symposium Coordinator ***By xena princess warrior on 06/25/2009 2:02 am***

"An honest man is always a child"

Yes, this is Adam. When Adam first caught my attention on Idol, I admired his virtuosity. But it was when I saw the child in him—the hand thrown over his eyes when Simon praised him, the delighted grin after Whole Lotta Love, the mischievous twinkle in his eye at the end of Beththat I fell hopelessly in love. (My favorite line in Ring of Fire is "I fell for you like a child.") ***By Juneau Underwood on 06/25/2009 7:06 am***

Glambertinas' Revelry!

Report on Landmark Meeting Gloria, Xena and Priscilla

Damn! Gloria beat me! OK, so I arrive at the mansion in which our mutual friend resides and when she saw my van drive up, she looked out the window—I later discovered that Gloria had been warned by her savvy daughter that I just might be a sixty-five year old man. Voilà—I'm not. I wondered why she looked relieved when I walked-in. Glorious Gloria is the Blonde Bombshell I had envisioned and resplendent in her Adamesque outfit—zipper from top to bottom—great for easy access, tons of metal and flattering to her already great figure. Now I know that when she's around, I won't be getting any of the male attention—I hate that. Each of us wore black patent leather strappy sandals and I was in a black and white sundress. Having had to do battle with M-I-L before I arrived, this princess warrior was ready to settle down for an afternoon that felt like we were playing hooky from school, well I can only imagine how that feels, since I never did it.

First—the refreshments—Pomegranate Martinis, which must be a secret recipe since we were not allowed to watch as she prepared them—and what will now be referred to as the "Fruits avec Chocolat Chaud sur Crème Frappé Adam" dessert or breakfast in bed or midnight snack if your nocturnal activities give you an appetite. Strawberries, raspberries, blueberries and pineapple dipped in luscious warm chocolate and then topped with whipped cream.

Gloria arranged the perfect Adam accompaniment as we lounged on the floor, watching her rather complete collection of videos—and here is the amazing thing—she has everything memorized! A veritable bibliothèque in her brain, she is definitely our go-to on a number of details. She knows everything each judge said to Adam after his performance! She quotes Adam before he speaks. Gloria will be preparing "Favourite Quotes from Adam" for us à la "I'm not skerrrrred."

The other guest, brand new Glambertina is known as Priscilla, Queen of the Desert, has a great sense of humour. Now I will fast forward to when the seminar completely fell apart and I am laughing with tears just recalling it—I think Cilla started it, anyway, I will blame her, since she's not here yet and don't tell her what I said.

As we were getting near the end of watching all of Adam's AI performances on a massive TV and we had drained our martinis, Gloria played "Slow Ride." Having watched this so many times, my mind wandered and I started to look for things only visible on this huge screen and there it was—there's no zipper on Adam's laminated-to-his-body pants.

We rewind, we pause, we do it again and maybe once more, and we're quite certain about this. Now we do need verification, a peer review, because of our alcohol level at the time, so please, every one of you must play this video as many times as you need, to say "yes" or "no" to the zipper. Another option would be to take one of the photos of Adam with Alison at the end of the song, blow-up the targeted area, perhaps get a magnifying glass and tell us what you see.

Of course, at the time, engrossed in our analysis of Adam's various garments, we wondered what might he wear under stretchy pants or trousers. Can't be boxers, briefs would have obvious VPL and we see that he's not "commando." We concluded that it must be some type of thong, probably custom made. The style of pant also shows up on "Crawl through Fire" and "Crazy" in a lighter-weight fabric, also a source of research. Do you wish you were there? We wished you were there.

We did get some serious analysis in, on Freudian theory and how it might apply to our reaction and subsequent elevated moods and feeling of self-worth, following repeated exposure to Adam. We have been told that men think about sex every 10 seconds? I forget exactly. Also, that they need fewer senses stimulated for arousal than women do.

We think it's possible that Adam has changed all that for women. We only need one sense at a time—either sight or hearing to become, shall we say—inspired, fueled, fired-up. Watching him and listening to him at the same time, simply reduces the time from exposure to "full speed ahead." Frankly, we don't want to be in the room when they do the "three senses" test—it could be "touch" or "smell," one of our favorites. We would end up sounding like Kara after RoF or Feeling Good.

Now, we are drinking coffee. . . . From Freud, we moved on to the subject of endocrinology—now who among us would have thought that "endocrinology" would show up here. Well, I have been waiting days for an opportunity, so I threw it out there today. The discussion of senses led us to talking about the importance of the level of testosterone in women's bodies, in order to reach that "multi-sensual" state.

How can Adam, using only our sight and hearing get our pituitary glands to produce this extra testosterone? Do we have any endocrinologists out there who could take a stab at this? I would ask my own, but I'm afraid that I would embarrass her and she would drop me as a patient.

If any of you wishes to challenge my version of events, please feel free to contact Gloria for corroboration.

About the French—ever since I heard Adam use "accoutrements" —French words keeping popping up in my mind.

By xena princess warrior on 06/26/2009 1:35 am

Six hours!? Felt like sixty minutes. Maybe we need a pyjama party.

I meant to include Gloria's illuminating demonstration of Adam-inspired Chakra vibrations, which brought a fourth dimension to the Adam experience, not to mention the smell. Gloria led us through an exercise to help us really feel those vibes and we did/do.

I told DH* and our Daughter who has been in on it all along, about our support group, how it evolved, and my furtive, late night writing. He's aware of this since I moved my computer into the bedroom and he's used to my periods of obsessive writing. I explained how I had found this amazing group of brilliant and sensitive women to talk to and how helpful and supportive all of you are to me.

He simply listened as he ate dinner and smiled with a bemused look on his face. He must have had an inkling that something was going on, since I have been happy, more affectionate and demonstrative, patient and accommodating. Laughing more. No complaints from him whatsoever. When we are alone again—I will tell him more.

Xena

*Dearest Husband **By xena princess warrior on 06/26/2009 10:21 am**

Glambertinas! So much going on, so little time. . . .

Zucchini Flower, I'm sure we are all reaching out to you in a big collective hug. I'm moved to the core to know that you've found joy and healing and strength through our writings.

Re: zippers, sounds like another MoALS topic ripe for ripping open. I have to confess I did not think those striped leggings that Adam wore in Slow Ride were flattering. I'm thinking it's time to resurrect the little game I started back around page 20 of "If I could do X for Adam Lambert." I started with X = "cook a fabulous meal," with the challenge of keeping him trim and sated at the same time. If that doesn't tickle your fancy, how about "If I could decorate his bedroom." (I find it sweet that Adam keeps mentioning wanting to buy a house.)

Other MoALS topics: I think I should take on the Adam as Muse, but I also volunteer throw in a thesis on "Deconstructing Adam's Tongue."

LOVED hearing about Xena, Beth and Priscilla's get-together. I can almost taste the fruit slathered in warm chocolat and crème. I will need to bone up on my chakras.

Finally, Xena, I also enjoyed a little *frisson* of delight when I heard Adam pronounce "*accoutrements.*" French is the language of seduction, no? My husband speaks it like a native. Maybe I need to ask him to speak French to me more often. Whilst on this topic, there was an amusing bit of advice in a recent New Yorker talk of the town, to the effect that once one passes the age of 49, it's best to state one's age in French. It sounds almost glamorous. I think I may try it out. "*J'ai cinquante ans, cherie.*" **By Juneau Underwood on 06/26/2009 1:55 pm**

I loved this interview! Adam's mind—another source of enjoyment! He used "Bromae" as plural for "Bromance"—if Bromance were a Latin word, Bromae could be the plural. French, Latin—be still my heart! I love those little asides he throws out there. He can't hide his intellect behind glittery eyes and tight pants, it shines through and for many women, it's another source of pleasure.

I have to use this in a fantasy and show the depth of this man. Henry Kissinger once said that "power is the greatest aphrodisiac," trying to explain why women were so attracted to him. I don't think it's as much power as it is intelligence for me.

Kris and Adam are such great friends, protective and supportive of each other—I repeat—when can I have lunch with both of them??

Xena **_By xena princess warrior on 06/29/2009 12:04 pm_**

Love it, GG80! I've been trying to develop the continuation of my fantasy, but my Muse keeps leading me into territory that probably isn't suitable for a family-oriented forum like this (kidding, but there are boundaries of taste). Trying to tone it down without losing all the heat, or exploring a whole different fantasy. Thinking about a vampire / Twilight take, but nothing yet. . . . **_By Juneau Underwood on 06/28/2009 9:45 am_**

Well ladies, here is my magnum opus.

There were recent references to articles posted to other Adam fan sites, that inspired this response and they reflected the writers' desire to imbue Adam with messianic qualities—someone who by his mere presence and force of personality and popularity, could change the world. They attempted to answer questions such as "Why now?" and "Why Adam?"

I challenge the claims that "we need it" and "he's filling a void" and "the world must accept it" and provide alternative responses to these questions.

Part II

Now I'm Getting Skerrred 29 June 2009

Now I'm getting skerrrrred. Imbuing Adam with the powers to bring about world peace, an end to famine and clean up pollution is a pedestal from which he is bound to fall, since as I have been reminded —he's only a man. By describing the current world in apocalyptic terminology, Adam is raised to the level of a saviour who will lead all of us out of these times, into something new and better, a standard bearer for causes.

Wow, I really don't think he signed on for this much responsibility. Besides, we're not paying him enough for that job.

My reaction was to protect Adam and his talents from others staking claims on his success. He did it himself. Claiming we were looking for someone like him??—I don't know who the collective "we" is, because I was not looking for anyone to do anything and certainly would not be looking to American Idol to present someone to change the geopolitics of the world, rescue a gloomy economy or fill a void in anyone's life.

If we were, why were we so shocked by how we reacted to him—instantly, in the gut? No one was rational—we were reacting to his performances and what little tiny peeks we got behind the AI curtain.

Here is all we knew—he's got the best voice in forever, he's creative about his performances, he plays a character for each song—complete with costume, jewelry, hair, make-up and set. He can manipulate every single part of his body to pose or move as he has choreographed himself and does that ever work—on us.

Claiming we "need it" implies that if we didn't "need it," Adam's talent and efforts would have gone unnoticed. Think about this—we would have heard and watched him and said "ho hum," who's next?? Really?

"Adam fills a void" now that is downright insulting to him, saying we are only using him to complete something we knew was unfinished. But, I believe that Adam pried open a corner of our hearts and minds and jumped in with both feet, assaulting our senses.

"People accepted him, flaws and all"—exactly what are his flaws? There are over 1200 comments here and I don't have to read them all to know that we have not heard about or discussed any flaws. No one is flawless, but I would like to know Adam's. They can't be the "open, honest, true and steady" description used in one of the pieces. They don't give any examples of "flaws."

No one within Adam's sphere of influence has to accept anything about him. Anyone can buy his records and listen to his music, just for the quality of his performance. They don't even have to know anything about him at all.

He was not invited

Let's not forget that this young man wasn't really invited into our world, he snuck in, camouflaged in jeans, t-shirt, hoodie and clean faced. Safely inside, he showed up in our living rooms tiptoeing at first, and finally, kicking and screaming, bending rules, putting up with insults, eye rolls, an invasive media and he did it graciously.

Each week he showed up as a different "Adam" from sleek crooner to hell-raiser and he somehow managed to focus on his art and his ambition to achieve his goal—the AI finale. He executed his strategy perfectly.

He won't be put in any existing music genre boxes and he has made such a splash, he can control his own destiny and produce magic on stage, on video and with his voice alone. He just wants to be a great entertainer whose music can make us laugh, cry, dance, love or make love, a tough enough goal as it is.

Attempting to put people into boxes and keep them there has been a problem for me, I keep breaking into the next one and people don't like that.

He was brilliant to not respond to the media's demands that he label himself the "gay" contestant so some could use him as a standard-bearer. He knew what they wanted and gracefully stood his ground and explained why. Claiming a winner for your side is always great, but what if Adam had failed as the "gay" contestant? Would they have abandoned him?

The Questions are, "Why Adam?" and, "Why us?"

We have been Socratic in our methods here, trying to understand our uncontrolled and visceral response to the beautiful Adam. We want to learn his place in the wider world as well. We know that we don't know anything, and in this forum ask questions to try to reveal the truth. (From Part I)

Why Adam?

Adam is truly greater than the sum of his talents and graces. Impossible voice, physically graceful and completely expressive in his performances, he compels us to respond to his message, from the tragedy of a broken heart, to the pathos of Mad World, to the sheer joy of dancing and sex. Our response is more than intellectual, and as one of our Glambertinas says, he creates vibrations. All this we learned from his carefully prepared strategy for AI and he succeeded brilliantly.

His Ability to Communicate

Then we held our collective breath until we heard him speak without constraint. Vocabulary, grammar, body language, eye contact and tone of voice are the subconscious checklist we have in mind and he gets full marks for each!!

He has the ability to speak his message in a voice appropriate to the likely audience while being utterly Adam the whole time. Talking to the Idolatry interviewer, chatting with Regis & Kelly or speaking to the Rolling Stone audience, provide evidence of an agile mind able to respond to each situation, a quick wit and a wicked sense of humour.

Good Character

But, is he a nice guy? Another test for us and he surpassed anyone's standards of "nice guy." We have seen his relationship with his mother, heard him speak with the students at his former performing arts school and his roommate Kris obviously adores him. Would we still be talking and writing about him if his colleagues on AI had not spoken openly about how he helped them?

But this generosity and niceness came through in his performances —politely acknowledging the musicians, smiling at the judges, being embarrassed at effusive praise. Hearing that he was a great friend to his colleagues, was not a surprise.

Honesty—we tend to worry about him being too candid and open about his life, but it's almost impossible for him to deny or contradict himself—two great qualities in any human being. Confident, affectionate, generous and grounded, he seems to possess such an abundance of enthusiasm for life that it radiates and affects us. He takes the blame and shares the credit. Who would not want to be the merest planet in his orbit?

After he trapped us with his talent and charisma, he fed us with his personality, and his excellent character—we are victims of Stockholm Syndrome and even with the door wide open, we refuse to abandon our kidnapper. We feel like we belong here.

A Man for All Seasons and Times

Adam is timeless, blessed with talent, beauty, personality and one performance on the Ed Sullivan show in 1962 would have been enough to inspire me to keep a scrapbook, tracking his life as closely as possible. Still have my Beatles scrapbook from 1963—it is paper, my Adam scrapbook is electronic, will it still be here in four and a half decades?

A performance on Ed would not have been a smoldering and spicy version of Ring of Fire with a Middle Eastern arrangement, but as we all know, he can sing in any genre and even if it were in Turkish, we would get the message and experience the song through his voice and body.

I was hooked by the sound of his voice singing Tracks of my Tears, and caught in the net when I sank down before his stunning image a few seconds later. That performance is easily transferrable to the '50s and '60s family entertainment show.

Adam's Talent and Personality are Transcendent in Time and Place

As Adam has said, there is no single musical sandbox in which he can be confined, so he can play in anybody's sandbox, he's got the toys. He is equipped for Musical theatre, choral, classical soloist, rock, pop and anything else that would have suited the time and place in which he might have found himself.

His personality and talents might have inspired Mozart, Bizet or Verdi to write opera for him. He's fun to be with, dedicated to his art, witty and flirtatious. Many aristocratic and artistic societies coveted individualists like Adam. They would have befriended him and he could have partied from dusk to dawn every night. He would not have suffered for lovers.

Such an open society is not confined to 2009.

Paris, London and Berlin would have loved him in the 1920s—recall "Cabaret"—and isn't it so easy to imagine him playing dress-up at the Moulin Rouge, surrounded by the high-kicking, scandalous can-can dancers at the turn of the century?

I would have paid anything to have seen him performing with the virtually naked Josephine Baker, oozing sexuality in her bananas skirt, at the Folies-Bergère. "Crawl through Fire" would have had line-ups there. Baker, who was more than the sum of Madonna, Lady GaGa, Britney and whoever is out there at the moment, was an exotic African-American and with Adam, what a dynamite duo they would have been.

From Woodstock to Broadway, to the Met to Studio 54—who would have locked the gate, the door or the velvet rope to Adam? Surely not the Andy Warhol Salon.

One of my great frustrations is the inability for some people to see past about ten miles around themselves or even as few as twenty years previous to today. The contributors I have quoted above could be an example of this myopic vision, though possibly these were the first thoughts that came to them at the time.

It's about Us Individually

Some of us have said that indeed "*he may be the awakening we have been looking for,*" and our next words expressed our shock and awe that he forced himself upon us. If any of us were looking for some kind of "awakening," would we be hunting in the AI woods?

Further, I truly believe it diminishes his extraordinary personal accomplishments if we claim that he is successful because we were looking for him and we found him, or that world conditions are such that "we need him."

He is the most gifted, creative, charismatic and hard working performer we've seen in a very long time, so surely this completely unique gem we describe is special. He is eager to please us and we have responded with as much adulation as any entertainer can get. He is a complete surprise and no one was looking for him, how could we when we didn't even know such a one existed? No one could have invented or even imagined Adam.

Below, I make the case that the collective "we" as used above, does not deserve to pat ourselves on the back for being "open" or "accepting" or whatever other favourable attributes with which we wish to endow ourselves, or that this tiniest of fleeting moments in the continuum of time is the only time the stars have been aligned to receive Adam.

When asked why he wasn't discovered earlier or why he didn't audition before, he responded that *he* was not ready and not that we were not ready for him.

These are the questions to which we seek answers here at the MoALS site.

I would have loved Adam, his voice, his beauty and his primal sexiness at twelve, twenty or thirty years old, which would have been in the sixties, seventies and the eighties. Then, we would never have known as much about him as we do now, which is both a blessing and a curse.

There was no ET, People or Perez Hilton, no paparazzi, no Facebook, My Space, videos or photos on the internet for which he would have to answer. Celebrity magazines promoted positive qualities and protected popular artists. His personal life would have been left personal.

Here's what I think he can do beyond entertaining us

If through his ability to draw us into his aura, mesmerize audiences with his performances and leave us feeling great about ourselves, he helps many individual people get out of their funk over the economy and any other worries and gives them a little more perspective on their lives—that would be great. He has already accomplished this with us, but it's not necessary to selling music and tickets. It's a value-added feature.

Adam as role model

Adam is very specific about how he wishes to represent himself as a role model—*to the weird kids out there, persevere and follow your own dreams and to mom and dad—encourage and support them.* I am raising one of those "weird" kids, so I can really appreciate what he wants to do and he is very much needed. Not only for gay and artistic kids, but any who feel ostracized.

Adam as Creative Inspiration

I believe Adam can and will, influence style and entertainment, particularly since he is the first in ages who crosses demographics with his appeal.

And how is this for special—he seems utterly unfazed by the media, impervious to their antics and by not jumping for the bait, they will leave him alone and he will eventually control his exposure.

Right now, we are the audience for any snippets the media can toss out to us. Once we have more of his music and videos available to maintain that connection with him, we should become satisfied with whatever Adam wants to give us.

This little collective of women, the Glambertinas, the MoALS, possessed with abundant but possibly suppressed creativity, have adopted Adam as our Muse, our inspiration to look deeply within ourselves individually and as a group.

We have the curiosity to wonder about our capacity for self-improvement, to investigate our opportunities, to express our fantasies, examine our personal relationships and to support each other in this process.

What a gift we have received from this young man.

We've learned that honesty won't kill you and if you believe you have a talent to share with others—get out and do it, because as Adam said, no one gets "discovered" anymore. Adam's message really isn't that complicated—if you want to do something different in your life, only you can make it happen.

We get this and are applying it to our lives to varying degrees.

Sometimes it's just survival to the next day after discovering we are not alone. This cozy meeting place helps me in many ways. Possibly through the sheer fact of our distant geographic locations, dear Glambertinas, we can gain a better sense of time and space, how through a shared obsession, we have found sisters over the Northern and the Southern Atmospheres to share our secret joys and sadness and the feeling that we get more than we give. This is a terrific bonus for belonging to the Glambertina Tribe and the MoALS.

I hope that Adam's fans around the world have been able to deepen the experience of enjoying the complete Adam, the way we have.

Let's conclude this detailed examination with what is really important in life.

• Share your happiness with your loved ones.
• Connect with people everywhere you go, share your smile and they will pass it on.
• Eyeliner, mascara and manicures aren't affectations; they tell the world that you think so much of them; they should only see you at your best, you put some effort into it.

• It is time to break out the gloss and glitter in how we present ourselves—sparkle, people!!
• You will light up the world.
• And there will be music and dancing!

With love from
Xena *By xena princess warrior on 06/29/2009 2:22 am*

Correction "North and South Hemispheres," not "Atmosphere"
X *By xena princess warrior on 06/29/2009 2:26 am*

Hah hah, I liked "Atmospheres." I thought you were playing (and subconsciously you were!) with the image of our cyber conversations, which are definitely transcending normal earthly, geographic boundaries. I love what you wrote.

You express so eloquently and precisely many thoughts that have been churning through my brain, but I didn't have the energy and discipline to rope them in and line them up into such a thought-provoking and satisfying essay. Bravo Xena!

I have some thoughts here regarding the phenomenon of celebrity. I don't think it's quite as simple as saying here's this phenomenal talent who would have been recognized and adored no matter what decade he appeared in.

There is something about the confluence of people with special gifts and the times in which they live. Some geniuses do go unrecognized in their lifetimes. There is something to the concept of the Zeitgeist and the yearnings of the crowd.

What is scary is when the crowd ascribes Messianic qualities to the object of their collective desires, and confuses the mythology they have constructed with the person. I've gotta run, but thanks for supplying so much scrumptious food for thought and more writing. . . .

By Juneau Underwood on 06/29/2009 11:56 am

Juneau—you are so thought provoking!! I barely finish what you have written and I want to talk to you about your ideas. I finally found the time, 12 hours later.

Your note sounds like you have more to say, shall I wait for your additional thoughts or may I "reply" to you?
Xena *By xena princess warrior on 06/30/2009 12:00 am*

gettin ready for the idols live tour! 1:31 PM June 30th from mobile web

I have detected a small, but potentially significant similarity among Glambertinas. Some of us share an obsession with Scrabble. My actual obsession with the game started about eighteen years ago and just before my family attempted an intervention, I stopped. Since then, I only play Scrabble on occasion, when appropriate, thanks to my family's refusal to play with me all the time.

I don't know about Gloria Beth though, who today informed me of her affliction. For all I know, she could still be obsessed with Scrabble and on Saturday, I discovered that my cousin, a younger woman who loves Adam, also loves Scrabble. What a dream—playing Scrabble while listening to Adam sing and enjoying a glass of New Zealand wine.

Far from being a distraction, Adam's voice seemed to quicken my mind's reaction and I managed to win handily. That tasty NZ wine must have added the extra punch to give me two seven-letter words in a single game.

So Glambertinas and MoALS—any other Scrabble players out there? If we find a few more, I will consider adding this to our Symposium: Women who love Adam and Scrabble

Mere coincidence or is there a connection?

Xena **_By xena princess warrior on 06/29/2009 1:25 pm_**

Part II of my Hollywood Fantasy. Enjoy!

The music is throbbing, the sitar notes skitter and swirl, sending waves of sensation firing through my nervous system. Adam's arms are around me, pulling me towards his chest. My palms are pressed against the luscious fabric of his jacket. Baby alpaca? I can't resist the urge to massage it, and then slip my hands inside. Now I feel his warm breath traveling from my hair down to my temples and alight on my cheekbone, caressing my skin. "Your skin is amazing," he murmurs, and I draw in a sharp, involuntary breath. "Oh shit, Adam, this is no time to get bi-curious," I gasp. "Let's not kid ourselves." Adam pulls back and gazes intently into my eyes, with a look of hurt. "It's all sexy, baby. It's all beautiful." I swoon inside. But I draw myself back from the brink, mustering what little will power I have left, and whisper fiercely, "please, don't play with me!"

Now that I can see around me again, I am startled to see that R and the Famously Gay Rock Star have closed in on us, riding the urgent throbbing music. The FGRS is sidling up to Adam. And R's eyes are burning with an unrestrained passion. Now R is embracing me from behind. I am pressed between him and Adam. I can barely stand. I feel

I am floating in space between two glorious seraphim. I'm gazing softly up into Adam's eyes. The FGRS is pressing up behind Adam, his hands are traveling over Adam's body. He wraps himself around Adam like a serpent. Adam's fingers are twisting through my hair, and through R's long silvery locks too; he's not resisting either. Bi-curiosity runs both ways. . . . We are entwined in a seething tangle of Want.

Abruptly, the FGRS pulls back, and he snarls, "F*ck, we gotta get outta here." Somewhere in the outer reaches of my consciousness, I hear a familiar noise—the soft snap and whir of a camera—and become aware that we are not unobserved. Something is lurking behind the draperies. The FGRS throws aside the drape, and reveals a glistening, porcine face: Perez Hilton. The sight of the self-promoting celebrity blogger drains the heat out of the room.

R grabs the camera out of Perez's hands and over his screams of protest, hits the delete. The FGRS and his band mates are already slipping out towards the back of the club. The bass player is barking into his cell phone, "we're coming out!" Adam grabs my hand and I follow. We scurry through a dark hallway and out a rear fire exit. A black stretch limousine is waiting for us, the driver deftly opens the door as we run towards it. We dive into the back, one after the other and collapse onto the soft seats, gasping with laughter. The limousine hums into motion. Where to? "Back to the hotel," says the FGRS. "Anyone up for a game of Scrabble?" [*To be continued, possibly . . . or not*]

By Juneau Underwood on 06/30/2009 12:16 am

Whoa Juneau! I haven't even had a coffee yet and my legs are too wobbly to get down the stairs. Your descriptions are so vivid, you must have had to stop several times to catch your breath and wipe your brow, as you practised each sweat-inducing movement and touch. Love, love, loved it!

And how thoughtful of you to include a Scrabble game! Now, there's a fantasy I could write. Scrabble with Adam. . . .

Xena ***By xena princess warrior on 06/30/2009 8:57 am***

I must say I thoroughly enjoyed concocting that last fantasy! Xena, how's that for a set up? I'd love to see what kind of Scrabble fantasy you can compose. . . . ***By Juneau Underwood on 06/30/2009 6:13 pm***

You kicked my brain in-gear with your set-up and I already have some ideas. For the sake of continuity, I think the setting will be the hotel, or maybe the limo takes a detour. It will be a high stakes game with a winner and a loser. Just how good is Adam?

By the way, took Adam to the hair salon and we had a great time, since both the colourist and the stylist are hip young women. Adam sat on my lap, on the cover of Rolling Stone, which I had taken with me to "read" and it took about two seconds for the girls to start the conversation. I told them about us, the Glambertinas, and they thought it was wonderful and want such a support group for themselves.

Xena

p.s. The Ottawa Citizen has a huge picture of Adam on the front of the Arts & Life section for an article about men wearing make-up, with "how-tos" and some biological justification for lining the eyes.

By xena princess warrior on 06/30/2009 7:16 pm

Love how you used Rolling Stone as a conversation starter. I'm afraid to bring up his name in conversation, and if anyone actually responds, I have to work hard to contain my giddiness. Last week I gushed a bit to my friend who plays with me in a string quartet, knowing that she's an admirer, and our violist piped up "Who's this Adam Lambert? All my musician friends are talking about him!" That gave me quite a warm and fuzzy feeling! Can't wait to see what you come up with in your fantasy . . . I'm trembling in anticipation!

By Juneau Underwood on 06/30/2009 8:56 pm

C., my heart is bursting reading what you wrote and I too was thinking how none of us would ever have met and how lucky I am. Those of us who "think out loud," need someone to talk to for the process to work. I am astounded that I have now written over 20,000 words here—on one, single thing we all have in common, our insane obsession with Adam. Just as interesting is the fact that we haven't been "discovered" which would have brought people with whom I couldn't connect.

You C., and all our friends here are the most indulgent group I have ever experienced, and I wish I could carry you around in my pocket all day long. You are never out of my mind and we have chats you don't even know about—until I write them down. I feel great every day and I'm able to cope with the stresses and strains of my life, even taken back ownership for part of it.

Thank you.

To Gloria, I have discovered an amazing way to get those vibes going. Put the CD in the car, crank up the volume, especially the bass and you will feel them. I almost forgot to turn right today and just made it through. A little bit of Adam/Nirvana in an otherwise mundane shopping trip, I didn't want to go home.

By xena princess warrior on 06/30/2009 9:16 pm

Happy one-month anniversary, all! I'm glad I sparked this . . . and that everyone is having so much fun with it.

By Allegra Huston on 07/02/2009 11:41 am

Dear Allegra, thank you for the inspiration. The Glambertinas and MoALS have been so provocative and fun, that I have spent way too many hours here. I don't know what would have happened had those words remained captive in my mind all this time, only to burst out uncontrollably, at the worst time. What an exercise in analysis, synthesis, humour and erotica—a blast.

Thank you for bringing us together.

Best regards,

Xena

By xena princess warrior on 07/03/2009 2:43 pm

Re: favourite Adam version

My love-at-first-sight was Tracks of my Tears, so that's who I connected with instantly and by the time he got to Whole Lotta Love—pow! man of my dreams.

Aren't his chameleon abilities one of the elements of his attractiveness?

You can place him in any number of our fantasy situations and there's an Adam who will fit right in—with panache.

What will he look like for our Scrabble game?

Xena

By xena princess warrior on 07/01/2009 10:10 am

Talk about "eye sex." That RS cover photo embodies that!

By Juneau Underwood on 07/02/2009 7:48 pm

▪

July 2/09 Adam posts a picture of his leather jacket for the tour on Twitter

▪

sneak peek of my Skingraft jacket I get to wear on the Idols Live Tour! http://twitpic.com/93r6f 6:30 PM **July 2nd** from Echofon

▪

PORTLAND ROCKS 10:58 PM **July 3rd** from web

The Messiah Pose

The photo, the imagery: lips puckered, serpentine belt, arms outstretched—head tilted back—eyes closed—bare arms—ripped jeans

I believe that Adam uses symbols to communicate with an audience as this does, or to keep him safe as his Egyptian God tattoo does. Every item of clothing, each accoutrement is strategically considered, as is the choreography.

Here's the Serpent in the Old Testament: *Now the serpent was more crafty than any of the wild animals the LORD God had made. He said to the woman, "Did God really say, 'You must not eat from any tree in the garden'?"*

The woman said to the serpent, "We may eat fruit from the trees in the garden, but God did say, 'You must not eat fruit from the tree that is in the middle of the garden, and you must not touch it, or you will die.'"

"You will not surely die," the serpent said to the woman. "For God knows that when you eat of it your eyes will be opened, and you will be like God, knowing good and evil." (Gen. 3:1-5)

My summary description

He's the dangerous boy your dad warned you about, tattooed, ripped jeans, earrings, long hair and that very symbol of lust and evil—the serpent. Makes him a "must-have-him" obsession for us.

In this pose he looks like that boy, asking for forgiveness for what he's just done, not in this standing pose, but lying down. Completely open in anticipation, lips awaiting a kiss, arms ready to fold around a loving body? Serpentine belt removed with one hand while the other feels for the z—oh no . . . have to stop or I'll fall off my chair, go unconscious, the police will bang the door down and find this open on my computer!!

For now, X

By xena princess warrior on 07/08/2009 8:57 pm

Asking for forgiveness? There's not a shred of guilt or remorse in that boy! He's asking for love. He's inviting you to go with him, wherever he wants to take you. And we'll all go there with him!!

By Juneau Underwood on 07/08/2009 10:40 pm

Can't he pretend to be someone other than Adam? You are right that he never feels guilt or remorse and has said so many times.

X

By xena princess warrior on 07/08/2009 11:27 pm

OK, Xena, you did have to bring up the Garden of Eden, and now I have to release my thoughts on this subject, although this is still a work in progress. Here goes nothing. . . .

"You will not surely die," the serpent said to the woman. "For God knows that when you eat of it your eyes will be opened, and you will be like God, knowing good and evil." (Genesis 3:1-5)

And the serpent is correct, for there are two trees in the middle of the garden: not only the Tree of Knowledge but also the Tree of Life.

▪

July 5/09 Tour begins at the Rose Garden in Portland, Oregon

▪

Our first show was so much fun!! Portland's audience was amaaaazing! 12:05 AM **July 6th** from Echofon

▪

July 7/09 Tacoma Dome in Tacoma, Washington

▪

TACOMA was badass! We're def gettin the hang of this! 50 more shows to go! 1:08 AM **July 8th** from web

▪

July 8/09 GM Place in Vancouver, British Columbia—pink bra thrown on stage

Now, this story always struck me as a complete set-up, for it is inevitable that Eve will be drawn to taste the fruit and to offer it to Adam. And why not? Does God really want his best creation to remain in a state of blind obedience, no better than a puppy? God has to want humans to have Knowledge, for without it, humans cannot appreciate the full glory of Creation. Without Knowledge, humans cannot aspire for transcendence, to become one with the Angels. But Knowledge also comes with a price: We are no longer happy, innocent creatures. We perceive our beast-nature and are ashamed of it. (Here one can truly say a little knowledge is a dangerous thing. . . .) We are cast out of the Garden, so that we may not taste of the other tree, the Tree of Life. And the rest is History, an unrelenting struggle between our beast-nature and angel-nature.

However, God offers another path back to Eternity, through an earthly Tree of Life, the Torah. In Torah, the way to Eternity is not through following rules (although there are plenty of them). The way to Eternity is through the experience of Transcendence in the here and now, by fully experiencing the miracle of creation, which is around us all the time, in every molecule we breathe, but which we generally fail to appreciate. We imagine that the sacred is something that stands apart from the every day. Sometimes it does help to put yourself in that kind of space. But the sacred is all around us, all the time, if we open our minds to it. (It's just so damned hard, when you have hungry children and deadlines, along with feelings of pride, guilt, shame, jealousy, covetousness, etc.)

We achieve transcendence when we reconcile our beast-nature and angel-nature. Which brings me to our latter-day Adam, he who embodies the beast-angel, so purely and vibrantly inhabiting his lovely flesh, brimming with erotic energy and overflowing with a voice like Praise. He is totally channeling the cosmic force. In him, "bad" and "good" merge completely. Sleazy morphs into sublime. When we consume him, we experience a shattering of those false dichotomies within us, and we feel Whole. Dare I say this is an experience of Transcendence? ***By Juneau Underwood on 07/09/2009 12:00 am***

Juneau, so true—thank you for this and if this is a work in progress, please send the finished work.

I hope this continues your thoughts as it takes us from the sacred to the profane.

Transcendent—yes, we have used this term before in describing Adam. He transcends:

- attempts to define him musically
- attempts to delineate different types of sexiness or sexual attraction "Sexy is Sexy"
- fear of exposure—he has none
- duplicity—he is consistent and truthful
- rules society might have about friendships and he's frank about it, and more. . . .

Here in this open yet safe haven, we have been describing a transcendental metamorphosis in ourselves, for over a month. We already knew the impetus for our journey—to understand how Adam "did what he did" to us, pushing us toward this introspective analysis, attempting to put words to feelings and to find a connection to others with the same experiences, to validate our own.

With no logical or obvious scientific reasons to explain our virtually complete surrender to him, we sought explanations and understanding. We are the type of women who are at least curious and at best, demanding to know what is going on with our minds, our bodies, our emotions, our relationships and Adam disrupted our routine lives profoundly.

But we liked this chaos he created in us, to bypass our internal censors and be perhaps Anaïs Nin for a few weeks, writing shocking erotica or reading shocking erotica or looking at it.

But our journey has taken us much farther than any of us could have imagined upon taking the first step, joining the caravan on a cyber pilgrimage, seeking more and more knowledge and comprehension of ourselves. Few can have participated without being affected in some way, with some better sense of well-being and assurance—we are not alone. We are not crazy, just jovial.

Better yet, as our creative muse, Adam has inspired us to be imaginative, to write, to share with each other as well as others. To create scenarios for others to enjoy as well as the pleasure the author gets from writing them. Has he not explained how he wants his music and performances to inspire sadness, happiness, to love or to make love and to dance?

Adam has lifted us to transcendence, not just spiritually and creatively but in other ways as well—and don't we know it.

We have morphed from landlocked caterpillars to airborne, brilliant, colourful, shapely, show-stopper butterflies in eyeliner, mascara, sequins and smiles oh, must add—red shoes for dancing.

There must be dancing.
Love
Xena

By xena princess warrior on 07/09/2009 1:25 am

Dearest Glambertinas,

This was a tough one. Adam and I had a lot of scenarios to try out before settling on this story—prepare your senses.

It's so late, because I kept going over and over it, perfecting each syllable, each motion, just for you, and I never wanted the evening to end, so it's now 5 AM.

Unfinished Business & Silken Dreams

"Cheri, it's so late—what happened?"

I've answered the door and Adam's standing there—disheveled—leather jacket and shirt are undone, shirt freed of the jeans on one side, silver jewelry left dangling on his bare chest, but I noticed something new there. Is it horn? It's on a black silk cord, so I grab it to take a closer look and lightly tug Adam toward me.

His tall frame sways forward, then back—his heat smells of faded Homme, something else masculine, musky and a woman's perfume—a hint of rose with a spicy background—perfect for evening.

"Adam, what's going on, where've you been?"

"I was partying with some friends at that new place after the show, we thought we were alone but turns out there was a bunch of—well, we had to leave in a hurry. I really need to unwind and get some sleep so I'm good for tomorrow—came here to crash—hope that's okay, Princess"—he kneels, looks down coyly, his hair falls in front of his face and when he looks up at me through that unruly fringe, and the fulsome eyelashes—well who could deny him anything?"

"C'mon in."

Great—I get shopping and sleeping—someone else is rubbing their scent all over him. I'm not sleepy and have been working here all day, so I make a plan to clear up some unfinished business with him. He'll get his sleep . . . eventually.

I turn Adam around and point him toward the bedroom door, his jacket slides off in my hands and I call after him—*"change and put on something comfortable"*

As he walks away with a slight stagger, I stare at the back of his low-slung jeans—so tight I wonder how he gets in and out of them—does he need help? His shirt clings to his back; little tendrils of hair have curled loose from the damp of his neck.

I follow, but enter the sitting room. It's decorated in crimson, purple, sapphire and curry, a lush room with silk covered walls—the floor splendid with cushions over Turkish rugs—a room designed for lounging and relaxing. Another world—sachets of exotic spices and flower petals are tucked into the folds of velvet and silk, ready to release their secrets when crushed under a hand or elbow, a shoulder, perhaps a back.

Oil lamps bathe the room in warm amber, leaving the corners dark and infinite. The sequin and crystal adornments flicker around the room like fireflies.

Yes, this should help Adam relax, but I have more soothing surprises and some unfinished business with him.

Emerging from the dressing room, sheathed in a silk robe, he carefully parts the rose velvet curtain and pushes in; humming something familiar—ahhh perfect, just the song I wanted to hear. His hair, hastily brushed off his forehead, reveals those smoky blue eyes and they've never been more languid, confirmation of his earlier exertions.

I take his hand and lead him to a stack of velvet and satin cushions arrayed next to a small ebony table and as we settle in, the blue silk robe Adam dressed in slides open across his thighs—all that dancing has paid off—toned muscles—powerful. He takes his time smoothing the robe between his legs, below the loosely tied scarf he's used as a belt, in a half hearted attempt at modesty. Now the top unwraps further, this he leaves alone—I keep this room warm.

Languorously, he leans back—then turns and rests his head in his hand. The silver threads in his kimono glint as he moves around—sparks of cool fire, a silvery aura.

"Princess, aren't we going to play Scrabble? I was hoping—I got some ideas to twist up the game. Been playing with the boys, they're not just pretty faces and—well, you know what I mean."

Oh, I know exactly what he means. Our delicious boy has attracted a bevy of blonde cuties, ready to do his bidding—didn't even know they could spell. This should be interesting.

"Does that mean Adam Rules tonight?" I ask.

"Please?"

"And if I win, Cheri, what's my prize?"

"Didn't you say something about unfinished business? Whatever it is, tonight we'll finish"

We shift our bodies around to face the table. Under our weight, the hidden buds explode and we're in Marrakesh, the Silk Road, the spice route—opium, dangerous with bandits, but we are oblivious in our tent, heavy with every sensual luxury imaginable. Warm cognac to sooth the throats and tingle the lips. Adam licks his in anticipation, takes a sip, and then kisses my lips softly—mmmmm stinging.

"Oooo, Princess. . . .

My young male servant arrives with a silver tray laden with luscious fresh figs, sweet plump dates, heart shaped, blushing two-bite strawberries and, warm, flowing chocolate with a sprinkle of cinnamon. Adam is licking his lips—while staring at the blonde boy, then biting into one of the huge dates with his teeth, closing his lips around it as it disappears into his mouth. Tonight Brad's uniform is a pair of loose, silk harem pants—amethyst.

"That's a tasty, fresh date Princess, I'll have more. Can Brad play with us too?"

"Maybe later Cheri, maybe later"

Adam lifts his torso from the cushions to sit up and cross his legs, now I know why he chose that robe—it slips apart with a whisper, while Brad is setting up the Scrabble board. To get relief from the oppressing heat, Adam opens the top of his robe and waves it to cool his body.

"*Tell you what Cheri, if you win the game, you may spend tomorrow with Brad—take him shopping for some new clothes, lunch. . . .*" Brad raises an eyebrow and lifts the corner of his mouth in a subtle smile—to Adam who winks back.

With that, Adam grins impishly, takes a strawberry, swirls it in the chocolate and makes an offering to me—I slowly wrap my tongue around to lick the chocolate, he takes the berry back, dips it again, I lick the warm and sticky elixir and quickly bite into the strawberry, juices trickle and I lick his fingers clean.

"Princess—the rules—whoever scores more points for each word per round, gets a wish granted, but it has to happen in this room, tonight"

I'm lucky with the first round; Adam puts down "queen" for twenty-four points—good start. But mine's better—I slowly place each tile on the board—l-u-s-t-i-l-y. That was good for ninety-three points!

"My choice Cheri!—I haven't had time to think of something, so let's just start and see where it goes—a back massage, merci."

I lie down with my back to him, face to the side, resting on cool satin; Adam frees the scarf of its loops, releasing the robe as he straddles my legs. He's warm and moist in the heat, his skin velvety against mine as he lowers himself, gripping my legs with his, pushing my small cover up my legs, my back and over my head, arms outstretched.

Brad has brought the orange blossom oil over and offers it to Adam, who leans down to breathe in the sweetness of the orange, lingering with almond—arching his back as savours it, eyes closed.

He dips his fingers in the bowl and rubs his hands together before he begins to massage my neck with just the right pressure—those soft, aromatic hands, not usually massaging a woman's body, but these days, stroking a mic stand or pressing and smoothing his inner thighs on stage. Small pulses with his finger tips, then harder with his thumbs, palms. As he wends his way down my torso, he wraps his hands around my waist with a little squeeze, palms on my back, fingers pressing around just below my breasts, he snakes down the rest of my body. Now bowed over me, feeling his hot breath on my skin, behind my ear as he whispers, "*is this what you had in mind, Princess?*" I exhale "*Oui, Cheri.*"

Unbearably intoxicated—the fragrance of the room—chocolate, cognac, orange blossom, spices and flower petals crushed together, cloying—light flickering, seductive music—Adam holding me down with his bare legs, while I shudder and close my eyes, I feel weightless.

When I open them again, Adam's face comes into focus above me, his eyes on mine, a big, confident smile, his hands caressing my hands and arms—and when he lets go, I rub my oily palms down my body slowly, to relieve the shivering and come back to earth.

Adam's robe is barely clinging to his shoulders now—he's so beautiful in this light—his cheeks glow and his body glistens, his hair fallen, his youth revealed. I reach up and press my hands over his chest to feel solid and earthbound, *thank you, thank you, merci, merci, Cheri, mon amour. . . .*

▪ **July 10/09** Arco Arena in Sacramento, California Sacramento

▪ : I love u. Sorry I didn't sign autographs outside. I have a killer headache. 11:39 **PM July 10th** from Echofon

After my victory with "lustily," I really hope he wins the next round and I can fulfill a wish for him—but I can barely lift my head so Adam re-arranges some pillows to lean on. Adam's losing steam and needs to lie down soon and get some sleep. Breathing slowly and deeply, my body takes in the oxygen I need. I'm cooling off, but my cover is gone. What a prize that was—wonder what he'll ask for.

Adam drapes a light cashmere throw around my shoulders, holding it in place with one hand, as he starts to work on his next word with the other. This time he doesn't do any better—t-o-n-g-u-e for fourteen points, while I play—h-a-r-d-e-n on a triple word for twenty-seven. Hmmm, that didn't work out so well, but Xena always has a plan "B" when it comes to getting satisfaction.

"Forgive me Cheri, here's my second wish. I can see you're fading; the air's scorching, so I will be gentle. You recline over here, put your head on my lap and stretch out your body."

Adam's lashes pull his eyes closed; I brush some hair from his face so I can see him. His body is dreamy, and his arms are open, reaching for me—it's that pose from the RS cover without a green snake or other accoutrements. Robe is open, body released, flesh revealed, he is unprotected, vulnerable, lying in mellow anticipation.

I reach for a strawberry, dip it cognac, then a swirl of tepid chocolate, leaning over his face, I touch the tip to his lips and his tongue moves quickly to grab the berry from my fingers and savour his catch in his mouth, sucking the chocolate before swallowing the strawberry. His tongue licks the droplets of chocolate from his lips.

He looks up at me with pleading eyes, mouth open to receive another and I succumb, feeding him another and another. Brad brings some warm oil, this time, sandalwood, cardamom, juniper berry mingle in their balmy bath and exude maleness, warm and ready.

Brad kneels at the feet of our Adonis, and begins with his thumbs on Adam's soles while my scented, slippery hands massage his shoulders—I work my way down. "*Meet you in the middle*" to Brad. The music speeds up, Adam is moving slightly, to the music, careful not to lose our hands on his body and gradually his body begins to almost pulsate, his breathing quickens, body twists. We push harder.

His body heaves up to meet our hands, pelvis, then chest, as we close in on him, reaching the tipping point, the point of no return, the peak, the pinnacle of Mount Olympus. Cascades of electricity move through his body, blistering our hands as we take the heat.

No longer looking vulnerable, Adam sighs triumphantly and brings Brad's face, then mine to his. Fevered lips singe ours—his arms around us, a satisfied smile, peaceful eyes, I shake his robe loose and pull it up, kiss on the cheek—"Slumber in sweet dreams mon Cheri, mon amour, mon ami"

After *this* game night, Adam and Brad can shop tomorrow and it's on me. That unfinished business? Will have to wait.

By Xena Princess Warrior on 07/11/09 5:00 am

▪ **July 11/09** Adam and Kris host American Top 40 for Ryan Seacrest

Oooh Xeenaaa!! I just arrived in Vienna, gateway to the sensual Orient, and am about to crash. This was the perfect bedtime story, evoking all the senses (almost all—how about a soundtrack, maybe Ring of Fire playing faintly in the background in an unending loop). I can taste the

▪ Oracle Arena in Oakland, California

cognac, smell the aromas and feel the supple contours of Adam's body under oiled skin. And the French is priceless. Very very sexy! Good night, darling! *By Juneau Underwood on 07/11/2009 7:14 am*

I can't express my happiness when you tell me your reaction. I write plenty, but never this or anything like it. I'm a policy analyst, so yes, lots of writing, dry and boring. I have a male friend who is helping me to get started writing more, I'll have to figure out how to fit in the stimulating stories, among my many interests. I recommend to all Glambertinas to try it out, for a good time. It feeeeels gooood.

Yes, unfinished business—I had the opportunity there, but squandered it on pleasure instead. I sensed Adam wasn't in the mood for what I wanted.

X *By xena princess warrior on 07/11/2009 2:53 pm*

Gloria, Juneau and Niamh, I am so glad you responded warmly to my story. Juneau, thanks for kicking my imagination in gear with your club fantasy and handing Adam over. You'll note that I had a moment of jealousy for you.

It took so long because I must have read it 100 times, over and over to make sure the story had continuity. I lived in that room for many hours, studying it, adding layers to it. Indeed it is the room Adam described in one of his interviews and that image stuck in my head so it was one of the inspirations.

Thanks for the pleasure of writing for you—okay and myself too.

Between Adam himself and you Glambertinas, I have a lot to work with for my stories/experiences. The fun with food—I had to keep tasting it until I had it right.

Glad you enjoyed it, my pleasure to write it.

Should I have put an X rating on it as a warning?

Xena *By xena princess warrior on 07/11/2009 11:05 am*

Thanks N. C. an "R" is what I was going for, thank you. Since I started this, right after Juneau's date, I didn't worry about the set-up too much.

I have hidden a few surprises in plain view, I'd like to see who finds them. Still have that unfinished business to deal with and I wonder what happens when we wake up?

X *By xena princess warrior on 07/11/2009 1:43 pm*

I'm salivating to find out what you have concealed up your silken sleeve, Xena. I detected the traces of my presence (on Adam) in your Scrabble episode. What I'm wondering is, did he come straight from the limousine, and if so, how did he get so disheveled? Or did he stop off first at the Famously Gay Rock Star's hotel suite for what turned out not to be Scrabble but something else? Did Adam yield to the ardent advances of FGRS? I'd better go drink some strong coffee so I can figure it out. Or perhaps a glass of champagne (with traces of cinnamon-laced chocolate lingering on the rim) is what's called for. . . .

By Juneau Underwood on 07/12/2009 1:34 am

Oh, Juneau, you stopped me in my tracks and I left you and Adam dancing on the beach to take this call.

Indeed Juneau, I knew Adam had been with you and a couple of others when I sniffed his jacket, I know your fragrance. Cute, seductive, but dangerous. It was you who left the limo first with everyone else, while Adam headed over to my place for some relaxation, rest and rejuvenation. He works too hard. Of course my green eyes sparked when I knew you were having all the fun, but Xena finds a way.

Given his multi-person activities earlier that evening, how could Adam have arrived buttoned up and hair combed? And he was exhausted. My home is an oasis of calm, a spa for rejuvenation of one's spirits, a restoration of balance. Desires are sated, for taste, for smell, for sight and sound and for touch. Playing games is integral to helping recover that playfulness we lose. Scrabble, played with Adam's rules works well, win or lose.

Now, I better go find out what you and Adam have decided to do next on the beach, or you'll be there all night.

Love

X

By xena princess warrior on 07/12/2009 2:12 am

Juneau, I am getting very emotional over the situation into which I have put you and Adam in the fantasy I've written and need to compose myself and sleep on it. They'll be fine where they are.

X

By xena princess warrior on 07/12/2009 2:48 am

Ahhh Xena, those orange blossom scented massages and Olympian eruptions will hopefully have quelled those green sparks, although being a Scorpio, I'm not immune to falling into the clutches of the green-eyed beast myself (indeed, I was aflame after reading about what you did after Adam was cast unceremoniously out of the limo by the FGRS—more on what precipitated that later, when I've had a chance to still my beating heart). Fortunately, Adam's energies are sufficiently abundant to satisfy us both. *By Juneau Underwood on 07/12/2009 4:40 am*

Dearest Juneau, There's nothing like a little competition to ignite the passion to please another of mutual desire. But, you and I are nothing if not generous, sharing friends and confident in our abilities to transcend any such jealousies. I agree with you that Adam is possessed of such gifts that we need not compete.

As a triple Libra, I must wrestle with a vision that is more than three dimensional, so forced to consider all possible explanations and options, requiring constant consultation, research and analysis, consideration of new information and opinion.

Living here among the hardest working Glambertinas, not to mention the MoALS, resourceful all, dedicated to searching and reporting everything they uncover to us—how can I conclude this project? Just when I think I have no more words, not a shred of anything more to give, avoiding news of our desired, one of our group will present a gift to arouse my curiosity once more, invading my waking and sleeping imagination and I become a slave again, images and words pour forth onto the page. I wish I had more to give, but words are all I have. I can craft no object of affection to bestow, evidence of my gratitude for his gifts.

I received some very bad news last night that shook my earthly universe and am grateful to have your friendship and all who contribute here and inspire me creatively. Sometimes our immediate world is too painful to consider. So happy to be here right now.

Love

Xena *By xena princess warrior on 07/12/2009 2:59 pm*

▪ **July 12/09** HP Pavilion in San Jose, California

▪ Dance with me and I'll Set you Free!!!" 11:46 **AM July 12th** from web

Oh Xena, I'm so sorry . . . I don't know what to say except to offer love and support and the hope that our community can offer you a place of refuge and healing. *By Juneau Underwood on 07/12/2009 5:06 pm*

J, this is a refuge some might consider artificial, but for us is real and truly connects us emotionally. Thank you for sending your love. I just posted something I know you will enjoy and writing it, I was transported to a different time and place.

Soon, I will go back to where I left you and Adam, to find out where you will go and what you will do. You must be getting cold by now.

Love

X *By xena princess warrior on 07/12/2009 5:27 pm*

Thanks, N. S., this is a great story, the naive mom, mere chauffer to the offspring, chaperone at best—sets eyes, ears on Adam then jumps in the net along with the rest of us.

If anyone thought there were many of us before, wait till they see the Million Woman March of the Glambertinas, Glamberts, MoALS, Grannies for Glambert, Adamettes, Adambombs and the rest, after this tour.

As I said to my daughter today, this is Gene Simmons' come-uppance for his remarks on Adam's sexuality "he's not a rock singer," "he killed his career by talking about his sexuality"

Get with the programme Gene, it's the 21st century, Adam is filling stadia around N. America—and we all know everything there is to know about him.

Undergarments flying, screaming, shrieking, freaking, fans on fire!

I predict that Adam will set a huge milestone and be the next Sexiest Man Alive. How do we make that happen? That would be the best. Priceless.

How could any man be sexier than the one who can remove the panties of women *and* men.

Makes one glad to be alive.

Xena **By xena princess warrior on 07/11/2009 10:37 pm**

Do you think there's a market for Gothic Erotica for women who desire an unattainable gay man? If there is, bring it on, baby! Truly, there is great pleasure in the writing, dreaming and experiencing.

Xena **By xena princess warrior on 07/12/2009 6:13 pm**

Welcome T. C.! From time to time, we have wondered if there were "literary voyeurs" reading here, but not revealing themselves.

So glad we have been able to help you validate your feelings about, and responses to, our recently dubbed Prince of Passion.

Turning On!! Transported back in time and space to a high school dance over forty years ago, I was riveted to a spot in front of one of the band members and couldn't take my eyes off him—he looked exactly like Adam does here, but had he moved and sung like Adam, I would have accosted him at the back door, tied him up and taken him home.

We look forward to reading more from you, T. C.!

Xena **By xena princess warrior on 07/12/2009 4:09 pm**

Apollo, God of Light and Truth

Part I: The Comedy

Casting Adam as Apollo, god of Light and Truth describes one who indeed shines his formidable beam into the darkest corners, to reveal the verities hidden therein. Brave and strong, Apollo slew the Serpent Python with his bow and arrow and wears his trophy to sheath his feet.

He has overcome those who claim to judge for others, to face us directly, in body and in soul.

Protecting his most precious corporal possessions, he has fashioned a shield of silver in the form of the dreaded Serpent Beast. Holding the shield before him, he proclaims it to us to prove his courage and supremacy.

Apollo, the beardless youth of the Ancient Greeks, is multi-faceted and is also known as a god of Music, Poetry and the Arts. How powerful is one who employs his gifts in the Arts to bring us Light and Truth?

Ancient images of Apollo show him with the lyre and the snake, a confident demeanor in his expression and his sturdy body, warrior and artist, in one combined. Unwrapped, yet unashamed and direct with his gaze.

His strength and power cannot be denied as he overcomes thousands upon thousands of mortals everywhere he alights, to invade their hearts, their minds, with nary an arrow. Some already worship his deity and come to bask in his light, while others wander in, out of curiosity, only to be struck deeply and then depart, not wounded, but in love, impassioned, inflamed with desire and generosity.

Shining with a small spark of Apollo's radiance, the converts join the rest of us in illuminating the world for others to see more clearly, the unlocked treasures of Truth and Love.

Xena

By xena princess warrior on 07/12/2009 5:21 pm

Pleeeeeease C., don't suggest images of Adam, dusters and aprons—I might write about it! I have to put those images out of my mind, immediately.

Thanks for the update and welcome home. New installment in the X/J epic due out shortly. Hope I'm not up all night.

Xena

By xena princess warrior on 07/12/2009 11:40 pm

C., none of us knew we needed anything B.A. (before Adam). Did I know I needed to write like this? NO. Truly our muse, Adam is. You C., and all who visit here fulfill my needs to know I'm not alone, to discover I have courage, I have heart and I have the ability to enrich others' lives for a moment, with my words.

Without the mystical, magical invasion of Adam, we would have carried on with our lives just fine, not even realizing there was more within us, not just to find our own happiness, but to share it with others. Sounding a bit cultish there, I know, but that's what I have gleaned from the women who comment here.

As to frilly aprons and feather dusters, do you think my servant Brad would wear an apron for me?

Love, X *By xena princess warrior on 07/13/2009 12:52 am*

I would dress Brad with strategically positioned feather dusters (with handles of braided leather that can be converted to other purposes). OK, I'm waiting for your next story with unseemly anticipation. . . .

By Juneau Underwood on 07/13/2009 1:44 am

Don't start!! feathers are nice and Adam likes them. They can be breezy, whisper soft against skin, hovering, . . oh no! no feathers before I finish what's demanding my immediate attention. You!

X *By xena princess warrior on 07/13/2009 2:15 am*

Juneau and Adam go Dancing

You, who smears and leaves her perfume all over Adam, his favourite dancing darling, tonight the space is pulsating, pounding—soul-moving music, flashing lights and steam rising from the tightly bound mass of humanity.

Adam and you—crushed together on the dance floor—a writhing wall of flesh and limbs surrounds you. Their collective pressure alone keeps you upright, before they all shift and you collapse, hair cascading behind you. Adam catches you—his muscled arm securely cradles your waist, bending his face to yours—have you fainted? Are you breathing? "Baby? Babe? Juneau?"

Lips to lips spark of life—pulls you up in both arms and Rhett carries Scarlett away to safety, to air, to space. Your diaphanous chemise billows, lights behind shine through to reveal your contoured beauty, barely concealed.

Pressed against Adam's chest, shirt open, you lean your head on his shoulder. Open your eyes and he might stop and put you down—eyes remain closed as new sounds and smells surround you—the ebb and flow of surf crashing on rocks, salty, cool air. The dance music fades in the distance, as the water music comes into focus.

His Homme mingles with your spicy rose fragrance, rising to calm the crispness of the ocean. Cool damp of Adam's flesh on your cheek, swaying in his arms as he strides along is—nirvana, heaven, paradise. How far can he walk with you cradled against his body like this? Please, keep going. . . .

Adam slows, kneels and gently places you down on a soft, giving surface—filling the contours of your body. With his hands, he carefully lifts your head to smooth your hair and brush out the sand with his fingers, arching your back to free your dress, before he lays you down and smoothes the gauzy fabric down to your thighs.

Opening your eyes, his are quietly concerned, gazing down at you, his hair with cobalt glints, flutters across his face from the breeze. Moonlight spills on the contours of his face, his body ethereal in the silvery air, whispering "*Juneau, how do you feel, Babe?*" Those devilish dimples in the corners of his mouth curl with relief as you look at him and smile back."

"What happened?"

"Don't worry; we're fine here for a while, before anyone misses us. We won't leave till you say so. I thought you just swooned like my fans—but you fainted." Relaxed now, you share a giggle recalling the sight of the women and men at today's concert—on fire! It was sweltering, swooning, crashing—normal behaviour for Adam's fans.

"*Here, take my shirt,*" he draws the garment around your shoulders, wrapping both of you, warmed by his body, smooth satin on your skin as Adam runs his hand through your hair, cheek, pulling you closer, curling his thigh over yours, your body pliable to his movements, he's singing "I will Always Love You," breathlessly, warming your face with his kisses, down your neck, he stealthily moves beneath your weightless cover . . . ah, bliss.

"*We'll stay here as long as you want, till you warm up and feel steady*" he squeezes you with a hug, leaving dimples on your skin. Adam's body radiates heat—you're warming up already and sit up. Taking your hands, he lifts you to your feet.

Shirt over your shoulders, he snakes his arms around your waist, yours on his shoulders and with his hips, pushes you slowly, from side to side, sliding your chemise up, grinding against you as he swirls the silky fabric over your skin—gracefully and enticing you to respond. You slowly return his movements, hip to hip, side to side, feet still. Your hands find their way down his body to pull him closer—he's already there.

You dance slowly, until the friction alights—driving you to a chaos of passion, bare feet slipping in the sand, bodies, hands sliding, grabbing, fabric tearing—until you find your balance again.

Finally the rhythmic, luxurious, soothing ocean music connects and you slow down again, your breathing calms, you're dancing to Ring of Fire now. Adam—the flame ignited, licking, flickering red hot, the sand turning to hot coals.

Unexpected, unprepared—undecided! Where's he taking you? Will you go?

Adam sings, softly, slowly, deeply, in a voice you've never heard before—intimate, invasive—you are incoherent.

"You need coolin', baby, I'm not foolin'
I'm gonna send ya back to schoolin'
Way down inside, a-honey, you need it
I'm gonna give you my love
I'm gonna give you my love, oh

You've been learnin'
And baby, I been learnin'
All those good times
Baby, baby, I've been discernin'-a
A-way, way down inside
A-honey, you need-a
I'm gonna give you my love, ah
I'm gonna give you my love, ah"

Drawing out each syllable, lips pressing your ear, "way down inside, I'm gonna give you my love" his voice, cascading waves of sound vibrate to your core and back up, as he covers your body with his. Your cheek on his chest you try to reach his ear, to protest his now obvious desire for more from you.

Before your words can reach Adam's ear, the wind captures them and scatters them on the beach. Is this a message you wonder? How can you decide?

What's left of your filmy chemise offers little modesty and no separation of your flesh from his, there is no doubt now of Adam's reaction to your touch, his warmth envelopes you like a velvet coat. Still swaying as one, the song lingers in your mind, your body; the words arouse—the pressure of moist, supple lips to your neck, to your blazing cheeks, to your lips, your body yielding—against your wishes?

Juneau, how long can you leave this unfinished business, this incomplete act, this desire allowed to lie fallow? Like Carmen, you tease, arouse and then abandon his passion, his body at attention, awaiting your surrender.

Is it Eros or Philia guiding your heart? Can the two co-exist as one? Have we faced this before or has Adam broken through another box, refusing to be restrained as either the erotic lover or to settle for a filial, brotherly love, like that which he shares with Kris? You know you'll both be unsatisfied with a platonic friendship.

Will this be the reckoning?!

Philia abandoned—it's Eros who is the wind; he's come between your protests and Adam's ears. He mimics your voice and whispers to Adam an answer to his supplications, which you cannot now deny.

Adam's urgency immediate, you are the flower, opening in the rising sun, the morning glory ready to be kissed by the dew of dawn.

By xena princess warrior on 07/13/2009 3:26 am

(Lyrics excerpted from "Whole Lotta Love," by Jimmy Page, Robert Plant, John Paul Jones & John Bonham)

Yes . . . yes . . . yes!! Holy multiple Adamgasms, Xena!! What a priceless gift you have bestowed upon hapless Juneau . . . she is swept away by your glorious words and visions to a neverland of passion and bliss. (Allow the editor in me to interject for a moment about your last image. Is it really almost dawn? I thought timing-wise Adam and Juneau are still enveloped by night. I envision a moonflower shimmering like angel wings unfolding to be caressed and penetrated by bright beams of starlight. . . .) Since you have warned me that something is about to intervene, I will simply hold and savor this image for as long as I can . . . have mercy! Love, J ***By Juneau Underwood on 07/13/2009 4:43 am***

J. The timing is really on the edge, you were at the party for hours before you fainted and time on the beach is compressed, you might even have slumbered there, wrapped in Adam's arms, legs, body—a cocoon of heat and beating hearts, momentary stillness, trapped in body and soul.

You're on Cleopatra's barge on the Nile, lovebirds coo in their cages, you are cushioned on a down-filled divan, gently swaying on the rippling surface of the water, sky glitters with the stars of a million exploded suns in the lapis sky—Marc Antony stirs.

He brushes your cheek, your lips with a plucked ostrich feather, black as onyx, down to your décolletage; your responses involuntary now, breasts rise in anticipation—with the greatest delicacy, your lover glides his instrument of pleasure where your body eagerly awaits it.

At the penultimate moment, you open your eyes, they're reflected in a pair the colour of blue topaz, framed in the blackest fringe of lashes—raised eyebrow, crooked smile, tongue parts lips, savouring

Would that help pass the time during the night, till dawn?

Xena *By xena princess warrior on 07/13/2009 10:48 am*

Thank you I. R. In my "Silken Dreams," Adam is tired and reluctant and somewhat passive, but manages to "perk up." In Juneau's original story, he's coming-on in a very complex, arousing, intense scenario and in "Dancing," he's quiet in demeanor, caring, gentle and ultimately, dreamy, the event evolves from the sexual tension that existed in Juneau's original story. He wants more, she does too, but she's conflicted, her intelligence makes this more than just an issue of physical attraction / satisfaction, torn between the two types of love we are limited to, she wonders if there's another way for them.

Stop me! I can't believe I am analyzing my own fantasy stories.

It is a large, but not impossible challenge to put an extremely sexy, attractive to men and women, gay guy in a heterosexual female fantasy, we have limitations within which we have to work, hence the need for lots of atmosphere, sensuality and metaphor—this is not male oriented at all.

He has been very candid about his sex life and stated that he lost his virginity at 21, after a period of unease and really opened himself up to the lifestyle when he was in Germany—and dyed his hair black, creating a new identity for himself. Hmm, haven't discussed what happens to people when they change their look drastically? Save for later.

So, I. R., present us a laid back Adam! And you women are unbelievable worriers! Adam is soooo happy!! Isn't that great? I will remind you that he is 27, who were you at that age? His accomplishments this year show his intelligence, focus, strategic thinking and the ability to finish the project. All qualities that work in his favour to succeed, happily, joyfully. Stop the worrying and enjoy his pride in himself at what he's done, anything less diminishes him and his maturity.

That is what holds people back—others who make them believe that they are too weak or lack something to succeed. How many of us heard those "warnings" from parents or others. Please be serene and don't get caught up in off-hand comments or third-party stories, make up your own mind and don't try to worry about how someone else might react to "bi-curious."

He's over six feet tall, handsome, about to be rich, very smart, affable, fashionable, outgoing and 27—he's been on his own since he was 19, travelled around the world and his mom does not look worried. I'm not skerrrrred!

Go Adam! Go Adam! Go Adam!

Now, I have to get back to that other boring stuff I do for pay.

Love and serenity to all

Xena

By xena princess warrior on 07/14/2009 1:20 pm

Dear Glambertinas, I've been holed up working on my next fantasy, which fills in the missing hours between the club scene and Adam's arrival at Xena's place. In the mean time, here's something I whipped off a few weeks ago for your consideration. . . .

What is a Muse?

It's one of my current favorite rock bands, as it happens (thanks to Adam), but that's not what I'm talking about. I'm talking about the Muse who is making me stay up late at night tapping away eagerly on my keyboard. The Muse who inspires me. That sexy, teasing Pan figure who I find myself so rapturously wanting to please with my stories, my sensibility, me. The phantom with whom I carry on witty and provocative conversations all day long. How am I doing? Were you impressed by how I just described that scene? How about with the way I look today, the way I just walked into that restaurant? Aren't I worthy of your phantom adoration and love? Can we be friends? I have an adult imaginary friend! Sheesh. . . .

What *is* a Muse? It's such a hackneyed Romantic concept, but I don't know what else to call this phenomenon. A Muse is a Being who *compels* us to create. That feels different from the support and encouragement that comes from one's real life partner, the one who is in the trenches with you, paying the bills, repairing the plumbing, waiting up for teenage children to get home safely, negotiating whose family to spend the holidays with—all the unglamorous, unending and essential tasks that go into building a life together. A Muse on the other hand is an idealized being who inspires expression. It's hard to embody that ideal when you're up to two AM clutching a screaming baby and covered in projectile vomit. It seems quite unfair to ask one's life partner to add being a Muse to the job description.

I understand for the first time why Picasso took so many lovers and wives. Duh!! A Muse must be gifted but also young and fresh—not

July 14/09 E Centre in West Valley City, Utah

Hey guys it's Adam, I got my Twitter running back. I want to give a shout to AINOW.com for the support. Thank you guys, love you all. 8:49 **AM July 15th** from web

July 16/09 Staples Centre in Los Angeles

a peer, but one whom you can instruct and impress, and whose radiance reflects back a flattering image. (Of course Picasso was a jerk who used up and disposed of his Muses.)

So what makes someone a Muse? What makes so many people find a Muse in Adam Lambert? It has something to do with his approachability and humility combined with swoon-inducing beauty of voice and physique. It also has something to do with his having struggled, been in pain, searching for love. You want to create something that will amuse him, comfort him, seduce and excite him. You want to meet him, become his BFF, become his lover. And you want never to meet him, to preserve him as a perfect being who can continue to stoke your engine. He can be the object of an exalted, pure and uncomplicated love, because he is created by Art. ***By Juneau Underwood on 07/17/2009 6:13 pm***

Juneau, what a lovely rendition of Adam as Muse. I don't think a loved one can be a Muse. Inspiration to create must exist in a separate life, an elevated force, mystical and one with whom we don't discuss mundane daily life decisions, like who will go shopping for food. Picasso took his Muses as wives, then his Muses as lovers who then replaced the wives, etc.

Living in our Adam Muse sphere, all our worldly needs are fulfilled, allowing us to luxuriate in his attention, and as you say, prepare ourselves for his approval, admiration and pleasure. I understand the dichotomy of your desires with the corporal one having the potential to cancel the idealized being with whom we are besotted and over whom we have some control.

So too, do we risk a reality check of us, visually and earthbound, when with our words, we can communicate images we can neither speak, nor realize. Who do you present, Juneau or Juneau's mistress? Am I Xena or the one for whom I speak?

It's not the former that would make me as nervous—as the second—that I wouldn't measure up. I need to maintain my idealized self in my mind and not invite the face to face comparison.

Xena ***By xena princess warrior on 07/17/2009 9:19 pm***

Cheeks looks exactly like Brad, my servant in the purple silk harem pants.

X ***By xena princess warrior on 07/17/2009 8:41 pm***

That interview—he quoted Shylock in Shakespeare's Merchant of Venice!! French, Latin, Shakespeare. "If you prick me, do I not bleed?" Thank you finding this, N. C. Fall in love all over again.

▪

Our fans are dying to know what kind of cologne you wear! (4:32)
Adam Lambert: Hahaha. . . . I wear Dior Homme. (4:32)
Comcast LiveChat **July 17, 2009**

▪

July 17/09 Adam receives the keys to his 2010 Ford Mustang GT Convertible

X

By xena princess warrior on 07/17/2009 9:32 pm

Dear Niamh Cat, Xena, Cleo and Gold Berry,

I have astonished myself by how much satisfaction I derive from writing and posting the thoughts churning in my mind. The simple act of expression is so cathartic. And when this triggers such new creativity and support from you all, that's just icing on the cake! OK, truthfully, it's more than icing. It has become nourishment too. You are all my muses now!

O for a Muse of fire, that would ascend
The brightest heaven of invention. . . . (Henry V, prologue)

July 18/09 San Diego Sports Arena in San Diego—Adam plays with a blue boa

By Juneau Underwood on 07/18/2009 4:50 am

Kings and queens! You remind me of the David Bowie song that I really wish Adam would perform—"Heroes." It gives me chills, it's such a beautiful anthem to the transcendent power of love:

I—I will be king
And you, you will be queen
Though nothing will drive them away
We can beat them, just for one day
We can be Heroes, just for one day

I love watching this live version:
http://www.youtube.com/watch?v=YYjBQKIOb-w

Bowie is so gorgeous in this with his hair blowing back. I wouldn't mind seeing a little more of his restraint in Adam's performances (if that doesn't sound heretical). Adam is like a powerful thoroughbred stallion who can do anything. If he can rein himself in a bit, I think it would be very exciting because we know what he's capable of when he lets himself go.

By Juneau Underwood on 07/19/2009 5:53 pm

(Lyrics excerpted from "Heroes," written by David Bowie and Brian Eno)

Instrument of pleasure . . . your pen is mightier than Adam's sword, Xena, You transport us into realms of unspeakably delicious passion. Time to return the favor. . . .

In Which Adam and Brad Express Their Gratitude

From somewhere not too far away, soft drumbeats thrummed against the curtain of sleep that was slowly lifting from Adam's brain. Not yet ready to face the day, Adam hung back in that delicious state of suspension between wakefulness and dreaming, afloat upon images and sensations of the previous night. mingled with fantasies of what might have happened. Memories of bodies pressing hotly into his, shimmering eyes gazing up into his own, tumbling hair, parted lips that he filled with prickling champagne from his mouth, strong, slender fingers sliding deliciously over his skin . . . his mind circled around the unfamiliar thrill of Her—Juneau? Xena? A tantalizing fusion?

Having been drawn only to boys and men, he was mesmerized by this new attraction. It felt transgressive. Was it possible to lose one's virginity all over again? He sighed, eyes still closed, and sent his mind wandering back to the unforgettable sensation of her skin, velvety as an apricot, stretched over toned muscles. He was surprised and excited by her strength. He wanted to endlessly rub his face against that glorious skin, redolent of spices and tasting of salt and crushed rose. And then there was her companion, an aristocratically handsome older man, with hair flowing to his shoulders. The way they gazed at each other, breathed and spoke . . . from the moment they walked into the circle of light at the club, Adam had felt an erotic force between them and was drawn to it like a moth to a flame.

In the back of the limo, Adam had inserted himself between them, much to the annoyance of the FGRS, who slouched with his band mates on the far seats. With each thigh pressing into the wonderful beings on either side, Adam chatted brightly while entertaining delicious thoughts of three-way erotic acrobatics, turning over the possibilities in his mind like a Rubik's cube. As the limousine purred down Santa Monica Boulevard, flutes of champagne were handed around. Adam took a sip and playfully bent over and kissed R, coaxing his lips apart and letting the cool, prickly sensation flow into his mouth. R stiffened in surprise, but he accepted the offering, drinking down the champagne and kissing Adam back. R reached out to Juneau—whether to reassure her or to draw her in, Adam would never know, for at that moment the limo slowed to a halt. The FGRS spoke in a tight voice. "I think we're done here." *Hey man, no offense intended.* "It's just gettin' way too hot in here. Y'all can do whatever you want. I just don't relish being a voyeur." *Oh man, I'm really sorry. That was rude of me. Really, I'll behave.* "Nothing personal. I just don't fancy being part of the audience."

The door opened, Adam and Juneau stepped out. R began to emerge but Juneau pressed her palm against his chest to stop him. "You have to fix things with him," she implored, glancing at the FGRS. R hesitated, but Juneau firmly guided him back into the car. "I'll call you. . . ." The limousine sped away, leaving Adam and Juneau standing on the sidewalk along Venice beach. "Aw crap!" Adam laughed. He glanced over at Juneau. Her fist was pressed hard into her lips, and tears were welling up in her dark eyes. Adam felt a pang of tenderness mingled with jealousy, a potent, confusing mix of feelings that felt very much like desire. "Baby. . . ." he murmured. "It's going to be okay." He started to put his arm around her when he felt her sway unsteadily against him. He caught her as she swooned, gathered her in is arms, and carried her out onto the sand, away from the streetlights, towards the primal sound of the waves.

If you should fall
Into my arms
And tremble like a flower
Let's dance, for fear your grace should fall
Let's dance, for fear tonight is all

In his half-dreaming state, Adam's memories swirled like sand in the breaking surf. Cooling breezes caressed skin. The sensation of her body, heaving with emotion. Breathing as one. Another cab ride through the night. . . . Warm velvet cushions. The smoky fumes of cognac. Silken chocolate and succulent strawberries releasing their juice in his mouth. Strong, warm hands (how many?) gliding over his body, scented with orange blossoms, rousing him from exhaustion. Waves of pleasure mounting in intensity, higher and higher. . . .

Adam became aware of a soft crimson glow, which he reluctantly realized was the light of day filtering through his close eyelids (still smeared with kohl from last night). Adam slowly drew in a breath, expanding his chest, and softly blew it out, then drew in another lungful of oxygen, exhaled, and carefully opened his eyes. His morning dreams had aroused him, and his gaze alighted on the sleeping form beside him. Her eyes were closed, her long dark lashes etched with exquisite delicacy against her smooth, pale cheeks. Xena. His eye traced the sculpted arch of her eyebrows, then drifted down to her full lips, which were parted slightly. He could hear her soft breathing. Someone had placed a pillow encased in spotless, crisply ironed linen under her head. Her luxuriant dark hair tumbled across the field of white. He glanced around the room. Last night's Scrabble board was nowhere to be seen. The low ebony table had been cleared of the tray of food. In its place stood a crystal vase holding a stem of white lilies, aglow in morning light. A blue silk kimono was draped over Xena's sleeping form. Under it she had nothing on. He glanced down at himself. He did not even have a blanket to cover himself.

Adam propped himself up on his elbows and was about to rise to his feet, when a golden form slipped in through the velvet-draped entrance to the room. It was Xena's servant, wearing a crisp white French maid's apron. The only other article Brad had on was a snug pair of black Spandex shorts that exposed a décolletage above his waxed and bronzed derriere when he bent over to adjust the kimono on Xena's supine form. In his slender hands, he wielded a feather-duster—a bounteous bouquet of black and white ostrich plumes. "Oh pardon me," whispered Brad. "I was about to do the dusting. Can I fetch you some tea or coffee?"

Adam was struck by how adorable Brad was. Huge brown eyes framed by long dark lashes. Beautifully chiseled lips . . . lips made for love. A slender, not overly muscular frame. "Tea or coffee?" Brad repeated. "Uh, coffee please," Adam stammered. Brad vanished through the curtain and returned a minute later with a silver tray laden with coffee in a French press and china teacups that Adam recognized as a Wedgewood pattern his mother had shown him. (She was decorating his new house.) As Brad set the tray down on the ebony table, Xena sighed and stirred. The kimono slid off her shoulder, but she settled back into slumber. Brad gazed at her worshipfully. "Shhhh," he exhaled. "She's been working so hard. Let her sleep." Adam whispered, "Uh, Brad? What happened last night?" Brad's eyebrows shot up and his beautiful lips curved into a bemused smile. "Xena's a remarkable woman," he replied cryptically. "And a mean Scrabble player. She beat the pants off you—or would have, if your pants hadn't already been off."

Brad pressed down the plunger on the coffee maker and poured Adam a cup. As Adam sat up to sip his coffee, Brad took up the ostrich-plumed wand and began dusting the cushions and the low ebony table with delicate, rapid flicks. "I need dustin'" Adam offered. Brad raised an eyebrow. "Oh really? Have you been getting dirty?" And with that, Brad ran the feathers up and down Adam's torso, eliciting an involuntary moan. "Shh, don't wake her up" Brad whispered fiercely. "Sorry," Adam mouthed silently. Brad raised an eyebrow, pursed his lips, and ran the feather duster over Adam's body again, pausing to make extra swirls in certain highly sensitive parts of the anatomy and making Adam gasp and giggle.

Xena exhaled and rolled on to her side, facing the men. The kimono slid down. Her eyes were still closed. Her breathing settled into a slow, even rhythm. Adam glanced up at Brad, then reached to take the feather duster out of his hand. Delicately, Adam reached out to caress the sleeping beauty's cheek with the furled tip of an ostrich plume, then slowly slid the feather down her neck, to her collar bone, over a shoulder, then across her luxuriant breast. A wave of goose bumps rippled across her skin. Her eyelids fluttered and her breath quickened. Brad and Adam's eyes met, and the men smiled. "She's been so good to us," Adam whispered. "We need to thank her properly and abundantly." And they did.

—

It was past noon. Brad was fixing a lunch of salade niçoise for the three of them, while Adam showered. When he emerged into the guest bedroom, he found his clothes laid out neatly on the bed, cleaned and pressed. Brad was amazing. As Adam slipped on his Alexander McQueen jacket, he felt something heavy in the pocket. He reached in and drew out a necklace of glittering dark sable-colored crystals. Juneau. Was R there with her now? Adam wondered. He was overcome by an urge to know, to be with them right now. Slipping the necklace back into his pocket, he finished dressing, ran his fingers through his thick, spiky hair and scrutinized his make-up in the mirror above the dresser. (A gorgeous art deco piece, he noted. Xena has such eclectic and impeccable taste.) Xena and Brad watched him curiously as he wolfed down the salad that Brad had arranged artfully on the Wedgewood plates. The morning's exertions had left Adam famished. "I'm so sorry," he told them. "I forgot I have an appointment." He hugged and kissed them both, and was out the door, leaving a faint whiff of Homme and a mote of ostrich down wafting in his wake.

By Juneau Underwood on 07/19/2009 11:23 am

(Lyrics excerpted from "Let's Dance," by Piet Veerman)

Oh Juneau, I am but a pool of scalding liquid, unable to push away this chair to gain composure, to face the mortals who await me. They have no idea—the power of words in your capable fingertips, to seduce, inflame, ignite and gently prolong the pleasure you have so carefully wrought.

The generosity of your spirit is overwhelming. My boudoir is bereft of ostrich feathers, an oversight I will correct as soon as possible.

The mote of ostrich down alights on my keyboard, I pick it up; touch it to my cheek, across my lips, a talisman to recall this night. The sweet scent of lily. Just inside my front door sits my collection of Wedgewood blue and white—evoking a flutter each time I enter or leave.

Bless you, Xena *By xena princess warrior on 07/19/2009 12:27 pm*

I do love foreplay, creating the perfect setting for one's imagination to take flight. I left plenty for you to play with, but I'm also waiting for you to take us to Brazil! The wonderful thing about Brad is that he will satisfy your every desire, so do send him out to fetch you all the ostrich feathers, scented oils and rejuvenating sustenance you could wish for. Okay, now that I have this one out of my system (for now), I can get to work on my vampire fantasy. Fun! *By Juneau Underwood on 07/19/2009 2:39 pm*

FYI on fantasies:

Leo: "Adam, how are you working on the record on the road?"

Adam: "It's been double duty, and it's been rough. I recorded all day yesterday [Wednesday] in L.A. But that's a secret. It's not for my record, possibly for a soundtrack. That's all I can say. It's not for New Moon, but that would be cool. It's a lot of work. It's like, OK go tour, go record, go write, go do press and photo shoots. But I stay pretty cool under pressure. *They have a masseuse backstage, and that helps.*"

By xena princess warrior on 07/19/2009 5:23 pm

Who's the lucky masseuse? *By Juneau Underwood on 07/19/2009 11:25 pm*

We could apply as a team—we bring our own equipment, oils and atmospheric accoutrements, as well as our assistant Brad and his extensive wardrobe which fits in a briefcase. Satisfaction guaranteed.

X *By xena princess warrior on 07/19/2009 11:44 pm*

Welcome back to the party Safari Gal and thanks for letting us know you're here! NYC—sounds like a plan to me—we could hold a little MoALS Symposium at the same time—better start interviewing for the boys who will look after us.

Who knew that we could write so much, share so much, laugh, cry, swoon and dream for 47 consecutive days? We are diligent in our project to uncover every morsel of pleasure Adam can provide, to share it with each other and those who are standing at the door, listening and looking in, or joining us when they can take a few minutes to feel, in our action-filled lives.

July 20/09 Jobing.com Arena in Glendale, Arizona

We sit and admire the beauty our Apollo, our Muse, has presented to us in sight, sound and imagination; and it's so wonderful, that we have to share our discoveries with others here, and ask for nothing in return. He is a unifying force isn't he?

Xena *By xena princess warrior on 07/20/2009 9:53 am*

Hi SweetSue, thank you for your kind words. Without readers, our writing simply hangs in the void between us, unseen, unheard, so we are grateful for your patient attention.

Oh, oh, I feel a dream coming on, Adam lying down, arms outstretched above his head, thighs bulge, those pedicured toes push against the arm of the sofa, arching his torso, his hand catches my wrist.

He draws me around and pulls me to sit on his legs, while I try to get to the arm of the sofa, where I can see him to talk, but avoid the contact with his body, the rippling thighs underneath me—I have to remain clear-headed—I know there's something important I have to do today.

"Adam, I don't have time for games today. I know you have some time before your tour starts, but shouldn't you be writing, rehearsing, having wardrobe fittings?"

Damn, there's that grin, dimples in the corners of his mouth, as he opens it to speak, those topaz eyes, innocently unadorned, pleading for my attention, feigned hurt, pout—how can he do that to me? What's he up to?

Flying down to Rio? . . .

Xena *By xena princess warrior on 07/20/2009 11:31 am*

Thanks Gold Berry, . . . I'm glad you enjoyed the latest installment of the fantasy. Much credit goes to Xena for raising the bar. I love it when you all suggest props or situations. It's so much fun trying to figure out how to work them into the story. I'm curious about what you found "brave" in my story. I'm truly intrigued as to what you are reading into it. Tell me! *By Juneau Underwood on 07/20/2009 7:21 pm*

We know how to have a good time, don't we? You neglected to mention his thighs, which were not discussed per se but played a starring role in Xena's Scrabble fantasy. There are still many anatomical regions to explore: his hair, nose, neck, hands (so expressive), abdomen (such a tantalizing glimpse in Ring of Fire), navel, shoulders, back, knees and toes. Foot fetish, anyone? :) *By Juneau Underwood on 07/21/2009 7:54 am*

My life
You electrify my life
Let's conspire to re-ignite
All the souls that would die just to feel alive

("Starlight," by Matthew Bellamy)

Chapter 3 Ignited Souls

Adam, I'm writing this letter to say goodbye. It is time for me to leave the excitement and fun of being totally obsessed with you, your music and all things Adam Lambert.

It's been four months of pure joy for me. You are my first and only celebrity obsession and it has been a pleasure having you on my mind constantly.

Adam, you reminded me about having passion, courage and living life with a positive outlook in spite of the obstacles. You showed me how to be a better person through your shining example and reminded me that being authentic and caring about others is what is most important. You also reminded me about how sexy life can be. I haven't felt like a teenager in a long time. . . .

I have some promises for you because I don't want you to think that I am abandoning you by any means. First, I will come by and visit you on this site and watch some videos and maybe even post occasionally. I will keep my thread of your "diamonds" updated regularly and will delight in reading the new gems that come out of your mouth.

Next, when your debut album is released, I will buy every copy I can get my hands on and share it with people who haven't had the pleasure of hearing your incredible voice. I will be at your Hamilton concert next month and will be screaming and dancing and having a great time. I will pass on the meet and greet because of concerns about your safety and not wanting to be involved with the crowd. The energy I send to you is that of a dedicated fan who is very supportive but also rational. I want you to have a long and successful career and will always remember this time with affection. I love everything about you

Adam—you have been sent to this earth to do some amazingly great things and I will be watching, smiling and cheering you on always.

Good luck, good health and happiness, Adam.

I love you forever.
Gloria Beth
Wednesday, July 29, 2009—10:16

Yesterday, I wrote a goodbye letter to Adam. I'm definitely not leaving him or this group but I had to say goodbye to the obsessiveness. It's time to get back to the world . . . the letter says it all I think.

I do not work and decided it was time to put some limits on my time spent Adamizing and start paying more attention to my husband, family, exercise routine, volunteer work, business ventures and. . . .

I will definitely be on this site daily and probably more often. I was starting to feel drained with the constant vibrations in my body. How much can one 54-year-old take???. . . Adam you are incredible!!

I'm going to accept that some days may be more difficult than others—staying away from Adam that is! I'm sure the process will be very interesting and I will learn even more about myself. http://www.adamofficial.com/node/395452

I hope you all can still love me. Nothing has really changed, but on the other hand, perhaps it has. I want to believe that Adam would approve! You guys too!

Love,
Gloria Beth **By *adams beth* on 07/20/2009 7:21 pm**

Dear Gloria Beth, I was very touched by your "dear John" letter and by the responses it evoked among other fans. You've made some special friends through this weird and wonderful experience. You are brave to take the step to move on. I've been trying to limit the time I spend actively obsessing about Adam. Once I've done that, I'll work on reducing the time I spend passively obsessing, that is, just thinking about him, which I do far more often during the day than any sane person should. What you are doing is very healthy and positive.

I'm sure Adam would be happier if more fans took this energy and directed it towards making their lives and the world a better place. For me, that day will come when I turn my writing energies to the essays and novel that I have put on hold for so long. I am already starting in that direction. Writing these fantasies has not only been a lot of fun, but it has loosened my creative gears and given me confidence that I can do this. I do hope you will continue to visit, read and comment here. This is about Adam, but also about so much more.

Lots of love, J **By *Juneau Underwood* on 07/20/2009 8:36 pm**

Dearest Gloria, we have become more than cyber friends and that is thanks to your initiative. You have been diligent in your research and keeping me informed, your enthusiasm is positively infectious, so our loss will be another's gain as you turn your considerable resources to other important interests. Do take what Adam has inspired and as Juneau says, make your own or someone else's world, a better place—a place with enthusiasm, beauty and music. Put on the mascara, the dancing shoes and shake a can of glitter—everything is better when it's glittery. Keep your favourite amulet nearby, to use as a reminder to smile, flirt and laugh a lot.

You have inspired our creativity and deepened our Adam experience. When I write, I will have you in mind always, Gloria. You don't have to say anything. In addition to your Collected Gems from Adam project, perhaps you could present. "Life After Adam—How to apply what you learned"

If you ever need some extra support, you know where to find me.

Much love,

Xena

By xena princess warrior on 07/20/2009 10:58 pm

About Adam and Love

Thank you Gloria. I agree with the sentiments about Love expressed in your earlier message.

Love must be expressed without reservation, without conditions and without expectations.

Before Idol, so many of Adam's cabaret songs described heartbreak and unrequited love and we all recall the 20/20 interview. He wants to be loved and to be in love.

Sharing the day's events, each listening to the other's story attentively, eye to eye, hand-in-hand, no one else even exists for those moments, no longer furtive or tenuous, but without reservation, from private to public—proclamations of love.

And a passion so fierce, it's barely contained within their sense of civility and propriety, but bursts forth as soon as they're around the corner.

While his fans and audiences loudly and demonstrably love Adam, they can't hold him and cuddle in the dark, hearing and feeling each other's heartbeats—tenderness swelling the lungs with drawn breath to slowly exhale. Skin-to-skin, fingers through hair, massaging neck, pulled closer, the long, soft kiss.

I think that in addition to the obvious libidinous attraction we express in our fantasies—we're also trying to fill some of the empty spots in Adam's life, with both intensity and gentleness, but our words can only conjure images, not flesh and blood.

We can describe warm, melted chocolate swirled with a plump and rosy strawberry, but our fingers can't reach his lips.

In the concert videos it's evident that the waves of love he feels from the live audiences overwhelms him with emotion and saturates him with adrenaline—the stage can barely contain his energy, even at the end of his set.

His movements exaggerated for the arena space, he extends every molecule as far as he can, then launches his voice from there, blanketing the lovers with his intensely sexual aura and magnificent voice, the signals unmistakable.

It's the give-and-take of the flirtation and foreplay—to be relieved by?? I can't imagine a whole Adam concert—they will need a first aid station, or hose-down the audience every so often.

Love

Xena

By xena princess warrior on 07/23/2009 10:56 pm

I need a hosing down after that, Xena. Your own love explodes over us propelled by the energy of your words and images.

By Juneau Underwood on 07/23/2009 11:22 pm

Hi J, it's a challenge to leave us out of an Adam fantasy, but it was serendipity that Gloria posted "Love," since I've been thinking about love a lot lately. Also, listening to Adam's sad songs—I love the sound of his voice accompanied by only a piano and to hear him speak—makes me feel more protective of him. It's comforting to know that he is on a bus full of friends and that includes Kris, to think of him alone after a concert is sad.

I wasn't going to write tonight, but after watching the Glendale Bowie medley video a few times, then listening to the cabaret songs, the contrast is overwhelming. He seems a slightly fragile boy in the sad cabaret songs like "I can't make you love me" or "come home," begging to have arms around him. In the Bowie medley video his exuberance is unrestrained, he's happy and he's huge.

Xena

By xena princess warrior on 07/23/2009 11:53 pm

July 23/09 American Airlines Centre in Dallas, Texas

The stars you wrote about were very troubled people, mentally, emotionally, socially—and they had abnormal early lives, whereas Adam's seems to have been filled with love, understanding and indulgence—helping him to overcome his feelings of being an outsider. Becoming a stage performer was simply a continuation of the desires with which he was born—enjoying dress-up and performing for its own sake.

No one imposed anything on him, they simply opened doors, made introductions and off he went. Possessed of immense talent, outgoing personality and the ability to express his emotions through performance is truly a magic formula.

That adrenaline high from an audience can be addictive to a natural performer and I suppose there is the potential for that feeling to replace actual, intimate, unconditional, reciprocated love with another. That would be unhealthy, but I believe Adam knows the difference since he has been hearing the applause for seventeen years now and he's fine.

Unless we are prepared to scour the world for suitable lovers or intervene each time we see him with someone, to test them like the suspicious father, we need to relax and know that he is a big boy and by his age, many of us were married and some had children. I'm not skerrrrrred.

Love
Xena

By xena princess warrior on 07/24/2009 1:45 pm

July 24/09 BOK Centre in Tulsa, Oklahoma

Hi E., I'm trying to stop worrying about Adam. He seems so much more grounded and smart about the world than I was at his age, that's for sure. I do hope he moves away from Hollywood. Now that he has made it, he should find some quiet, less celebrity-obsessed place in which to settle. I've spent some time in L.A. and I feel it's an insidious, toxic place—glittery, beguiling and exciting, but corrupting too.

By Juneau Underwood on 07/27/2009 12:44 am

July 25/09 Verizon Arena in North Little Rock, Arkansas

July 26/09 Adam visits Graceland with the Idols

Fedex Forum in Memphis, Tennessee—Adam wears his hair in pompadour style

Hi C,

I have mostly worked with adults during my career, but have had the opportunity now and again to employ or work with adolescents and young 20s. Some of these kids have not had much experience and don't have connections, so I become a reference for them and provide them with some guidance on how to reach their dreams. That has been wonderful—and now with my daughter's friends—I have the pleasure of presenting art, architecture, science, history to those who have never been to a museum or an art gallery—they become engaged and discover new dimensions to the world.

Hasn't Adam, through this site presented these remarkable women with a wonderful place to think about what matters to us, to learn how we can inspire others?

What we can't give back to Adam—we pay forward to our students, loved ones, friends and here—even strangers whose face and name are a mystery, but who matter so much to each of us, that we welcome, respond to, soothe pain, share joy, entertain with some fiction or laughter—each other.

Love, Xena

By xena princess warrior on 07/28/2009 1:03 pm

Dear Gloria Beth,

I want to comment on something you wrote on page 144: "*He said his greatest accomplishment is 'falling in love.' This irritates me a bit . . . it doesn't feel right . . . maybe I am jaded!?*"

I'm curious to know why this irritated you. When I heard Adam say this, I was quite moved and amazed. I took him to mean that he was able to give his unconditional love to someone else, to abandon himself to another. This was about his giving love, not about being loved back. That takes real bravery. I think it shows great wisdom (and a romantic soul) to recognize that falling in love is not simply about finding a deserving object of love. It's about being up to the challenge of giving yourself, letting go, and making yourself utterly vulnerable.

By Juneau Underwood on 07/25/2009 3:23 pm

"One of the posters talked about Adam being created by a goddess. I think it must be a goddess with a hell of a sense of humor. She made this beautiful, talented, sexy, funny, and humble man then made him gay. Now, I would think that would be something a punishing God would do.

The Goddess's gift to women is gay."

Punishing? Not at all! The Goddess is pure genius. By making Adam gay, she elevates him to something beyond a sex symbol. He arouses such powerful feelings of love, but because he is sexually unattainable, our feelings spill over and touch other things in our lives. It's really astonishing how many of us posting here have written about how Adam has inspired us to change our own lives, project more love into the world, make more love with our partners, etc. I'm trying to imagine whether he would have had such an effect on us if he had been straight.

By Juneau Underwood on 07/26/2009 7:42 am

I'm with Juneau on this one. By making him gay, she has assured us that he can maintain his distance—on his pedestal—where we admire, worship and bestow our offerings of thanks and love. Had he been straight, think of the emotions we would have to deal with when he showed up with the "other" woman! Too painful to think about. Bad enough I'm jealous of Juneau in our fantasies—a flesh and blood female love would have me throwing myself into a pit.

Don't even want to think about it. I do like seeing him with his female friends—that's nice.

Xena

By xena princess warrior on 07/27/2009 3:15 pm

Indeed, if he showed up with a girlfriend, the dark side of my Scorpio nature would probably rear its toxic tail. Best to keep that safely hidden under a rock!

By Juneau Underwood on 07/27/2009 6:41 pm

Thanks J., I think we would have to start a whole new nasty place where we could gossip and post bad pictures of "her"—our target.

X

By xena princess warrior on 07/28/2009 12:40 pm

July 28/09 St Pete Times Forum in Tampa, Florida—Adam gets a red whip and rhinestone handcuffs

That would be very bad and Un-Adam! The jealous twinges you inspire with your fantasies, however, are quite delightful. Keep 'em coming!

By Juneau Underwood on 07/28/2009 6:52 pm

Just came across this in a New York Times article about Polyvore, a fashion site that lets users pull together fashion ensembles. Here's the last paragraph: "It could also give buyers information about trends in real-time, faster than monthly magazines, said Jess Lee, Polyvore's product manager. This fall, for example, watch for recent trends bubbling up on the site: exposed zippers, fingerless gloves and butterfly prints."

Is it purely coincidental, or did the inspiration come from a certain wildly compelling Idol known for accoutrements and themes that fit the above-described? He is quite the trendsetter.

By Juneau Underwood on 07/27/2009 8:46 pm

"Or is it that ADAM has filled some void in our lives that we didn't know we had and the rest of them didn't have this emptiness that needed to be filled?"

My life was full, but Adam tore into me and displaced so much that I thought was important. Now, I have discovered I can live without reading two or three or even four newspapers a day, listening to annoying hosts on news/talk radio with whom I hold one-sided screaming sessions, thinking about my frustrating work—all the time.

More than filling a hole, Adam opened one up and jumped in when I wasn't looking. He brought along all of you and my compulsive writing. Must be getting crowded in there.

J., I think you might be correct about us being ahead of the curve.

X

By xena princess warrior on 07/29/2009 12:29 am

Funny, just a couple of days ago, I was thinking about throwing a whip onto the stage when I see Adam. Mine wouldn't be such a dinky toy! Mine would be at least six feet long, braided, in dark leather with metal studs—much more dangerous! Of course, I can only imagine the objects that will have been thrown at His Hotness by the time the Idols make it to Providence. The mind reels at the possibilities.

By Juneau Underwood on 07/29/2009 8:55 pm

▪ **July 29/09** Revealed that Adam has recorded a track for the movie 2012

Just viewed the photos Cleo posted early this morning—yikes!

Foxy Adam

I am sitting here in a public place, my screen facing the window—and I just had to blow them up. What a collection of posters—wallpaper!!

Adam—he sparkles, glitters, mesmerizes us with his eyes, seductive movements—hips thrust, arm outstretched, graceful fingers beckoning to look closer, to attend to him.

Removes his outer wolf pelt to expose his swelling biceps and move freely, like a sinewy cat, joints loose, stretching out to us, forcing us to look closer at the goods he is displaying, phallic mic upended as he sings. The seductive voice of the sirens—calling us to dangerous rocks.

Is Adam of this earth? Must be from a planet in a constellation far, far away—Vulpecula—the Fox. The male fox—the vix.

Eyes communicate eternal sex, the Vix is sleek, quick, smart, cuddly when asleep. He runs, looks back, winks, licks his lips, throws his head back, then stares us down with laser eyes and fingers to lips, blows a kiss.

Glambertinas meantime, live in the constellation Andromeda—the Chained Maiden. They try to chase that vix—he calls to them, he taunts, he teases, he arouses, but they are chained and strain at their handcuffs to escape—to run, whip in hand—to catch him, to devour and quench their burning desires.

The Chained Maidens must keep their distance or lose the object of their desire forever.

Trying to stay cool while all of you keep throwing me heat.

Xena *By xena princess warrior on 07/30/2009 11:37 am*

I'm down on foxes since a family of them wiped out our Bantam chicken flock. A wolf is more noble (OK, I was brainwashed by Jack London when I was a child) and powerful, and wolves sing, whereas foxes cough. A panther is beautiful, but I still come down on the side of the wolf because panther's are solitary, whereas wolves are social, and Adam is definitely social. Plus he can be such a playful puppy at times.

By Juneau Underwood on 07/30/2009 4:46 pm

Dear GB, E., Xena and BD, interesting discussion about whether there is something we have in common (besides our love for Adam), and why we have all been swept up in this delicious madness. I've been struck by how diverse we are. I've never in my life had a fan obsession for anyone. I have never joined a fan club, written a fan letter, gone out to buy a magazine just because the object of my adoration was on the cover, never spent day after day listening to one man's voice, or changed anything about how I dress or act because of an object of adoration. The iPod that my husband gave me several Christmases ago lay untouched in my desk because I didn't have the motivation to learn how to use it.

And then along came Adam, sneaking into my consciousness at first, then intriguing me week by week, and finally laying siege to my heart. A few extra neurons fired when I saw him audition, and then Satisfaction made me think this kid has something. With Ring of Fire, I realized he was quite unusual and amazing, and then it was a bit of a bumpy ride for me in the weeks that followed, when I wasn't sure whether I liked what I was seeing or not. It's when Kris won Idol that I started obsessively combing through the AI performance videos and YouTube to prove to myself that Adam was really as huge a talent as I thought he was and should have won. And then I found myself hopelessly hooked. I still can't quite believe it. And if I hadn't come across this site, I wonder if my obsession would have been fed to the degree it has. I have to hand it to the creators of American Idol. It is a truly diabolically genius marketing machine.

For some of us, Adam is filling an emptiness that we were feeling. And for others, like Xena, E. and me, Adam ripped open a hole in our lives that we didn't know we had, and we are having a fabulous time exploring what that means. It's incredible to me how many of us have taken actions that we would never have dreamed possible even two months ago. We are feeling creative, writing insane erotic fantasies, designing jewelry, sprucing up our looks, feeling young and in love, and making wonderful friendships here. It's all GOOD!!

And now onto a matter of truly pressing importance. Adam's concert hair: up or down? What's your preference?

By Juneau Underwood on 07/31/2009 7:38 pm

Bromance is in the air! Isn't it wonderful? I don't think it's because women are getting more crass, at least not in my experience. Women are perhaps being more open to men about our friendships, and the men are wondering why it is so often hard to have this kind of intimacy and support with one another. ***By Juneau Underwood on 08/02/2009 8:34 am***

E., I also have imprinted in my brain the image of Adam's eyes welling up after Black or White. I think that was a seminal moment for him, not only because he was feeling his dream starting to come true, but also because that was right after the media were in a feeding frenzy over the "kissing photo." His song choice was a statement, and when the judges and his audience embraced it, it must have sunk in that he wasn't going to be consigned to the margins any more, that it was going to be more than OK. That's how I read it, and I'm as emotional about it as if he were my own family.

GB, I'm with you on Starlight. It's an exceptional song (I've been listening to Muse's original every day) and is such an amazing fit for Adam in every way. The melody is a perfect showcase for his vocal range, the beat and instrumentation feel very now, and the lyrics so full of longing and sadness ("Starlight, I will be chasing your starlight, Until the end of my life, I don't know if it's worth it anymore"). It feels like a portent of his future and taps into our collective anxieties for him. A perfect storm. ***By Juneau Underwood on 08/02/2009 8:31 am***

OMG SweetSue, what a thrilling recounting of your Adam live experience. I am all out of breath and my heart is beating way to fast. All my concerted efforts of the past couple of weeks to rejoin the living and become a responsible, NPR-listening, work- and family-focused, upstanding citizen have just crashed and burned. I'm back in Adamania land. I don't know how I'm going to survive until September 13 when it's

▪

July 31/09 Arena @ Gwinnett Centre in Duluth, Georgia

▪

August 1/09 Time Warner Cable Arena in Charlotte, North Carolina

▪

August 2/09 Greensboro Coliseum in Greensboro, North Carolina my turn. I'm thrilled that your husband now gets it. Thanks for all the practical advice too. I may have to go out and get that shimmery blue dress I tried on a couple of weeks ago, and I will make sure to invest in waterproof eyeliner and mascara, as well as bring tissues.

By Juneau Underwood on 08/03/2009 8:15 pm

I have to say that physiologically, this IS an addiction. All the signs are there: thoughts of Adam run obsessively through my brain circuits, out of my conscious control; whenever I have a fix of Adam, I experience what has to be a surge of dopamine through my brain's reward circuitry (nucleus accumbens and locus coeruleus, for those of you who want precise anatomical info; btw locus coeruleus means "azure spot"—the color of HIS eyes); my moral universe has tilted; and when I need another fix, my hands tremble reaching for my iPod, just like a nicotine addict reaching for a pack. . . . However, I have not yet committed any crimes! And I don't think I'm damaging my body by indulging in this particular addiction (apart from stubbing my toes and walking into the occasional wall).

By Juneau Underwood on 08/03/2009 11:33 pm

Oh Cleo, That was an absolutely vivid, hot, hot hot description!! Now it's my turn to be a complete puddle on the floor. I love how you and your daughter glammed yourselves up. I love how you describe each song experience, and how you were all drenched in sweat after just five songs. . . . I guess I'd better start giving serious thought to what I'm going to wear!

By Juneau Underwood on 08/03/2009 11:52 pm

Finally got our tickets. Second row south side of the stage. Should be able to toss something from there! My daughter might object though. She has offered to do my hair/makeup for me and we will sparkle!
X

By xena princess warrior on 08/04/2009 3:01 pm

With sadness in my heart, I've decided not to return to #Idol—Paula Abdul on Twitter **August 4, 2009**

August 4/09 Verizon Centre in Washington, DC

Dearest Prima Glambertina Cleo

Thank you so much for all the effort you put into bringing your envy-inducing Adam experiences back to us and after all your evocative words—this morning we have your vivid photos to brand the images in our minds. How did you keep your hands so steady? How long did it take you to unwind after the show? Especially from such an intense high?

You and your daughter look wonderful and so happy, we really must all meet together in Hamilton, where I will be accompanied by my eighteen-year-old daughter as well. She has been my supporter and cheerleader on this journey and deserves to be there.

Only ten days—will I be ready?

Love,

Xena

By xena princess warrior on 08/05/2009 9:18 am

C'mon I.R., when I started writing on this site—and you know what I have written—I was petrified that someone would find out, including my husband and family, but bit by bit, I started to let people know, even though most haven't read any of it.

My husband knows everything and he's just fine. I have since made the decision that after almost 57 years of living as if the CIA and the Mounties have files on me, I am going to do more as I please and face whatever consequences may come.

My daughter is coming with me to the concert and she has plans for how I should dress! I now hope we run into someone I know. They would be shocked.

I don't know how you can read our friends' accounts of being there or watch concert videos and not be overwhelmingly motivated to buy a ticket. I made mine my birthday gift.

The only regrets I have are those things I didn't do, not those I did.

Love

Xena

By xena princess warrior on 08/05/2009 8:36 pm

There is an interview where Adam describes what it's like on stage, the exchange of energy and how the audience invigorates him when he feels tired. It's just as we discussed some time ago, the relationship of performer to audience and he explains why he prefers to perform as himself rather than a character in musical theatre.

And no wonder—he has more facets to his personality than the Hope Diamond—macho/aggressive/demanding to introspective/ethereal/sensitive/emotional to effervescent/sexy/playful/flirty dancer boy—and that's just Adam on stage.

Thanks to such evocative live concert descriptions from our Glambertinas and by watching Adam perform, we can see and almost touch, feel and yes, smell him live—a few feet away. He connects with as much of the audience as he can—he's not just looking out into space, but looking at someone, smiling in another's direction, a little nod, a wink—in front—way back.

From the first time we heard him speak on AI, we knew he was a special personality and he has held our attention ever since, not just musically and visually but intellectually and erotically as well—what a dynamo! Adam fires-off every feel-good chemical in our bodies—in any setting, from relaxed and casual to all-out, no-holds-barred, sexual heat.

Saw Michael Jackson perform in person—unbelievable, watched Prince and Bowie and Elvis along with all the others and not one has had the effect Adam has had on me.

He has more intellectual depth than Elvis, is more gregarious and wants to personally engage us more than Prince or Bowie and is sexier than Jackson. Does anyone have a superior voice, vocal range or variety of musical styles? Voice was enough to hook me before seeing him.

He can front an orchestra, stand next to a piano, unplugged, electrified, café or stadium, solo, group or duet.

Even Adam's interviews are good—he can think, is quick-witted, generous, self-deprecating and he's not shy about talking—we would like to have dinner with him, or go shopping or anything else that's enhanced by a loquacious, enthusiastic partner. Wait for the bus? Stand in line at the grocery store?

To be fair, as a seasoned musical theatre performer, Adam has to be a dancer of some ability and what we are watching is a concert performance, where he holds the mic (and uses it as a prop) and performs in front of a band. With the exception of the two examples below, we haven't seen many choreographed videos, nor has he performed wired—with a hands-free mic.

What I can say is that with his ability to move different parts of his body in different directions at the same time, his acknowledged rhythmic sensibilities, his gracefulness and his love of performing, he can probably dance.

Oh, just imagining sitting in the second row, pheromones expanding in the humid air, flying on the point of Cupid's golden tipped arrow to our hearts and minds—now forever bound to our Apollo.

By xena princess warrior on 08/05/2009 5:52 pm

▪

August 5/09 1st Mariner Arena in Baltimore, Maryland

▪

IM BAAAAAACK!!! bubble tweet coming any minute! 7:13 PM **Aug 5th** from web

▪

My latest BubbleTweet -> http://bbltwt.com/n5r99 9:08 PM **Aug 5th** from web

▪

My latest BubbleTweet -> http://bbltwt.com/dv4ht 7:18 PM Aug 5th from web

Beautifully put, E. I've been mulling the dancing question. I love to dance, but very few men that I've been romantically involved with share that passion or comfort level when it comes to expressing themselves in this way. I wonder how much of this is cultural and how much is innately biological. By the way, no one has remarked on what a beautiful speaking voice Adam has. Even when he is answering an interviewer's question, it falls like music on my ears.

By Juneau Underwood on 08/05/2009 11:57 pm

Astaire and Kelly were my idols and because of them, especially Fred, I took jazz, tap and ballet dancing—as a young adult. My teacher was a wonderful straight guy who adored women, flirted shamelessly and was married. What about all those straight guys we danced with in the disco days? John Travolta? Dirty Dancing? We just have not had this type of solo entertainer for a long time.

When I performed, I loved backstage—costumes, make-up—but the lights, applause and action—there's nothing like it. I don't think we're going to see any impromptu, unchoreographed dancing on stage—as you said, Adam's a perfectionist in every detail of his performance.

I didn't like Elvis, too old fashioned for me and really, none of the others—although straight—worked as hard as Adam does to get a "rise" out of us. He makes us feel sexy and alluring—we want to be manicured, pedicured, coiffured, eyelined and glittery. We want to flirt and get a man's attention. It's not just about him, but about us too.

Don't you just love that Boy Next Door quality? what a contrast he is—onstage as the Rock God Seducer and then the cute, cuddly, funny t-shirted boy right after. He makes sure we feel close to him and he lets us know how much he loves his fans, whether in interviews or on stage and as you say, perhaps his gayness contributes to this.

Bowie seemed aloof and Jagger seemed contemptuous and angry, while Adam is joyous, sensitive or with Whole Lotta Love, demanding to give us his love with a promise of absolute satisfaction. The others weren't really "loveable." Impressive talents and entertainers, but not someone I would go shopping with.

Love

Xena

By xena princess warrior on 08/06/2009 1:17 am

Ha ha ha! I love how C. has gotten so loose and comfortable with letting it all hang out here! I think we need a collective whipping to snap us out of our Adam-induced haze. We need to be punished!!

By Juneau Underwood on 08/06/2009 11:20 pm

Hi ladies, I'm scrambling to catch up on all the posts. . . . I was never a fan of Prince's, which is why I completely forgot until now that my husband did a project with him once. I was so uncurious that I never asked him what he was like. As for further establishing my non-fan credentials, I got to know a certain famous rock band a number of years ago when we were spending a lot of time in Dublin. They had just released an album and the guitarist brought the CD over to our house to give to us. A number of years later the thought occurred to me that perhaps I should have asked him to sign it. Another time, he and I were chatting about how terrible the traffic in Dublin was, and I advised him to take the DART (the train). He looked at me like I was out of my mind, and it took me a second to realize that this was not an option for him. I am a complete dork! ***By Juneau Underwood on 08/06/2009 11:17 pm***

I can't wait to see the Julia/Julie movie. I remember watching French chef when I was growing up, but I didn't fully appreciate her impact until I read her memoir. Her descriptions of post-war France resonated for me. My family lived in Geneva in the 1960s and we visited France pretty often. The sights and smells are imprinted forever in my memory.
By Juneau Underwood on 08/07/2009 5:58 pm

Wonderful! Adam's unplugged "Starlight" was the taste of honey warmed in the sunshine—kissed with orange blossom.

During a 'chat' bit on the stage, Adam mentioned that for New York, the audience was quite tame and had not thrown any bras on stage. One of the hosts started to mention "family—morning. . . ." Adam cut him off, turned to the audience and exclaimed "Good Morning America!!"

Such a busy day—can't keep track of everything. There are about twelve or thirteen teenagers in my basement celebrating my daughter's friend's birthday—we are party central and most of the kids end up sleeping here too. Our dog is so restless, she's barking at my ankles and I am trying to focus on all this Glambertina work! Don't kids and dogs understand priorities?

Love

Xena ***By xena princess warrior on 08/07/2009 10:15 pm***

Well D.! Thank you for such an enthusiastic expression of your feelings —and ours. So glad you wrote here for us today, so we can know you and to join us as a fully participating Glambertina. We understand the overwhelming emotions Adam can stimulate in us and as our muse, he helps us put words and images to express those innervations, as you have done so eloquently here.

So glad you finally decided to walk through the door and join us in the salon of Adam appreciation and discovery. We hope you continue to write here, we are good listeners. Did Adam help you get through some of your difficulties?

Warmest welcome D.,

Xena *By xena princess warrior on 08/07/2009 12:25 pm*

Sorry, D., I should have said "warmest welcome back." I think you were the first to suggest Adam as Sexiest Man Alive?

By xena princess warrior on 08/07/2009 12:32 pm

You are welcome Cleo—I agree and this might become my desktop photo for a while.

This is where his sublime beauty is particularly evident—the perfect symmetry of his face from widow's peak, entire hair line, eyebrows, eyes, cheekbones, nose and luscious lips, in natural light, foliage backdrop. A male Nefertiti for me. *By xena princess warrior on 08/07/2009 9:58 pm*

A male Nefertiti! Spot on brilliant, Xena!

By Juneau Underwood on 08/07/2009 11:32 pm

Thanks J! Great you have some time to catch up with us here. Did you ever "meet" Nefertiti in Berlin? Did I tell you my Art History prof and Nefertiti story? *By xena princess warrior on 08/07/2009 11:45 pm*

Yes, I did have a moment of silently communing across the millennia with the beautiful queen when I was in Berlin some years ago. I do recall a story you shared with me about your art history professor. Didn't he decide how the bust would be displayed? One of my past boyfriends was a dealer in ancient Egyptian art. He's still a dear friend. He is one of those rare hetero males who is completely comfortable being an aesthete—sensitive, voluble and emotional. He always dressed beautifully in Armani, loved to prepare wonderful meals, and spoke so eloquently about art and life. When we would visit a museum, as we'd go through each gallery, he'd say "which piece would you want to take home with you?" That opened my eyes to a different way of seeing and appreciating art. I use that line on my girls to de-glaze their eyes whenever I drag them to a museum. Anyway, I remember him rhapsodizing about the bust of Nefertiti and looking at pictures of her in an art book, and his telling me I needed to go see her in Berlin.

▪

August 7/09 Good Morning America with Kris Allen and David Cook. Adam performs an acoustic Starlight (Muse) and

▪

Little Lies (Fleetwood Mac) with Kris and David

▪

Boardwalk Hall in Atlantic City, New Jersey

▪

New York!!!!! GMA was fun this morning! What a treat to sing w David cook and kris allen!!! 8:58 AM **Aug 7th** from Echofon

Do you think Adam appreciates the visual arts? I wonder if he regrets not having had more of a formal, liberal arts education. Wouldn't it be fun to open his eyes to the great art and literature of the world? I was very excited to read in that LA Times interview that he had sung in a classical choir. I would love to hear him sing the tenor part in the Missa Solemnis. . . . ***By Juneau Underwood on 08/08/2009 1:12 am***

Juneau, yes—he's done every type of music—even his version of country ROF. The musical performance possibilities for him would be unlimited and I do include opera or tenor solo arias. Recently I was listening to Annie Lennox and thought they would make a great duet.

Do you have "the Prayer"? Adam sings in English and Hebrew.

In my experience, those of us who appreciate the performance arts also appreciate the visual arts and literature. Adam has spent some time travelling the world and lived in Germany for a while. He could not have missed ruins and art scattered about like bread for pigeons in Italy.

He has an innate sense of style, so his eye is good, as is his ability to see beauty. We have had numerous glimpses into the "entertainer's" mind, and we have yet to plumb the depths of his knowledge. My favourite little examples of course—French, Latin and Shakespeare spoken in perfect context "If you prick me, do I not bleed?" Without a formal, post secondary education, he's picked up a lot.

And you know, Juneau, that travel is a great source of knowledge—cultural, social, political, geographic, etc.

Oh, imagine making a plan to illuminate the great works for him. The grand themes of the canon of western civilization from ancient mythologies through ancient art, architecture, literature from Beowulf to Shakespeare and on, all the way to the present, inform any creative endeavour with our collective cultural history. Moving to the Eastern, oriental arts, then African and Pacific. So much to cover—we'd have to be selective.

Another fantasy to dream about. Taking Adam to the Louvre? The Pyramids? To Nefertiti?

Xena ***By xena princess warrior on 08/08/2009 2:21 am***

You're right of course that travel of itself can be a profound learning experience. I feel confident, as you do, that Adam would have made the most of his journey through foreign lands. He has such an open, curious mind. I would love to know more about what he saw, what made an impression, what he learned. . . . He lived in Berlin during a time of historic transition. What did he notice and make of it? And I would love to lead him through a gallery of ancient Greek sculpture of breathtaking male bodies. ***By Juneau Underwood on 08/09/2009 8:40 am***

August 8/09 Prudential Centre in Newark, New Jersey—first Jock strap onstage

Sadly, the interviewers are so incurious that they don't ask him the right questions. In one of the recent interviews he did talk about the travel with the cruise and with the tour, and the locations, about some of his favourites and the fact that they had lots of time during the day to tour the ports and the cities where they performed, which he did. But the questions veered off in another direction after that.

You naughty girl—just had to mention "breathtaking male bodies"!!! did you do this on purpose??

Love

X ***By xena princess warrior on 08/09/2009 2:33 pm***

That's why you and I have to take on the job of interviewing Adam. And I am totally into breathtaking male bodies. When I was at the Kunsthistorisches museum in Vienna with my 15-year-old, I expressed admiration for an Athenian youth's pert marble buttocks, much to my daughter's mortification. (Of course my mind raced to how much Adam would enjoy what I was seeing.) My daughters want me to be innocent. ***By Juneau Underwood on 08/09/2009 6:59 pm***

Innocent mom? Too late for me I'm afraid—thanks to Adam. I was pretty good at keeping Xena hidden for over 50 years, but she is the one who responded so ferociously to Adam and I'm stuck with doing what she wants. The "other" me led her life so carefully, to avoid any embarrassing explanations to any future child, but she has given up and it looks like Xena might win the battle of the identities. So much more fun.

By the way, I've got Adam on a beach again, this time with both of us and you remember that Brazilian? I'm hoping he shows up. He might have marble buttocks, perhaps you can check that out.

X ***By xena princess warrior on 08/09/2009 7:25 pm***

Seeing how open Adam is being about his life, I find myself dredging up memories of my youth and indulging in a bit of nostalgia as well as self-examination. How much I might share of this with my daughters, I don't know. They are too young anyway. Maybe in ten years. . . ? Maybe

I'll write about it in an unpublished memoir that they can discover locked away in a safe box after I've shuffled off this mortal coil.

As for the serious question about that Brazilian beauty, his buttocks are not of marble, but of hot, active muscle, please!!

By the way, I have been tormented by the chest hair question. I'm speaking of the dark stubble on the Rolling Stone cover. Someone asked why it wasn't reddish or blond, as one might expect. Hard to believe it would have been dyed, although nothing is beyond the manipulations of a skilled and unscrupulous image artist. Do you have a hypothesis? I'm losing sleep over this one. ***By Juneau Underwood on 08/09/2009 11:20 pm***

Juneau, you are nuts some times. Losing sleep over chest hair colour? Without looking through my extensive photo collection, aside from Rolling Stone, any bare-chested pictures show him hairless, painted green, hairless glowing gold, hairless with just a singlet on.

I can't stand the thought of you losing sleep, so I promise we will get to the bottom of this! In the meantime, the fun is about to start on the beach and you and I are missing it. While we talk over here—he's gone off to talk to some boys.

X ***By xena princess warrior on 08/09/2009 11:44 pm***

Guess I'll have to watch the (Good Morning America Idol Concert) show again because I missed all that "checking-out." What I did see is that as usual, Adam looked directly at the person speaking or performing. Is Andy the guitarist who was next to/in front of Adam during "Lies," who when Andy's playing was highlighted, watched him, just as he does with whoever is singing or playing on stage with him, any time?

Stage training teaches that you either watch the person speaking or dancing or singing or simply remain still and unobtrusive, otherwise, you will upstage whoever is performing at the time. Adam, as a professional, has always performed that way with others, whether fellow singers or band members. And, if Adam is ogling someone, lucky them! wish it were me.

Hmm, gesturing with one's hands or using one's expressive face or modulating one's voice to enhance mere words are all excellent communications tools and the best speakers use all of them—Adam is very expressive and uses his body, shoulders, neck, eyes, brows—everything —which is one of the reasons we love to watch him do anything. Read the phone book? He looks directly into the camera to speak to the audience and focuses on the interviewer while they are talking.

▪ **August 9/09** Photoshoot for Elle Magazine with Kris and Allison

▪ Newark, New Jersey #2 Adam wins Teen Choice Award for "Choice TV Male Reality/Variety Star

▪ At photoshoot w Kris and Allison getting glammed up!!! I love New York!!!!! 8:24 AM **Aug 9th** from Echofon

▪ Looooooooooove and am deeply grateful to my fans who made idol a dream come true. I feel that I express that love in my performance.Thank u 9:24 PM **Aug 9th** from Echofon

If there had been a woman on stage, and she had a solo bit, Adam probably would have been watching her. Lucky girl!

Where did you find this, Gloria?

By xena princess warrior on 08/07/2009 9:49 pm

This is terrifically interesting, Gloria! Listening to the GMA video earlier, I was blown away by Adam's new "acoustic" take on Starlight and thought, wow!, he's such an amazing improviser. Just flawless instincts and timing. I've noticed universal praise for his pitch control, but no one has mentioned his nanosecond rhythmic precision. Really impressive. Anyway, this blog post has me in even greater awe of Adam's technical prowess. That he can go through a horrible sound check and then nail the live performance is beyond amazing. And did I mention I really LOVE this version of Starlight? Reminds me of his stripped down Tracks of My Tears. ***By Juneau Underwood on 08/08/2009 12:05 am***

I think Gloria's David Cook Fanboy is jealous because:
1. Adam didn't flirt with or stare at David
2. Adam didn't even notice Fanboy
3. Fanboy likes Andy and can't compete with Adam
4. "Adam should have worn a plaid shirt?" Yikes!
Any others? ***By xena princess warrior on 08/07/2009 10:29 pm***

Globert. Really? Is that as in "Global Lambert" fans?? What about Canadians? Are we "Canberts"?

Something very powerful about a man who inspires a whole new language, isn't there? And powerful is sexy.

I love his interviews so much that I am going to make a CD of them from my recordings, then I can listen to his speaking voice as well as his singing, while driving my car. ***By xena princess warrior on 08/09/2009 6:50 pm***

Hi Xena, I'm joining you on the countdown to 3K. I think between the two of us, we account for about 20 percent of these posts. Such greedy bitches, aren't we? :)

I found an excellent YouTube post of Adam's Starlight for the Good Morning America concert, so that you can save it in QuickTime. I'm going to do that now . . . I love the Muse full rock band version, but this stripped down version is special.
http://www.youtube.com/watch?v=wlxvApQDcnE

By Juneau Underwood on 08/08/2009 12:39 am

How many adjectives, nouns, verbs and adverbs can be written about a single person who only reached our consciousness a few short months ago. But what a person!!

Soon we'll have written enough words for a couple of Shakespearean plays or a Charles Dickens novel—with fewer characters. There is only one hero, one protagonist, one leading man with an exclusively female chorus.

Perhaps a Rock Opera would be more appropriate to tell this tale of women obsessed with a star who outshines the Milky Way. With a few words, a few notes, a smile, a gesture, a hip motion, we melt like volcanic rock in uncontrollable steamy streams of lava.

Such strength removes any obstruction on our path—to perhaps breathe in the same air, to maybe a nanosecond of eye contact with our Adonis—he who slays serpents to protect us and then soothes our fears and inflames our torrid passions with his music.

That voice of sweet, rare nectar, a tonic of restorative and seductive powers.

Love

Xena *By xena princess warrior on 08/08/2009 1:29 am*

Thanks for marking this milestone Xena. I see the raw material here for a fascinating play (off off off Broadway, maybe the first Blogosphere theatrical release?). If the topic weren't so "frivolous," it would be great for Anna Deavere Smith. Not that I consider what we do here frivolous. This is a dead serious form of fun. OK, I must go to sleep. I will have Adam's unplugged Starlight to carry me off.

By Juneau Underwood on 08/08/2009 1:49 am

Sending you something on art and literature—you'll see it tomorrow

Listening to *Missa Solemnis* which should help me unwind as I imagine your idea. *By xena princess warrior on 08/08/2009 1:57 am*

Thanks Gloria—Kris and Adam remind me of a couple of soldiers who have been attached at the hip in the trenches. Looking out for one another—they develop secret codes of words and gestures, little signals. Out of mutual adversity, a bond forms in those situations and no one else can "get it," because they haven't had the same experiences, travelled through the same minefields. This doesn't always happen of course, the chemistry still has to be right, but when it is—look out—

and don't get in between. They shared a bedroom and bathroom for months—there's not much they don't know about each other now.

Examples in my own life include working on election campaigns—it's 24/7, pressure cooker and at the end, surviving on coffee and cigarettes, pizza, beer and if lucky—some good scotch. If you're fortunate, there is someone else who's there when you are, in synch with your strategic thinking and you feed each other, so when it's over—it's a huge break-up, a devastating departure.

In business & maybe in school, you worked on very lengthy team projects and formed deep bonds with other women or men—it's war in the trenches without the blood. Guys like Adam and Kris are the lucky ones who have someone—who is going through the same experiences—to talk to about it. We're lucky too—we have each other.

For us, it's the Adam vs. everything else in our lives. Much as others try to accommodate us and smile indulgently—we return to the scene of the crime—over and over—to validate our obsessions, our feelings and our experiences. Pity the poor woman who has no one else she can connect to—living underground, surreptitiously sneaking peeks—maybe there's one standing in our doorway who visits us to make the connections she needs.

For any unnamed, shy Glambertinas, we can only hope that we help a bit by being here, writing, sharing and connecting with you.

There is an important element that Kris and Adam have and we are missing—the flesh and blood—the touch, the hugs, the eye contact, the smile—so we have to make up for this gap with our words, photos such as Gloria just posted, performance clips, media clippings. We can feel that we are in the same room at the same time. Tough work? Yes, but it's worth it.

Love to all who live here and those standing in the door, thanks for being my buddies in the trenches.

Xena

Gotta fit Kris into the Rock Opera

By xena princess warrior on 08/08/2009 10:48 am

OMFG, what a sight to wake up to on a Sunday morning. And here I was all focused on baking some croissants and catching up on some serious work, but you just blew all of those thoughts out of my head. I can't believe I've become such a connoisseur of Adam videos that I can recognize where this one was filmed (Atlantic City, right?). He's actually caressing the GB in this one. Maybe because it's Atlantic City, he felt it was OK to go a bit further? I think this one is going to end up on the GlamBulge's Daily Tweet. By the way, the audio quality on this one is about the best I've heard. If anyone peeks over your shoulder while you're watching, you can say "I'm watching it for the sound quality." Like that old line about reading Playboy for the articles. Yeah, right!

OK, I think I smell croissants burning. . . .

By Juneau Underwood on 08/09/2009 8:55 am

I did mention that I was trying to focus on more intellectual topics. So distracting to have to watch Adam gyrating around every time my fingers subconsciously navigate me over to YouTube. . . So here's my more serious thought for the day:

Have you all gone to see Julie & Julia? It's really delightful. I was in a packed house in Harvard Square to see it last night. There's a wrenching moment towards the end of the movie when Julie receives a call from a reporter who tells her that Julia Child "hates" Julie's blog. Julie is utterly crushed. She has been fantasizing about meeting Julia Child in person. Julia has become her Imaginary Friend who has been guiding and approving of her as she struggled through the recipes. To hear that the real Julia disapproved is devastating. But Julie's husband rescues her with his wise insight that it's the "Julia in her head," not the real Julia, who is the one that matters. (You might pick up on the Imaginary Friend idea, which I posted about previously with regard to Adam.)

I've noticed that my own muse, Adam, has become a bit blurry and less present in recent weeks. I don't find myself carrying on the same kind of intense, focused internal conversations with him that I then feel compelled to write down. I am if anything more obsessed than ever with following the Rock God's every move, watching his interviews and concert videos, and I wonder if this has something to do with the fading out of muse-Adam. I find this distressing because I really want and need my muse. I hope the cause is nothing more than the temporary distractions stemming from the daily hubbub generated by the concert tour.

Or . . . perhaps what I need is a deadline, like Julie. I'm wondering if my Glambertina friends on wowOwow are going through something similar as we get swept up by the overpowering feelings that attend anticipating and seeing Adam in the flesh.

By Juneau Underwood on 08/09/2009 9:02 am

My interest in the nature of an artistic muse has been awakened by my personal experience with the manner in which Adam (the Adam who

It can charge you up and make you feel like a million dollars and at the same time, it can make you feel like you got run over by a train. There is so much energy coming at you all the time. In New York, I wanted to just give everybody as much of me as I could because everyone was so supportive and showing so much love http://www3.signonsandiego.com/stories/2009/jul/16/1w16adamm201519/

lives in my head) has inspired me to explore and be creative in new ways, including posting on this site, putting my fantasies into text, writing about other matters that have long been swirling impotently in my brain, and taking stock of my life.

The real Adam has inspired me to do these things, but the mental-Adam is the one who drives me to action. I wrote in an earlier posting that he has become an Imaginary Friend with whom I carry on a dialog. This Muse-Adam is my imagined reader, observer, personal fan club, who tells me I'm fabulous and doing a great job.

In the movie, Julie clearly is feeling this way about Julia Child, although it's not really mentioned explicitly except near the end when Julie's husband talks about the Julia in Julie's head. I also find it fascinating that my muse is probably most powerful as long as he remains an imaginary construct. If I were to meet Adam in person, I don't know what would happen to my Muse-Adam. It's a scary thought because Muse-Adam is changing my life. Does this make any sense?

By Juneau Underwood on 08/09/2009 1:00 pm

"I don't want to meet Adam in person, lest he look past me to a cute boy standing behind me."

You know, I don't think he'd do that. He is so polite, makes eye contact with the person in front of him, and I'm sure because you are so intelligent and cultured, he'd take a genuine interest in what you have to say.

I've been sneaking Adam into the family in dribs and drabs, and actually saturated my younger daughter during our drive to Maine with Adam songs from my iPod. Although she kept complaining ("are you going to make me listen to Adam Lambert all the way to Maine?"), I was happy to hear her spontaneously singing Black or White, Born to be Wild, Mad World and One afterwards, so I may have succeeding in infecting at least one family member! And yes, we are fortunate to be witnessing the birth of this spectacular new star, and that he lives in a time when he can be true to himself.

By Juneau Underwood on 08/09/2009 6:23 pm

You ladies make me laugh! Let's stand up for sexy mature ladies. We wear our battle scars proudly and have plenty of love to give the world. Those callow youngsters can think of sexual attraction in only a very narrow, narcissistic way. They can't conceive of the nature of the erotic tidal wave that has washed over people of all ages in the wake of Adam

Lambert. It's not about doing it with him (awesome as that would be). I think Adam's very un-attainability has made women of all ages feel it's safe to express their love for him. They know they don't stand a chance, but it's not a personal rejection. ***By Juneau Underwood on 08/09/2009 6:10 pm***

We are almost as obsessed with each other and what we have to say, as we are with the object of our affections. We compulsively check the site and refresh our email to find out what's going on here. Out of range, we drive hours to find a cyber connection or rely on blackberries and even if we can't respond, we read.

We have explored places where others fear to go. The sheer volume of creative writing, articulate observations and deep analysis is mind boggling—everyday brings news, photos, opinions, videos and Glambertina comments!

Xena ***By xena princess warrior on 08/09/2009 7:08 pm***

Well said, and I don't want to see you posting any more until you deliver us to the steamy shores of Brazil, Xena!

I must say I'm as addicted to this community as to the Object of our Adoration himself. You all make me smile, feel supported and alive. Xena is right that there is not another blog like this one. I do browse the other Adam sites from time to time, and the level of inanity and snarkiness astounds me. I don't know why people feel they need to tear each other down. I feel like I need a hot shower after spending time in some of them. Whereas here I feel it's a cold shower I need! So much heat and passion along with the intellectual stimulation. It is a compelling mix. I love you all! ***By Juneau Underwood on 08/09/2009 9:29 pm***

Oh Yes! Downunder—

I love clever minds. I love clever, sexy, kind minds with good looking men attached even more!

And yes, Copacetic, we Canadians understand the meaning as it is American, a bit Canadian, and we know, not English.

You mention Scrabble—a former obsessive/compulsive project of mine, now under control. Some time back—I received a challenge to write one of my fantasies about Adam, with Scrabble in it. Juneau flung down the gauntlet by including it at the end of hers, and I did it.

Now you mention "Trivial Pursuit"? Another old favourite board game. Do I need to write a story about T. P.?

His vocabulary, quotes and foreign words—including French and Latin and Shakespeare—absolutely stimulate my endorphins. I think he tries to humble his intelligence to fit in with the AI crowd. When I take off on a single word like "bromae" or accoutrements—we aren't even close to done with our research. And we are only now really getting to know him better, since he does so many interviews.

And those double entendres—well, they were in my second little Adam fantasy—sitting in the dark corner of a bar, holding hands, flirting and laughing at his naughty jokes. "I like the top."

Sounds to me that if I had to take a long bus trip, he'd be a great seatmate.

Do you have a project for the MoALS Symposium? You might present something on "The Meaning of Adam Lambert's Talents, Activities and Knowledge"—there is more to this man than meets the eyes.

What do you think?

Xena

MoALS Symposium Coordinator

By xena princess warrior on 08/09/2009 10:40 pm

Let's not forget that Adam sings beautifully in Hebrew. I also read somewhere that he read voraciously as a kid. I suspect he's an autodidact. Wouldn't it be fun to send him to the Glambertinas' Finishing School?

By Juneau Underwood on 08/09/2009 10:33 pm

Absolutely! I volunteer to teach him physics and biology. And astronomy, with Brian May as a guest lecturer.

By Juneau Underwood on 08/10/2009 12:03 am

I choose Art History and architecture and it will involve a lot of field trips to view the works in person.

By xena princess warrior on 08/10/2009 12:13 am

Hi Xena,

Here's a draft description of your courses. Please provide feedback. I will compile suggestions and produce a final curriculum to present to our student. Love, J

Architecture (Prof. X. P. Warrior). A comprehensive survey of world architecture, including ancient Egyptian, Greek and Roman, medieval to modern European, Indian, southeast Asian, east Asian, and concluding with contemporary masterpieces of Latin American, Oceania and

Japan. The unifying theme of this survey will be towers and their enduring meaning through the ages. You must commit to extensive field investigation (may be done as part of a work-study program) and dramatic impersonations of architectural works.

Art History (Prof. X. P. Warrior). This year, our celebrated art historian will instruct on the much-anticipated topic of Eros in Art: A Global Perspective. She takes "around the world" to a new level of sophistication. This course will included tactile exploration of classical Greek sculpture and very close examination of Grecian urns, Mughal and Chinese miniatures, Japanese woodblock prints, and comparisons of 20th century masters including Schiele, Picasso and Koons, among others. Silk scarves, gloves and magnifying glasses will be supplied. Please notify professor if you are allergic to latex. Requires field investigation; recommended pairing with Prof. Princess's survey of architecture course. Work-study OK.

By Juneau Underwood on 08/10/2009 2:24 pm

OMG Juneau!!!! I am laughing so hard, tears are washing my keyboard! Just to let you in on something—you and I have together, taken Adam to study ancient Greek art and we have today, focused on the male form. Adam's a hoot! It is the first day of "Eros in Art" and he has really taken a liking to it—enthusiastic, bright and curious student, who participates fully in all activities, shows leadership and creativity in developing new ways of studying. Plays well with others.

Towers—whew—where to begin—love the newly shaped, curvaceous modern ones, smooth and shiny and very organic.

Have to get back to our story—I can't have it occupying conscious mind space while attending at Town Hall.

Juneau—I thought you had other intellectual pursuits to which you must attend—well so do I.

Love

Prof. X. P. Warrior, Phd.MFA.BFA—specializing "teaching art and architecture to the adult male student" successfully and leaving them panting for more.

By xena princess warrior on 08/10/2009 2:39 pm

Wow!!! Thanks to all who voted for the Teen Choice Awards! I'm honored to win "Choice Male Reality/ Variety TV Show Star" thank you soo much 8:42 AM **Aug 10th** from Echofon

I have yet to view a gay man's residence without an obelisk—why don't women have tall, slender, pointy objects too? And hetero men—round, organic and curvaceous shapes—the world is a bit mixed up. We will try to correct this and your recommendation is totally welcome! (I love using "totally," it reminds me of Adamspeak)

It's not me E.—it's all of you! If I didn't have the Glambertinas, I would be hiding in a dark room, bedcovers pulled over my head. But, thanks to all of you wonderful women, I have managed to stay out of the dark tunnel of depression—the bottom—and have been moving back up the roller-coaster, where it's exhilarating and beautiful, if a little dangerous.

Love Xena

By xena princess warrior on 08/10/2009 3:11 pm

OK ladies, I'm asking all of you to review your course descriptions. Xena is working on hers (see above). Here's Calculus, and I threw in my Astronomy course too for your feedback.—J

Calculus (Profs. C. Lambert and A. Beth). Calculus is the study of Change (is gonna come). Calculus (plural calculi) may refer to any method or system of calculation guided by the symbolic manipulation of expressions. Ability to express and manipulate are prerequisites for this course. Newton used the methods of calculus to solve the problem of planetary motion, the shape of the surface of a rotating fluid, the motion of a weight sliding on a cycloid. In this class, calculus will be applied to solve the trajectory of a spaceship attempting to dock with a Venutian space station, and whether an extra-dry martini should be stirred or shaken. Extra credit will be given to students who propose and solve an original problem related to the motion of a weight sliding on a cycloid.

Astronomy (Prof. J. Underwood and guest). Why astronomy is cooler than astrology. This cosmic survey begins with a review of our own planetary system (is there life on Mars?), Milky Way galaxy and the space-time singularity in which we currently find ourselves. The second half of the course will probe the harmonics of supermassive black holes and space travel. We will visit ancient astrological sites (Stonehenge, Teotihuacan, Machu Picchu, Vezelay, etc.) and ascend to high elevations (Mauna Kea, Chile, Australia, etc.) to obtain crystal-clear, varied perspectives on the night sky. Air mattresses and down-filled silk quilts will be provided for optimal prone viewing positions, but participants must bring their own heat. During our stop in England, Prof Brian May will lecture on interplanetary dust and astronomical themes in the music of Queen. Travel will be coordinated with Architecture and Art History.

By Juneau Underwood on 08/10/2009 5:54 pm

C., I was pondering whether to mention limits. Adam might take it the wrong way. But you're right, it's a key concept. I like the questions you raise, especially about the penalty. We professors will have to give that careful consideration: what punishment to mete out if Adam transgresses.

By Juneau Underwood on 08/10/2009 8:29 pm

N. S.! wondered when you would submit your proposal and you did not disappoint! Adam needs to be well-rounded and geology is a must.

By xena princess warrior on 08/10/2009 9:52 pm

Woo hoo! Will add Geology to the curriculum! Is "sudduction" a clever hybrid of subduction and seduction? Very nice! And what of the self-exciting dynamo hypothesis of terrestrial magnetism? It seems to convincingly explain the wanderings and occasional reversals of the magnetic poles. Who would have thought science would have so many delicious double entendres?

By Juneau Underwood on 08/10/2009 11:12 pm

oh yes, love the poultry—slippery hands and fingers pulling legs, thighs, wings, free of their ligamental attachments. Teeth bite juicy flesh, copious amounts of wine.

Please include our special Adam dessert—

"Fruits avec Chocolate Chaud sur Crème Frappé Adam" dessert or breakfast in bed or midnight snack if your nocturnal activities gave you an appetite. Strawberries, raspberries, blueberries and pineapple dipped in luscious warm chocolate and then in whipped cream.

By xena princess warrior on 08/10/2009 3:37 pm

We're setting the bar a little low for him, don't ya think? I am working on a curriculum that will prepare him to meet world leaders and chat with Noble laureates. I noticed also that he speaks in complete sentences without falling back on fillers. And in such well-modulated, dulcet syllables—a speaking voice worth swooning over.

By Juneau Underwood on 08/10/2009 2:49 pm

How can we expunge, expurgate and exorcise those barriers to your imagination and your libido? Just came out of the shower to prepare for dull meeting, wondering if I can sit and write while the meeting's on—oh such risky business! But as I stepped out, a new thought for the current story just can't stop the flow. You keep reading, I'll keep writing!

I was the "keeper of the rules," modest and ladylike, manners to be proud of, never a complaint from a teacher, didn't know how to flirt but somehow attracted my husband. I was the girl the boys could bring home to mom, dad and grandma and not worry—still am. Except this group of women—who knows there's Xena inside the familiar face and she's a harridan. ***By xena princess warrior on 08/10/2009 4:49 pm***

These two [Alison and Adam] are so great together—the choreography has become a "guideline" so they are more impromptu and spontaneous—personalizing the words too. And we get to see Adam up close and personal with a lovely girl.

I'm in the second row floor on Friday—I'm thinking maybe an ostrich feather—a shout out to Glambertinas! I thought the jock straps could have been more interesting—studded, sequined, silk, satin, metallic leather—colourful? Maybe rainbow coloured!

Xena ***By xena princess warrior on 08/10/2009 12:54 pm***

Gunmetal black leather jockstrap festooned with blue ostrich feathers and black rhinestones. Start sewing, Xena!

By Juneau Underwood on 08/10/2009 2:57 pm

I think that would be one he would not fling back—it's a keeper. My daughter would die! ***By xena princess warrior on 08/10/2009 3:13 pm***

Do it! Here's a place you can start shopping:
http://www.jockstrapcentral.com/productdisplay.php?product=09002

By Juneau Underwood on 08/10/2009 6:01 pm

In my mind, he and all of the Glambertinas are sitting in a room together and talking to me all the time, provoking and encouraging me and then your responses! I'm addicted to the audience the way Adam is—we "use each other" in a good way—energy flowing in both directions is powerful inspiration. I'm sure it works the same for you, don't be shy.

Adam has spoken many times that he loves this effect he has on women and men and that he deliberately works to provoke our desire, physically, musically and with his sometimes naughty mind—some of us just happen to visualize and write it down. *"It's all good" "I'm making 'gasms? that's great."* I take that as more than permission, it's encouragement.

Hugs, kisses and love to all of you, you make my heart sing!

Xena ***By xena princess warrior on 08/10/2009 3:03 pm***

Hi Niamh Cat, I have taken the liberty of assigning you as co-instructor in Biology for Adam's Finishing School:

Biology (Prof. J. Underwood and Prof. N. Cat). The science of Life—what could be more profound or beautiful? This course will review the fundamentals of molecular and cell biology—DNA, protein synthesis, intracellular signalling and all that—and move up to systems, organisms and evolution. We will explore the Origins of Symmetry in life forms and species characteristics driven by sexual selection (butterflies, the peacock's tail, exotic male genitalia in the insect world). A section of the course will be devoted to the evolution of homosexuality, a seeming paradox if one considers evolution only in the context of the selfish gene, but which makes perfect sense if one considers Richard Dawkins' model of the Meme, a cultural idea or symbol that, like a gene, evolves through selection pressure to give rise to self-propagating cultural systems. We will debate the hypothesis that homosexual individuals, being free of the burdens of physical procreation, are able to devote themselves to creating and propagating memes (e.g., in medicine, science, arts, literature), which have contributed to the overall survival and well-being of our species. Extra credit for writing an advanced thesis on why women love gay men. ***By Juneau Underwood on 08/10/2009 6:53 pm***

Holy Toledo, I don't think we're in Kansas anymore. . . . So is this photoshopped? Or is this a Kradam coming out announcement?

By Juneau Underwood on 08/10/2009 8:43 pm

GB, what can I say—it was like opening Pandora's box—the light glowed so fiercely—I had to slam the lid shut! Then, I took a deep breath, a sip of wine, closed my eyes, clicked and very slowly, squinting at first, I gradually opened my eyes, then closed them again. The ethereal beauty of the image in thought and execution, heart racing, quick a cold cloth, I'm overheating, melting into my chair—"turn up the air conditioning!" ***By xena princess warrior on 08/10/2009 9:42 pm***

I find it astonishingly wonderful that we women are so completely open to being turned on by an image of two men locked in an erotic embrace. The thought would not have even crossed my mind a few short months ago (although come to think of it, yeah, I thought the sex scene in Brokeback Mountain was delicious). No jealousy (maybe a little envy), just a simple volcanic overflow of Eros.

By Juneau Underwood on 08/11/2009 5:33 pm

J. I could not believe my reaction and how it moved me—I think this particular piece of art is the reason. The two men share more than mere affection and we know that about them. We know them as individuals and as a "couple"—they are yin/yang to each other—no? The role the artist cast for each—Adam, the worldly, sexually charged, tempting devil, tall enough to embrace the fair haired, smaller, innocent, unworldly, modest and angelic Kris, in a pose of sexual desire/satisfaction—which is it? the ambiguity the artist carefully constructs adds to the sensual eroticism, and the mystery of time.

Has Kris come into Adam's arms for comfort and solace, yet arousing Adam's desires? Has Adam taken Kris into his arms as a protector from the darkness of the world, outside their confined sphere? There's light surrounding them, within a void of darkness. No, the light emanates from them, they glow and radiate their love which we can feel.

Can Adam feel erotic love, while Kris returns a filial love and the two be happy for long? Or, does Kris feel the pull of Eros, but resists the powerful temptation to act, remaining the angelic virgin in the relationship?

I think that what we envy is that they have a special bond, a unique love, they complete each other and that's what we would like to have in a friend.

FYI, I wrote this without looking at the picture since yesterday, it is burned onto the backs of my eyes, like watching an eclipse without protection.

X

By xena princess warrior on 08/11/2009 6:20 pm

I'm speechless. Like watching an eclipse without protection. You are a mistress of the English language.

By Juneau Underwood on 08/11/2009 8:10 pm

If I'm the mistress, you are the Queen. Just reminded me, I have great description for the fantasy.

gotta go

By xena princess warrior on 08/11/2009 8:27 pm

C., your Newtonian physics is spot on. My only quibble is that there's nothing "sneaky" about Adam's hand. It's pretty brazen and in-your-face, IMHO. Seems to have a mind of its own. Pretty soon, Adam's hand (GB's friend) will have a twitter account of his own.

By Juneau Underwood on 08/10/2009 11:18 pm

I will add "Applied Geology" with a focus on spelunking under "extra credit." Thanks for the excellent suggestion. He's going to have the most kick-ass education in the history of pop stardom.

By Juneau Underwood on 08/10/2009 11:21 pm

All those math classes are finally paying off! Who would have thought geometry and calculus could be so much fun?

By Juneau Underwood on 08/10/2009 11:52 pm

It will be kick-ass, hands-on, interactive, intellectual, stimulating—with field trips to exotic locations, in luxurious comfort.

And when classes are over, our hair comes down, we remove our spectacles, drop the books, calculators, microscopes, gyrating objects and pick up the sherpas, the bellboys or whoever is attending to us that day—to show us local night life—to study the local rituals, the entertainment, music, dance—anthropology field work.

Back to my story—you've been swept up by a tall, dark, stranger and you're not back yet. I hope you haven't left Adam and me behind—we'll worry, then have another drink.

X

By xena princess warrior on 08/10/2009 11:53 pm

Women of Glamberta! You are intoxicating me—I can't stop laughing out loud—someone in this house is bound to call for a paddy wagon and straight jacket. Hauling me out the door while I sing Let's Dance and try to get the attendant to dance with me, or at least do some pelvic thrusts.

Earlier, I barely got out the door for a meeting that took less time than I did to dress, do hair, eyeliner, mascara, lipstick and 4" pink pumps to match the silk jacket over a simple black sheath. When we walked out of the council chamber after 25 minutes, I told the men "It took me longer to dress!"

Sadly, no one thought it meant we had more time for cocktails—remember the '80s?

But, you're better than a shaker of martinis to bring on the joy and laughter! Group therapy at its best—I do feel sorry for people who unfortunately, don't have a group of brilliant, funny, sexy women to party with on a Monday night.

Love X

By xena princess warrior on 08/10/2009 10:06 pm

OK, here's another course description for the Adam Lambert Finishing School curriculum. Prof. E., your feedback is requested. Others may pitch in with helpful suggestions.

Health I—Food and Physique (Prof. E., assisted by all faculty). Science and esthetics come together in the art of healthy cuisine and maintaining a gorgeous, love-ready bod. Oops, did I really let that drop? Oh well, never apologize! In this course, students will be challenged to take a set of raw ingredients and transform them into a love feast capable of making your object of desire cease to object to your desires. Past challenges have included meals made entirely of zucchini, another restricted to foods with four-letter names, and the all-time challenge, a meal comprised of gonads, vegetable and animal. Not for the faint of heart. Biology is a prerequisite. Each class ends with a session of 200 stomach crunches and 100 push-ups, assisted by the professor. Bonus final project: Fruits avec Chocolate Chaud sur Crème Frappé Adam" dessert or breakfast in bed or midnight snack. Strawberries, raspberries, blueberries and pineapple dipped in luscious warm chocolate and then in whipped cream. Extra credit: Use methods of molecular cuisine to transubstantiate the above dessert into a form that will float in warm, scented bathwater. ***By Juneau Underwood on 08/10/2009 11:50 pm***

I'm limp, my wrists are weak, I can't type—you're killing me!

Is the bath still-water or Jacuzzi?

X ***By xena princess warrior on 08/11/2009 12:07 am***

I have had SUCH a fun day. I need to slow down. . . . The bathwater is still. That's so we can hear Adam cooing sweet endearments while he feeds his beloved, morsels of the molecular gastronomic delicacy. Maybe the Jacuzzi makes an appearance in the hydrodynamics class, the section on female erotic response. ***By Juneau Underwood on 08/11/2009 12:19 am***

E.!! Hand to mouth—smothering laughter—close the door MIL must not hear

I volunteer to be the sous chef or pot washer. Perhaps you'll use fine, translucent Limoges porcelain, Baccarat wine goblets, antique sterling, ivory handled fish set, and I imagine the linens will get rather soiled during prep and consumption—every object and living thing will need a gentle, careful, but thorough hand washing and hand polishing, before and after. no cloth required.

You're the best—Professor Emeritus de gastronomy

By xena princess warrior on 08/11/2009 5:26 pm

Nothing but the best, naturellement. I can guest lecture on a Japanese kaiseki meal, served on a glossy black lacquer table with jewel-like morsels of the most rare seasonal delicacies served in priceless antique tea bowls, stone and earth scarred by the fires of the kiln. We'll be seated on grass-scented tatami mats, and soon Adam will be so uncomfortable that he will have to stretch his long thighs and we will tumble to the mats as our silken robes escape from their brocade bindings.

By Juneau Underwood on 08/11/2009 5:40 pm

I think that today, I wrote and read my way out of my depression and spent most of the day laughing like a crazed hyena. I think it's been the funniest day for comments and so voluble! It's Monday—don't we have jobs to go to or at least think about?

Where and how did we find these women? It can't be us, we're sane.

Got to go read Adam's Ultimate interview pt III
http://latimesblogs.latimes.com/americanidoltracker/2009/08/adam-lambert-the-ultimate-interview-part-three.html

By xena princess warrior on 08/11/2009 12:30 am

I did say that my life was full and so did GB.

Thanks so much for your concern AAH—I've been on what used to be called manic/depressive cycles since my twenties, but my periods of "normal" were long, so I went way up and way down about every ten years. I'm on medication and had 12 years of psychotherapy, including behaviour modification, starting in 1990.

For me, depression is kind of a permanent state of mind and it's primarily chemical, but events can trigger one. The anti-depressant I take smoothes out the highs and lows of my cycles, but I believe stifles my creativity by virtually eliminating the manic phases, however since May/beginning of June, my mind managed to break through and take the roller coaster up to the top. Other than Adam and having all of you to talk to, nothing changed in my life and I began to feel that rare "happy" emotion. So, I followed the "if it feels good, do it" philosophy and it worked fine until July 15th.

Woke up in the morning and knew it was the last day. Actually wrote it up, how I felt—the day begins with Leonardo di Caprio on the front of the Titanic shouting "*I'm the king of the world!*" and fewer than eight hours later, darkness descends and I'm collapsed. I didn't contribute much after that, until late last week again. I kept reading—nothing "inspired" me, but I believed that I could move up the roller coaster of happiness if I kept reading and trying to write and it worked!!

Yesterday and then again today, I feel that I am going back up—hurray! It's a miracle to me, but after so many years of experience with this, including a lot of study, I thought I would try this method to prevent a total crash and it worked!

I am going to try not to race to the top, where it drops again, but will take it slowly this time. ***By xena princess warrior on 08/12/2009 12:12 am***

There are indeed two parallel universes we have found ourselves in: The Universe With Adam Lambert and The Universe Without. I'm so happy to have such magnificent fellow travellers! I imagine there are countless other parallel universes that we simply haven't discovered. Another topic for the physics course I'm working on!

By Juneau Underwood on 08/11/2009 12:23 pm

Only Neil [Adam's brother] could meet a guy in a bar, and he turns out to be the co-inventor of K-Y. ***By N.C. on 08/11/2009 11:18 am***

Well Gloria, my daughter is getting so excited, she might throw me up on stage and she keeps reminding me that we have a lot to prepare before.

I am responding here to some posts awhile back with Juneau. My daughter has been thoroughly corrupted by all of you—I am but a messenger. So Juneau, on her own, Xena II came up the idea of a blue sequined and feathered jock strap as a "gift."

Warning to those of you we will meet on Friday—the acorn does not fall far from the tree and you will have a live witness to my life since June 3rd. Maybe I'll forego coffee/lunch ahead and just send her. She was an EMO kid and now, like Adam, she has no filter when she speaks, which at first I worried about—remember how so many of you were worried about him? Thanks to her, I'm not skerrrrrred anymore and Adam has reinforced that in me.

Love

Xena ***By xena princess warrior on 08/11/2009 5:05 pm***

Physics (Prof. J. Underwood). The crown jewel of human scientific achievement (I'm not showing any bias here am I?), physics is the rigorous analysis of nature in order to understand how the universe behaves. This course will cover the fundamental theorem of Emmy Noether (a woman who kicked the butts of most other mathematicians of her day), who proved that the Origin of Symmetry is linked to the laws of conservation (of energy, linear momentum and angular momentum). We will debate the possibility of traveling via wormhole among Parallel Universes (With and Without Adam).

We will also devote some special evening sessions to pulling the plug on G-String Theory and calculating the mass and angular momentum of an extraterrestrial object sighted recently on YouTube known as the "GlamBulge." The class will make a field trip to the Large Hardon (oops, Hadron) Collider, which occupies a vast tunnel excavated beneath the Franco-Swiss border, for the spelunkers among us. Mandatory laboratory experiments on vibrations, waves, and energy transfer via quantum dots.

By Juneau Underwood on 08/11/2009 2:20 pm

If I can come on the field trip, I will carry on my own back, the necessary tools and equipment—vibrators for the vibrations, water jets for propulsion and waves. Appropriate music to inspire the necessary contact needed to feel the energy transfer experience—deeply and thoroughly—every inch of it. We might observe the effects of said energy transfer on the recipient and the producer. I will also bring a fire extinguisher. ***By xena princess warrior on 08/11/2009 5:15 pm***

You must have been a Girl Scout. Good of you to remember the fire extinguisher. ***By Juneau Underwood on 08/11/2009 5:48 pm***

Of course, that lesson on vibrations needs a variety of tools from the mundane to the most exotic. Speed control—along the entire continuum of movement, surface texture—rough, smooth, soft, supple or hard. Temperature—from hot to tepid to cool. Size—does it make a difference? What effects can be produced by employing different shapes and sizes—alone or in combination? Manmade or natural materials? e.g., Ostrich skin vs. vinyl—Firmness—rigid to flexible

For the waves, we should include ostrich feathers and peacock feathers to determine the features of each, in creating waves of air movement and compare their effectiveness.

This is all physics isn't it? I only had first year biology, so forgive me if this sounds too simple and feel free, all you scientists, to augment these learning experiences with other experiments. Adam must be able to attain a very high level of practical knowledge, so I rely on the experts to use their judgements.

I'll get back to researching the list of sites to study the meaning of symbolic and realistic phallic objects—from the prehistoric to the modern. Are they symbols of power and lust or fertility and how do you know?

Xena, Prof. Architecture and Art

By xena princess warrior on 08/11/2009 6:51 pm

Dear Prof. Xena, You are doing exceptionally well with the physics. I want to draw your attention to a that should be added to your trove of experimental equipment. That is the OhMiBod, an implement that comes in various sizes and shapes that plugs into an iPod and pulsates in time to the contents of said iPod (need I guess which artist would be stuck on endless play?). Here is the web site: http://www.ohmibod.com ***By Juneau Underwood on 08/11/2009 8:05 pm***

Ah! I certainly see the value in this exceptional teaching device—it's extremely efficient in its workings and combines the vibrations with the waves—sound waves. We should study how different musical sound waves flowing into the device produce different movements and the effect of those movements on the subject. From slow, sensuous ballads in a deep basso profundo to Adam's Ring of Fire to lively, heat producing dance numbers—Let's Dance.

Recognizing that this is a manmade, artificial augmenter, how does it compare to the actual, natural, expandable, one-size-fits-all, real thing—utilizing the same sound waves to induce the vibrations. Testing its effectiveness, efficiency and sustainability.

so 21st century

Xena, still Prof. Architecture and Art History

hope I don't get suspension for this one, don't want to lose tenure

By xena princess warrior on 08/11/2009 8:46 pm

I could use some inspiration on this one. The latest addition to the Adam Finishing School curriculum. Xena, maybe your daughter can help.

French Poetry (All faculty). Mostly because it would be so awesomely sexy to hear Adam speak French. Poets covered in this class include Apollinaire, Baudelaire, Breton, Cocteau, Genet, Rimbaud. Class field trip to Le Père Lachaise Cemetery in Paris, with a wine-tasting celebration at the tomb of Jim Morrison. Detours to sex clubs in nearby Pigalle will cost extra. Students must supply own whips and handcuffs. Entrance fees may be waived if you wear a bejeweled, feathered jock strap. ***By Juneau Underwood on 08/11/2009 5:50 pm***

Juneau, I lost it when he spoke one word in French “accoutrement,” listening to him read French poetry?? In a below ground cafe, French accordion playing in the background, a little Edith Piaf to get us in the mood. Drinking absinthe, smoking Gauloise, wearing dark, unstructured, careless robe, jupe, chemisier, chandail—or capris like Audrey Hepburn in Funny Face

Darkly painted eyes, pale skin and deep, dark, red lipstick.

We will need to be in Paris for several days—there’s a lot of Art and Architecture to review there. La Tour Eiffel is included in the study of towers in architecture and the museums too numerous to mention here.

Xena ***By xena princess warrior on 08/11/2009 8:48 pm***

I may not sleep for the next 52 hours. It’s 7:39 pm on Wed. now and in a little over 52 hours, Adam will be giving us a whole lotta love and finish off by asking us to dance with him. Someone might have to prop me up by then.

We’ve all talked about our starving families, piled laundry, missed deadlines—now I have a flooded basement, husband out of town, daughter out and I am writing to you. A small flood, but still, water in the basement and after doing the least I could do, I’m back here. It’ll dry up on its own—won’t it? ***By xena princess warrior on 08/11/2009 7:45 pm***

E., fortunately I have a husband and daughter who eat to live, but occasionally appreciate a special meal from me, which I enjoy doing.

Took daughter and friends to a concert today, returned, picked them up, drove past our town to drop them off and then back home. Daughter is in the basement mopping. It’s Quid pro quo around here.

By xena princess warrior on 08/11/2009 11:49 pm

Since I’m doing foreign languages today (see French Poetry above), here’s another course:

Hebrew, the Language of Love (Prof. A. Lambert). This Finishing School espouses the view that students learn by teaching, and teachers teach by learning. Hence, in this class, instruction will be in the hands of our star pupil, who has capably demonstrated his ability to vocalize in Hebrew with conviction. Whether he understands what he’s saying, who cares? It’s enough to make any Jewish mom proud. Professors auditing this course are required to closely study all of Adam's YouTube videos in which he sings in Hebrew. Remember: L'fum tzara agra (no pain no gain)!

Shalom Chaverim! *By Juneau Underwood on 08/11/2009 8:31 pm*

DF, you are so right, that's what he has produced here. Women who are more than smiling but laughing out loud, feeling sexy and every day, almost every hour, celebrating and collaborating on fantastic projects, endorphins flowing, synapses sparking and all we have to accomplish this, is one sense—sight—of words, but Adam provides the sounds and the pictures—he's our conduit to each other.

I think he feels pretty good about that.

By xena princess warrior on 08/12/2009 12:28 am

So, just looked at the latest biceps photos from Cleo—how much would it cost to kidnap him and keep him somewhere wonderful, just for ourselves? What would we be willing to sacrifice? Could we compromise?

By xena princess warrior on 08/12/2009 12:38 am

New Zealand might be a good hiding place. Do you have luxurious seaside resorts? Perhaps a private Pacific Island—Johnny Depp has one.

By xena princess warrior on 08/12/2009 12:41 am

We'll have to bribe husband with something really special

By xena princess warrior on 08/12/2009 7:41 pm

How beautiful is that???? Okay, NZ is definitely on the list. Perhaps we could move him every quarter to different locations?

By xena princess warrior on 08/12/2009 2:05 am

▪ **August 12/09** Nassau Coliseum in Uniondale New York 2

This is perfect for the Finishing School. We can add golf to the phys ed requirement. *By Juneau Underwood on 08/12/2009 8:33 am*

▪ TwitterParty !! 8:28 PM **Aug 12th** from Echofon

Please, please—may I have golf? It's the only sport I play—have for about thirty years and love to watch it. Men with shafts—biceps peak out from under short sleeves, bodies firm and taut as they torque their torso around, then the release, knees first, thighs, hips and finally the wrists, club head makes contact with the dimpled sphere.

I have stylish outfits, not tacky ones and the most beautiful "princess" golf bag—it has no shoulder strap to carry it. Only goes on a cart, by a valet. Matching hand-made snakeskin golf shoes in a bronze/copper metallic finish—they glow in the sunlight.

Although my driving can be erratic, my short game, when I start closing in on the green, high irons in play, beautiful arcs as the ball explodes off the wedge, spinning—at the peak of its trajectory, it spies its target, the hole with the flag staff still in it.

Can't avoid the stick, so my ball bounces off and drops 11 1/2 inches from the hole. Oh well, there's another stroke on this hole, hope the putter's hot today. Caddy Brad has the putter in his hand and wipes it carefully with the shammy—special emphasis on the head—can't have any flecks to deflect the ball from its target.

Slow, smooth practice stroke, maybe another, then loosen the shoulders, feet still and supporting, easy grip on the shaft as hands slide to find the sweet spot, draw it back, eye on the ball, then release, move the club head through ball smoothly, cleanly—to roll toward its destiny—follow through, lift head for the final—there it is! The satisfying spiral of the ball as it slides down the sides of the hole and mercifully lands on the bottom.

Just think, this happens eighteen times on the course before we return to the clubhouse for a post-game analysis of swing, stroke, stance, exploding sand shots, then the herbal massage, sauna, the shower, cocktails on the terrace, seafood dinner in a private beach-side gazebo lit by a glowing sunset of hot colours.

There's my application—do I qualify as Adam's golf instructor?

Prof. X. P. W.

By xena princess warrior on 08/12/2009 11:51 am

"Adam is the true man for a new age, one where sex is ageless and genderless. If that is the case, WOW, he will conquer the world . . . the dawning of the Age of Aquarius."

Dear E, you couldn't have expressed this thought more beautifully, and I believe what you say is true. I have occasionally wondered whether Adam is mortified by how many Boomer women are in love with him, but I see that so many younger people, and men, also are fans, and realize we have a skewed perspective here at wowOwow. He has truly universal appeal. He just won the Teen's Choice Award, and Young Hollywood, after all. I think he will bring together people of all generations, genders and nationalities in a way that we've never seen before.

As for his not coming out for meet and greets, I'm sure he is on the brink of exhaustion. He really has to conserve his voice and his strength. And in New York, I read that his mother had a huge group of friends there (I think she must have grown up in the New York area), so he had to choose between spending hours signing autographs or spending precious time with all the family and friends who came to the concert. I am glad he chose friends (including dozens of women his mother's age!) over fans. He's a good son.

Regarding whatever anxiety or self-consciousness you are feeling about your age, all I can say is that the age of my friends ceased to be relevant once I became an adult. I have always had friends of all ages. What they have in common is "aliveness" and an intelligent engagement with the world. You certainly exude that. You energize me! As long as you send out energy into the world, and find friends who soak it up and radiate it back, you will never be over the hill. If your friends are energy sinks, it may be time to seek out new friends!

By Juneau Underwood on 08/13/2009 10:49 am

Hamilton countdown—Xena team update:

Shopped today for essentials & obtained following—sheer black tank top with very shiny silver sequins all over the front. Slinky silver shirt to wear over (off during show) and I'll wear the most flattering trousers I have.

Shopped for the jock and didn't purchase, but researched—that was tough, because I have never been in one of those "naughty" stores—ever—I promise—pinkie swear.

Then to craft store where I found glitter, iron on multi-coloured glass crystals with a star shape for the centre. Feathers! hot coloured! oooo, they are soooo soft. will finish project tomorrow

By xena princess warrior on 08/12/2009 8:55 pm

Adam is up to his trend-setting mischief again. Did you see the New York Times article today on men's hairstyles?
http://www.nytimes.com/2009/08/13/fashion/13CODES.html?pagewanted=1&8dpc

Men are getting very adventurous with their hair, and mixing up styles in fresh ways. Here's what the article says about our hero: "And however you thought Adam Lambert's hairstyle pegged him, it was clear to "American Idol" audiences that musically, at least, the man's got range."

By Juneau Underwood on 08/13/2009 6:27 pm

No we're not all gone, some of us are still working away on preparations. I am embellishing a men's thong, Xena Jr., is doing cover art for the CDs

I made for the others and she has plans for a sign as well! I bought her a new SLR camera which she needs for school anyway and of course there are the outfits and accoutrements to coordinate—we may not get to bed tonight. Two OCD perfectionists—too painful for words—trying to get something done together. It either comes out great, or we can't even start. At least we've started hmmmmm—the aroma of coffee just wafted by, I think it's in my imagination, better make some, it's going to be a loooooong night.

Keep talking amongst yourselves—I'll just be quiet and glue glitter to everything. ***By xena princess warrior on 08/14/2009 12:02 am***

I was going to hold off on more Finishing School course descriptions until after Hurricane Adam had swept through Hamilton, but tomorrow's much-anticipated concert offers a too-tempting opportunity for close inspection of the anatomical organ that is the focus of Prof. Gloria Beth's class, that I just had to put it out there. All for the advancement of knowledge and the greater good, of course.

Health II—Oral hygiene (Prof. A. Beth). In this course, the mouth receives the respect and affection that is its due. We will appreciate the paradox of the lips, sculpted like marble yet yieldingly soft as a breast, its hue so like the velvet underpetal of a rose. We will master the delicate art of parting those lips with fingers, gently and firmly, coaxing them wider apart until we have an unobstructed view of those admirable incisors, cuspids, bi- and otherwise, and molars, forming strong arches to frame that acrobatic muscle, the tongue. We will learn the importance of the salivary glands, conduct a vocal cord health check, measure the diameter of the esophagus, and learn the correct technique for palpating the Adam's apple. Extra credit for evening seminars devoted to candlelit bouts of oral poetry, including "I crave your mouth, your voice, your hair" (Pablo Neruda), "My mouth hovers across your breasts in the short grey winter afternoon in this bed we are delicate and touch so hot with joy we amaze ourselves to. . . ." (Adrienne Rich), and "I have a fire for you in my mouth, but I have a hundred seals on my tongue."—Rumi ***By Juneau Underwood on 08/13/2009 11:48 pm***

▪ **August 13/09** Adam shoots cover for new album with Warwick Saint

▪ @perezhilton. Thank you very much for bragging bout me that was sweet. I'll stoop: i'm more of Top. Not an offer though, I'm taken. :) ha 12:35 **AM Aug 13th** from Echofon

Thanks for appreciating my latest effort! Regarding whether Adam's smile has been enhanced, who cares? I do note that he probably had excellent dental care as a kid (his mom was a dental hygienist—this class is an homage to her). He could have had braces, who knows . . . and who in the entertainment industry doesn't at least have whitening done?

Time for people to get over being snarky about men who care about their appearance. I saw what you posted on the Authenticity thread about how clothing can be an expression of a person's authenticity, and I extend that to hair and make-up, and to some extent to cosmetic surgery. It can also do the opposite, of course, and be a mask or distortion of a person. With Adam, I feel his appearance is part of his artistic expression, and he is using it to express the many facets of himself. I love that it's complex, and not just one dimensional.

By Juneau Underwood on 08/14/2009 8:07 am

Oh you are wicked! I thought about testing for gag reflex control as well . . . great minds think alike! ***By Juneau Underwood on 08/14/2009 12:26 pm***

E., delighted to report on great progress here in Adam's workshop! we now have the male thong almost finished—there will be photos. Basic black with graphic outlines in bright silver glitter, the frontispiece is a riot of fuchsia, purple and blue feathers of a very soft, perhaps ticklish feel and over all, there are scattered sparkly glass beads. Definitely a visual treat to behold. ***By xena princess warrior on 08/14/2009 1:34 am***

Dear Xena, I want to make sure you receive the feedback below regarding your data-collecting expedition tonight. I am promoting you to a tenured professorship! We will need to produce a brochure of the Adam Lambert Finishing School. ***By Juneau Underwood on 08/14/2009 2:56 pm***

Dear Prof. Warrior, I greatly appreciate your undertaking this arduous piece of research on behalf of the Finishing School. Not only have you taken the initiative to upgrade the data-capturing apparatus, but you have had the foresight to bring along a data-capture technician in order to ensure that you will be able to concentrate fully on the most important task of close observation and synthesis of the phenomenon under study. In addition, you have taken a highly creative approach to the design of the bait to entice the experimental subject closer to the observation post. You must publish a full account of the effect of said bait upon the subject. (As an aside, you must tell us your own response whilst purchasing the bait ingredients, which I presume included an item that you are not in the habit of buying. Or did you get it on-line?) I am impressed by your list of subject's anatomical parts which you intend to document. Please don't forget to investigate the shoe-size question. That one has taken up gigabits of the blogosphere, and it's high time we end this silly debate with some real data. Excellent work, Professor! You can definitely have the Mistress of Golf class position, and I will advance your case for tenure at the R.I.F.S. (Rock Icon Finishing School).

Good luck on your expedition tonight!!

Prof. Underwood

By Juneau Underwood on 08/14/2009 7:48 am

Just got Adam's instructions for the day:

"We did a surprising amount of work before the tour started, we had about a month. I got a lot of co-writing done, some great initial vocal material recorded, and just general collaborations with different producers. [. . .] Just clap and scream and have a good time. It's not about you guys getting my attention, it's about you living your life in a positive way. When you dance and move around it creates a different reaction from the audience—they love it. And getting a sense of interaction with them, I love that." Adam was saying of the recent weeks and his work.

Ladies, we have surely understood and are executing his orders "*it's about living your life in a positive way."*

By xena princess warrior on 08/14/2009 10:22 am

August 14/09 Brian May is blown away by Adam's song from 2012 http://www.brianmay.com/brian/brianssb/brianssb.html

V'adoro, pupille
saette d'amore,
le vostre faville
son grate nel sen.

I adore you, eyes,
lightning bolts of love,
your sparks
are welcome in my breast.

("V'adoro pupille" from Handel's
"Giulio Cesare" [trans. by R. Burstein])

Chapter 4 Pilgrims Progress

Hey ladies.

We five plus Mom J. and daughters Cleo II and Xena II are in our room reading Adam gems and drinking wine and eating. Wish you were here. Vibrations starting thinking about Adam. . . .

We are watching the clock and wanting the time to go quickly because we will be with Adam and at the same time we want time to slow down so we can savour every moment.

Oh the dilemma! Will keep you posted. . . .

Hi ladies . . . we are having so much fun . . . talking about our Muse Adam . . . wish you were here with us . . . Hugs C xo

Hi everyone, N. S. here. Having an absolutely amazing time sharing Adam stories with the wonderful Famous Five ladies here. Gloria Beth's hotel room overlooks Copps and we can keep an eye on critical activities happening below, while we partake of wine and other sumptuous goodies. Adam videos play in the background and we're getting totally into the mood. We'll be thinking of you all tonight, wishing you were here, too. Full reviews tomorrow. Muah!

Nails done, blue spiky hair, red lipstick, false eyelashes, sparkly clothes, finally I'm ready to face the stage and try valiantly to catch the eye of our study subject. Equipment at the ready, zoom tested, group shots taken, data collector has an excellent plan to execute her instructions to gather evidence of our field trip for all Glambertinas, MoALS, Professors, Instructors and students.

Copps Coliseum in Hamilton, Ontario—dildo hits Adam on the leg during WLL

Visual reports will follow as available.

Prof. X. P. Warrior

By adams beth on 08/14/2009 4:10 pm

Wow Adam's EofH, I've seen you here before and in the doorway watching, probably hearing our laughter and tears while we talk. We believe that there are not enough in the sisterhood and love more to join in. You put "totally in love with Adam" on your letter of application, so you have met the single and most arduous qualification to write and to talk with us.

You will find that we have a number of "women of science" among our group, made up of great women—very chatty, open, affectionate and fun. You're safe here—negativity is almost non-existent as you know, which attracted the rest of us too.

We look forward to getting to know you better, as you make your contributions to the conversation. There are no actual rules about writing, so please just write! Whatever you want. We have other Glambertinas who sounded like you at first—now they are writing beautiful pieces.

Xena ***By xena princess warrior on 08/15/2009 2:59 am***

Juneau, give that man an award! Brian May is a genius.

By xena princess warrior on 08/15/2009 3:03 am

You read it here first: I predict that this song will be nominated for a Best Song Oscar, and Adam will be singing at the next Academy Awards.

By Juneau Underwood on 08/15/2009 10:36 pm

Hi E. E., Thanks for pointing out this link. I think Frank Rich is spot on (my favorite Times columnist along with Nick Kristof). And I do think Adam is deeply significant culturally. I don't see him as the driver of change, but he is a catalyst. He is himself a product of the profound cultural shifts that have been occurring in this country and in the world, and the way the world has embraced him is an indicator of that as well. And now we are seeing the chemical magic happening before our eyes, as Adam is brought together with the audience that has been waiting for someone like him. At the same time, we are seeing the hate- and fear-filled reaction to this change, which is becoming increasingly loud, violent and demagogic. It's a very unsettling time, and yet I also feel giddily optimistic. ***By Juneau Underwood on 08/16/2009 8:31 am***

Ladies, just want to say wowowowowowowowo!!!!!XXXXXX I can die now. I was six feet away! I could see the rhinestones around his eyes, little trickle of perspiration on his temple. Will have to write later as I have to get up in a few hours. Don't worry, nothing will be lost in my memory, Adam branded my brain with a hot iron.

Data technician had a fantastic spot at the barrier—we have shots and poses never seen before! We had a panic about the equipment—it was too good, so not allowed. Gloria stepped into the breach—always the girl scout—prepared, or is that a boy scout? never mind, so this camera was a bit challenging, but given the technician's vantage, it worked.

We are fortunate that the data technician did return home, since Adam made—deep eye contact with her twice and smiled at her. She almost leapt across the barrier to grab a boot lace so he could drag her across the stage. I was worried that she might run away and join the circus—uh, Idols Tour—she was so mesmerized.

What a trooper! She has requested a "guest comment" which I will post for her, she wants to share her religious epiphany with all of you. This might have been a life changing experience for her.

Have to go and get rid of some of the bright blue in my hair before I lie down on a white pillowcase—or—maybe I'll just find a blue pillow case.

Love to everybody!

Xena

By xena princess warrior on 08/15/2009 3:23 am

Ahhh Xenaaaa! I can hardly wait to read your next post, and to hear from Xena II. As for having a chance to examine the primary data, what can I say? I'm going to have to keep some tea towels close at hand so I won't short out my keyboard.

August 15/09 Blue Cross Arena in Rochester, New York

Blue stains on that white pillowcase . . . a new scene detail, you devil! We have to keep that sexy servant Brad busy, don't we? Trails of glitter across the floor, and telltale traces on somebody's skin. . . .

By Juneau Underwood on 08/15/2009 5:41 am

Top Ten Reasons Adam seemed a little different last night

10. He had a new concert hairstyle. Extreme Xena!! Spiked up and gorgeous. . . . As the evening progressed, it fell down, down, down. (Priscilla is deaf from hearing the scream "His hair is down" a million times) Explanation: Post sex hair

9. Adam can play football. During WWL a missile was thrown and hit Adams leg. He immediately kicked that missile into the audience with amazing form and power. He definitely has been hiding this talent from us. Explanation: Post sex energy

8. Adam seemed a little tired. Explanation: Post sex exhaustion
7. Adam's voice sounded fantastic but huskier (Priscilla thinks higher) Explanation: Post sex injury? Kick to the GB????
6. Armpit was hairless. Very smooth!! Explanation: Pre sex waxing (Manscaping)
5. Adam's crotch circles were definitely much looser and sexier Explanation: post sex limbering
4. When Adam descended into the stage, he forgot to say he loved us. Explanation: post sex depression (He misses his bb Drake)
3. Sneaky was fairly quiet last night. He did his thing a couple of times. Explanation: Post sex shock/bruising
2. Adam's dancing was out of this world—more moves and more exciting than any seen previously. Explanation: Post sex frenzy
1. Adam was right there, a few feet away from us in person. Beautiful. Sexy. Gorgeous. Hunk. OMG.. Adamgasms. Surreal. So real. Incredible. Fabulous. Glittery. . . . Positive Adjectives ad infinitum. . . . Adam in the flesh "igniting all the souls who would die just to feel alive.". . . Explanation: Adam

Gloria Beth and Priscilla Quothed ***By adams beth on 08/15/2009 9:17 am***

▪ Please support my charity!!! Www.donorschoose.org/adamlambert Let's help some kids out!!! 1:24 PM **Aug 15th** from Echofon

http://www.youtube.com/watch?v=XC5D3SWgwTg
OMG—Do you hear "get my camera" and two voices talking—spoiling the sound? that's me and Xena II. The battery on Gloria's camera just died!! panic!! those screams are coming from our corner because the person filming was standing right next to XII and the second highest pitch scream is hers. I'm sure you can hear me too.
X ***By xena princess warrior on 08/16/2009 2:58 pm***

"Are those Xena's undies on the stage????"
"Yes . . . they are Xena's undies . . . the feathered thong. . . ."
"Yes! Oh, if he had only seen them."

Cleo, first of all, thanks for the vivid description of your unforgettable night. I am living this all vicariously through the fantastic Five of the north. Re: thrown object, I agree it looks more solid than a piece of lingerie. Adam looks like he could have been a decent soccer player if he had been so inclined! And re: his sexual temperament and being Born to be Wild, my favorite lyric in that song is "take the world in a love embrace." And he sure has! ***By Juneau Underwood on 08/16/2009 7:52 am***

From my excellent vantage point, it was missile shaped and hard—looked like a vibrator to me.

X

By xena princess warrior on 08/16/2009 2:24 pm

Supremus Magnum Opus

Once is not Enough

Pilgrimage of the Faithful Fabulous Fierce Five

By Xena

Once in His presence is barely a whiff, a mere whisper of he who is; the Prince of Passion, Rex Erotica, King of Kink, Potentate of Pulchritude and long may he reign!!! Honoured throughout the universe—new titles and lands are bestowed upon him. Can a Nobel be very far? Perhaps a Prize for bringing peace, love and understanding among all sexes, hope for the "weird kids" that they can become lithe swans emerging from duckling confines, for sprinkling liberal amounts of glitter and glamour on every being he encounters, inflaming passions in those whose ardour may have diminished.

The Pilgrimage

This auspicious day, the town was teaming with the Ruler's entourage, the streets lined with his subjects, who have arrived with offerings to His Highness, to honour the GB in its magnificence and the one who carries it. The day is appropriately blue sky, sun and hot. The subjects' attire advertises their love and as they greet each other on the streets, they share knowing smiles, shouted greetings "Adam Forever!"—out in the open, they celebrate in anticipation of what they are about to witness—the first visit of Divine Monarch to their community.

With only artificial images and sound—the believers are spellbound, as if in the thrall of Mesmer. Just as the shepherds followed that star—the pilgrims have travelled by foot, by horse, mule, chariot and caravan to this Holy place—to bear witness, to worship, to validate and confirm their feelings before his flesh and blood, GB and Sneaky. In homage, they have painted their nails with black and rimmed their eyes in kohl, glints of blue in hair as the sun shines on them—the blessed.

I'm travelling by chariot pulled by two black Arabians, ebony ostrich feathers at their foreheads—they move and wave as the horses toss their heads at a gallop. I am accompanied by a young protégé, an apprentice scribe and court illustrator, Xena II. Reluctant at first, she wished a favour of me, so here she is and it could be a life-changing experience

■ **August 16/09** XL Centre in Hartford, Connecticut

for one so young. She helped with the preparations and so earned her place next to me.

We had taken our time preparing ourselves with potions, lotions, paints, eyelashes—even to grinding some bright blue lapis stone to mix with lotion to paint on our hair. Sorting through various accoutrements, I settled on a black and silver colour scheme, shiny and glittery, bold silver necklace, studded leather bracelet and a fingerless fishnet glove.

The previous night, we spent hours preparing an elaborate gift for the King, the Star. A man's black undergarment embellished with silver sparkles, blue, fuchsia and purple feathers. It has become customary to fling such gifts onto the stage during the King's performance, in the hope that one will obtain an additional, very special blessing—that he a) sees it, or b) touches it, or c) plays with it!!!

The Faithful Fabulous Fierce Five

A group of members from my sect, the Glambertinas—the Faithful Fabulous Fierce Five—FFFV have planned to convene in one place, to walk—perhaps levitate—the final yards to the venue together. Until today, most of this group have only communicated through messenger and are meeting for the first time—they will make final preparations together before the big event. Xena II and I have brought token handmade gifts of CDs with Adam's music to give to our friends of the sisterhood, to comply with the Potentate's latest encyclical to share with others rather than send gifts to him. This is a rare collection of music—he made most of it before he ascended to the Peacock Throne and we have hidden a rare gem within.

The Ecstasy Of Adam Adherents

This aspect of the pilgrimage is as important as our evening of celebration for the life of our Beloved King of Kink, soon to begin. Gratitude must be shown to the Universe for aligning the stars, the moon, the planets to allow the Age of Aquarius Adam to commence and flourish, to inspire love in all its forms, erotic and filial, friendship, beauty, smiling, eyeliner, eye contact, nail polish, pedicures, black hair and more sex. . . . We women, of course with our exceptional perceptive abilities, were filled with the lantern of Adam knowledge within seconds of hearing his voice or seeing his image, we "got it" and prove it every day.

Our responses were profound and brought us to a state of ecstasy with the merest contact, sighting, a few notes of his voice. We did this over and over and over again, avaricious for more Adam. We searched for information and finally found others entranced, touched—maybe shoved, perhaps scorched, consumed, rocketed to Adamgasms by his performances and we have yet to breathe the same air, share the same small square of dirt beneath our feet, as the corporal Apollo.

The Arrival And Final Preparations

Finally, we have disembarked the chariot, and grooms have taken our steeds for water and food. As we approach the door, about ten feet away, laughter greets us ahead of our entrance. Priscilla opens the door and we are treated like the prodigal daughters—we immediately know who everyone is, we hug firmly, exclaim our joy for accomplishing this much—*Wow! we made it! What a special day—I knew you right away*—first our wonderful Glambertinas then we meet Adam!

Finally we have arrived and chaos ensues as some of us greet each other for the first time, yet we know one another immediately upon sight. My heart fills and I can't contain my happiness or stop smiling. At this holy moment, I cross the room to the shrine, kneel and reverently genuflect, humbled in sight of the icon and giving thanks for these wonderful women whose friendship is a blessing.

The Shrine

Centred in the shrine—what has become an iconic image of the King of Kink, dressed like a member of the Kiss tribe, but young, beautiful and sparkly—remember those eyes, we see them again. There's also a smaller icon and Glorious introduced her as C., Sister Kiwi of Downunder—our sister sect of Glambertinas from a distant group of rabid adherents. Spiritual Leader Glorious insists that we carry this icon for the day and record her presence among us.

Gloria includes Sister Kiwi's icon in our commemorative photos, as she symbolically represents those who could not be here, but are with us in spirit. We send you our final words, we watch the videos, we present our offerings to each other—signs, thong, glow sticks, just as we prepare to depart on the last leg—only two hours to the beginning of the show, in one hour, the doors to the coliseum will open and we will join the throngs of fellow worshipers, shuffling, pushing forward, shoving to get closer to the stage from which Adam will sing and deliver.

The Book

Gloria presents an illuminated manuscript—detailing important statements about Adam, phrases of love, lust, offers to carry his baby or his make-up, praise from judges—inanity from judges—and his own brilliant, wise words, double entendres, wit, French, Latin, exposing a complex mind, a loving soul within a beautiful, graceful, fluid body, oozing sex from every pore and a face with eyes that could launch a thousand ships—or Adamgasms.

We are beginning to suspect that Gloria, deeply grounded in Adam spirituality, had joined a monastery, where unmolested, she could carry on her ministrations for world peace and to study the art of Illumination. Only life in a monastery could provide her the blessing of time, time to research, correspond and to produce this life's work. Of course she had to wear headphones and carry an iPod at all times, since the monks are silent otherwise and aside from ancient Gregorian chants at service, there is no music. Finally the book is completed—before she has torn out her hair or throttled a couple of monks and after consuming the forbidden wine she has secreted into the monastery, she is expelled.

Leading us through a final lesson before we depart for the Coliseum, Gloria reads various of the judges' statements and we are expected to know the name of the judge and Adam's song. Next to the author herself, Daughter of Cleo proves an adept student of Adamatrivia and knows many answers. Cleo, be proud of your daughter, so smart and possessed of internal and external beauty, so comfortable with a group of pilgrims she has not met before.

Research Begins

I and my young cohort take some time for her to eat and build some energy for the show—we descend underground where we discover other pilgrims, some serving food, others simply walking about, bedecked in Adam regalia, members of different Adam sects. Xena II asks if she can record their images for a project her superior, Xena P. Warrior, esteemed MoAL Scholar has undertaken—to record the faces of Adam's subjects for the study of their demographics.

Entering the Coliseum where Adam the Magnificent will enthral his subjects in a few hours, we arrive early to ensure the best vantage points. We can barely contain our excitement as we survey the currently empty seats, soon to be filled with teeming throngs and as we approach our designated location, we are in awe. It is impossible to believe that we will be immediately in front of him, a mere six feet to separate us, but requiring a sturdy, forged metal barrier to hold us back.

The Show Begins

While we wait for the Prince of Passion to appear, we enthusiastically respond to the courtiers who precede him on the stage. In our Adam-ized state, they are all beautiful, graceful and sing like songbirds. Glambertinas are generous with praise for others, whether deserving or not. The performers looked surprised at the loud clapping, shouting, hooting and screaming, as well as at the gifts tossed at their feet. As Northern Spirit observed, I danced the entire time.

We are given a brief respite before he will enter and receive us, our adoration, our praise. We dare not leave our standing posts, lest the hordes fill them, so we do not even sit for a moment, cannot leave for water, fortunately a fellow Adam pilgrim shares with me, a sip of cold beer.

Pyrotechnics explode—screaming wenches, in painful agony, their bodies and souls about to ignite in the heat, a baptism in the ring of fire—the sound of a thousand canons firing in rapid sequence.

Momentarily deaf and blind, we blink awake to the thickening smoke just above us, fire light illuminates the core of the billows as they gradually, slowly—oh I am gasping—eyes riveted, trying to see inside, he's in the room—the clouds begin to transform—now the shining, silvery, genie is taking shape—the stage is getting smaller—will it be adequate to contain all of Him? He explodes in voice and body, powerful full-body movements, choking the golden, shining rod in his hand, at the very top, before he removes it and stalks the stage.

This is no corporal, grounded being but something ethereal, enthralling—once fully formed from the gusts of smoke we see the source, with his sex on fire, before a note has been played.

From the tips of cobalt on the shards of hair atop his crown, to the glittery, bejeweled eyes—unforgettable—his Beth eyes—I will see those eyes forever, in the heaven just above me, awake or asleep.

Adam flings the mic like a woman he's grabbed by the hair. Long already, he extends the smooth and glistening rod to stroke it in our direction. This is the hardest working prop I have ever seen and obviously appreciated and well-used by Adam—at least four days on then one day off.

He is as a bullfighter, dressed in his suit of lights, sweeping his body aggressively, swaggering to the bull, taunting and fearless, jumping aside at the last second, he finally reaches us to declare, to our raging excitement—that he will give us every inch of his love!! He charges forward, sways provocatively to prove his magnificent love. He shows us where his love is, deep down inside and it's not his heart, he pounds his fist to show us again—every inch of his love.

Oh no, he's moving toward me! I'm not ready—I didn't check my lipstick, how is my hair? He takes long strides and stands right above me, *Xena don't die—you have to record this moment for others*—as his shoulder drops, Sneaky pushes down his thigh *"I've been year-er-nin'"*—so have I!—Sneaky slowly slides back up—not a second stroking! Ooh, down then up! I am so jealous of that appendage.

Until now, the cavernous space was cool—it's become a screaming steam room with thousands of people exploding with testosterone, especially in our corner—the all-Adam cheering section and we feed off each other—that energy exchange Adam talks about. Is the roof still on?

Adam moves away—*"no!! Come back, come back! I need to look at the rest of you, up close, at almost touching distance—I don't have enough information yet!"* The air is electric and I catch the sullen security guard from the corner of my eye—what's *he* thinking? He deflates me momentarily but I focus on Adam and recover. I don't care what he's thinking now.

I am in shock since the moment he stood directly in front of me, six feet to his boots and another six to those beacons, that siren voice—they entice me to the shore to crash on the rocks and break me apart. Nothing else existed at that moment, I don't recall the song, or any details about his body—just that other-worldly, perfectly beautiful, flawless face, icicles of obsidian hair fall casually over his forehead, directing my eyes—to stare into those eyes with the magnetic pull of the tides.

He's returned in front of me—I want to reach, to jump, to scream like the girls, but if he looks at me, I need to be dignified, I must be looking at his eyes, not anywhere else, to treat him like a human being, a beloved man, and not objectify him . Besides I am rooted, I can barely breathe, let alone move—what am I supposed to look at again? But try as I will, my eyes won't be pulled any lower—I can see individual rhinestones around his eyes, like runway lights leading to his core and now I just want to look at his eyes, in my mind. Just as we knew, there's plenty behind them.

Remember all the "eyes" in the videos and the photos—even "Beth"? None can come close to reality, a few feet away. On this night, they are cobalt blue, Xena II and I agree. They change expression as the music, the words change in mood.

Eyes in vicinity—all else drops away, GB, Sneaky, biceps—just eyes, larger than life, chunks of hair loosened by his stalking, dancing, posing, stomping—drift down his forehead, further drawing us into him, through those openings to his soul. The sound of his voice, the vibrations, emerges from his—*no, no!—don't leave, don't turn, just stand right there and sing only to me!* It won't take long, then I will collapse in ecstasy over the railing, arms and legs flailing, impaled at my waist—complete loss of dignity—*then you may turn around. Then you can go to look at others, hook them too*—why should I be the only ragdoll in the building? Ravaged in Ecstasy like Ste. Thérése, a golden pointed arrow shot by Cupid—into my breast.

Face and body equally adept at expressing sexual aggression, teasing, seduction, never let up, he's wearing us out and it is only near the end, that I can see droplets of dew on his temples. Those pretty, smooth lips—open wide, pout, snarl, smile, grin—eyes wide, narrowed, incredulous, sideways glances, downward, upward and framed by the most expressive eyebrows. Like his body, he can control each part of his face individually, allowing him the broadest range of expression. If his performance is "theatrical," then bring on theatrical!!!

His eloquence enhances the sincerity of his performances—he never lets up, never relaxes—voice, body and face in synch and in constant motion while he's on stage.

Alison

With Alison to play with on stage, his smiles widen to a grin—when she sings, his eyes are on her and focused—would that I could be her. She responds of course—hair like northern lights, moves wildly with her, like a hot aura. Back to back, bodies in unison, they bend and rise as one. I want to hate her, but it's impossible—she already insinuated herself into my heart with her stage-filling, deep throated, confident solo performance. There is so much more improvisation now, they are so comfortable and their excitement shows. It's all so natural for them.

They share private jokes and laugh, are we even here for them?—they are in their own world until the moment almost at the end, when they stop, recalling the audience, they turn to acknowledge us—before their final note and with flourishes from his hands, Adam plays the lingering instrumental notes in the air, releasing pent up adrenalin, before they fall into each other, hugging, they lose their balance and Adam's arm is outstretched as Alison walks away. He turns and takes a drink of water from a bottle next to the drummer.

No Video Could Ever Reproduce Adam's Dance Moves In Fame, *Or,* **Let's Dance**

His body as a whole—who can dance like that? I can see his outline, his body moves as though boneless, a long, sleek whip, cracked by the gods to move—the only words I can come up with—in a single, smooth, sinewy, serpentine motion, around his core—there are the waves!—they emanate from his body and crash into mine. He's far enough away that I can take him in from head to toe, the undulations are unbelievable, in spite of the heavy trousers. Trim, tight body—he works the stage so hard—no gym needed for him. Just whatever rigorous workouts Drake and he manage when they can, probably contributing to his spiritual, emotional and physical health.

A little closer and I can focus on his torso—as he sucks in his abdomen, then expands, pushing GB toward us, there's not an ounce of excess anything visible—please—take off the vest!! Maybe if he comes close again, I can rip it off.

Like his perfect face, he has a perfectly proportioned body, from head, neck, chest, shoulders, waist, hips, legs and of course—feet. He's the RS Adam, the primal, sinful Adam of the green snake, the beautiful, seductive Adam. "*Take me, I'm yours*" I heard him say that, I'm sure.

Unless you are watching in 3-D, you have never seen him dance—really.

As he descends below, right arm stretched up, his muscular arm clearly defined, left is below and he turns his head briefly to the left, in our direction. What caught his eye, did he look at someone? A mystery to be resolved.

Obsession Sustained

People had hoped that the concert might close the circle on my obsession—hardly—it's just enhanced it. I want more—I didn't see everything! Damn reality and responsibilities—I want to follow the buses and just watch from the audience until I have every square inch of his voice, body and motion, mentally imprinted. This will cost me in family and friends, but now, Xena II would be right beside me—anyone else? I'll drive, I'll get a bigger chariot and more Arabians. I have to get over him sometime, but not yet. The time was so short, I feel cheated—one cannot read the entire works of Shakespeare once and appreciate every facet at many levels, so too with Adam. Truly—once is barely a taste, a sample to entice you to buy the whole product.

Afterward I will seek penance and silence at the Convent of the Pining Heart, for the rest of my life.

Xena II and I are almost the last to leave, as we are in the opposite corner to the exit, still in our own world and don't notice the activity around us until we look up to a virtually empty coliseum and the stage is being struck by some workers, security people have emerged from their hiding places, I feel fantastic and fatal at the same time. Sad, almost heartbroken to leave, yet I am smiling at everyone, making eye contact, greetings sung out.

Final Farewells and Promises to Meet Again

With Priscilla and Glorious, we return to our meeting place, I am hobbling because "vanity thy name is Xena" and while I brought three different pairs of footwear—none are flat. Glorious and Xena II go ahead to review the visual recordings of the day, while Priscilla and I seek refreshment to quench our thirst and build our energy. The name "Priscilla" must mean "fair of face, patient listener and man magnet." She patiently receives my tumult of words, left-over from the day that must be cleared to make way for the next.

We call the valets who bring our horses and chariot around for us, to embark on the journey home. My cohort, Xena II and I, have completed a bonding project and it's true—we know each other better and are closer, she has a truer appreciation of my obsession—she looked into his eyes and he into hers—and now she knows some of my best friends—helping me appear less eccentric. How bad can I be? Look at my friends—they're smart, sophisticated, generous, caring, lovely, enthusiastic, funny and nice!! Pilgrimages serve to bond believers, but the process began months ago and simply culminated tonight.

Xena II has shown me empathy, defended me, helped me when I crashed and now, beside me, I believe I have the most supportive daughter, a cheerleader, a co-conspirator. How fortunate am I? I must take the road to Glorious to lay offerings at the shrine—we have made arrangements.

Xena

By xena princess warrior on 08/17/2009 3:58 pm

Dearest Cleo, the inspiration for the mother/daughter project came from your example. When I saw the photos of the two of you, I wanted the same experience and it turned out Xena II wanted it as well. The happiness of being with her in that "pit" of excitement, her hugs of gratitude—worth everything. Now, I did worry what you might think about our rather embellished appearances, but forgot as soon as I saw you and we hugged so tightly. We don't look like that every day—just for rock concerts and Glambertinas.

XOXOXO

Xena *By xena princess warrior on 08/17/2009 5:42 pm*

Dearest Xena, your have utterly outdone yourself this time, and how could you not . . . this pilgrimage and entry into the sacred sanctum are the consummation of months of questing, meditation and rising fervor, all directed towards this ecstatic encounter (I won't say final encounter . . . we are going for multiple Adamgasms, I have no doubt!). I am in complete awe of your creative powers. How ingenious and utterly right to meld imagery from the pagan past—I'm thinking of ancient Macedonia, Persia and Greece, because of Xena and Alexander the Great—with the rock arena rituals of our time! And after admonishing the more extreme fans to not turn Adam into a Messiah, here you are playing into that temptation with both sincerity and a delicious sense of irony. King of Kink! You make me laugh out loud at the same time that you inflame me. And I predict a 3-D Omnimax film of Adam Lambert for the not too distant future. We can all go see it and blow our circuits forever. Come down to Providence to re-live this experience with me! Or perhaps we should rendezvous in Manchester NH for the final blow-out.

A Whole Lotta Love,

Juneau *By Juneau Underwood on 08/17/2009 10:23 pm*

- **August 17/09** Recording with Max Martin

- Onto to stuff that matters: in NYC to record song with MAX MARTIN!!! Soo excited. This album is getting so great!! 7:31 AM **Aug 17th** from Echofon

Hi Juneau, so glad you enjoyed it, thank you. Tried to walk that fine line between authentic messianic and my love of the pagan, mystical and mythical rituals, keeping it on the secular side with monarchical references, but religious undertones.

More interesting to mix it up and invent my own society. As a Macedonian—Persia and Greece as well as my own culture live in my DNA and each borrowed, stole or appropriate elements of the others' art, architecture, cuisine, education, mythology and social structures, enhancing each others' culture.

3-D Omnimax—30 feet tall Adam—well there's a study model for us.

Thanks so much J.

Love, X *By xena princess warrior on 08/18/2009 12:13 am*

My pleasure GB, to document our trip and the magical encounter of the FFFV. Glorious is such an obvious title for you and I am sure the others will agree and it will help illuminate you to all the other Glambertinas.

Love X *By xena princess warrior on 08/17/2009 4:52 pm*

Glorious is also the final track on Muse's album, Black Holes and Revelations. It's an exhilarating song, and seems a fitting anthem for you. Go listen to it! *By Juneau Underwood on 08/17/2009 10:39 pm*

Here's a little palate cleanser after that fantastic banquet of images and words from Xena. The latest course offering from our Finishing School. As a tribute to Xena, I have featured an opera favorite of hers:

Music—Advanced Opera (Profs. Princess and E., with assistance of student body). This course is restricted to students who have demonstrated extraordinary mastery not only of vocal technique but also of stage movement. Ability to provoke eruptions of Eros an absolute must. Student(s) will produce and perform an Aquarian Age adaptation of Bizet's opera, Carmen, in which the lead role of the wild gypsy seductress will be performed by the student who satisfies the above-stated prerequisites, without regard to gender. Professors will take turns in the role of the hapless Don José and the bullfighter Escamillo. Taking the Oral Hygiene course concurrently will be beneficial.

By Juneau Underwood on 08/17/2009 11:33 pm

I love how the camera caresses his body. Glitter and perspiration enveloping him in one sparkly package . . . and such a wondrous view of those crystal "runway lights" into the windows of his soul.

By Juneau Underwood on 08/18/2009 8:47 am

Hi J. this video should make it quite clear to everyone what happened to me. When "he was with me" his face didn't glitter or glisten, so much as glow, as if lit from within, his eyes—the openings into that internal glow—you cannot look anywhere but into them. His eyes sparkle because they are blue, the light enters then reflects the light, this is the beacon effect, like the light from a lighthouse—starts as a pinpoint and explodes outwardly. Adam's are the maximum effect—he knows how to work them.

Now to working those eyes—as I explained, he can move each part of his face individually, eyes, eyebrows especially. The raised eyebrow at the end of Beth. Hence his powerful ability to express emotions and get that to the back of the room. If I were a stage performer in musical theatre, I would not want to share the stage with him.

The emotions in Mad World are not what I saw though—I had Whole Lotta Love, Slow Ride, Fame and Let's Dance—mostly ferocious, aggressive eyes or laughing, happy, joyous eyes and face, you just want to get up closer and dance with him!

What we are missing in this show is seductive eyes—Ring of Fire—Satisfaction—seductive/impish

I don't think there's anything he can't say with his eyes.

X

Byxena princess warrior on 08/18/2009 10:43 am

I hope he's saving the "eye sex" for his solo tour . . . he will definitely have to have the fire brigade on hand to quench all the people who will spontaneously combust when he turns on the full wattage.

By Juneau Underwood on 08/18/2009 10:15 pm

E!!! How brilliant that you have found this—you can all finally see exactly what I was looking at. Those eyes in that face. The camera with the telephoto can move up and down, but when his face is just above yours, your eyes are pulled into his.

Here's a hotlink to the same miraculous video.
http://www.youtube.com/watch?v=y8U1CchG1bM

By xena princess warrior on 08/18/2009 1:18 am

Now you can see what I was saying—yes that was the view of his eyes from my vantage point—scary isn't it? And Xena II's

By xena princess warrior on 08/18/2009 9:53 am

Robert Sebree's studio shots turn up on the internet

Love the clothes, love the accessories—red shoes! shirt, tie, leather! these would be great poster shots

This would be one of Adam's "perfect days," playing dress-up and having his picture taken. Wonder who the designer is.

By xena princess warrior on 08/18/2009 11:37 am

Priscilla's favorites are the ones I love too. The shiny black jacket matches the pants in my first fantasy! I love the mesh bag. Interesting that he looks so slim in these photos. By the way, I personally prefer him with a paler complexion, as in these photos (and in the photo on the Adam Official web site), rather than with the bronzed look that some Hollywood stylist told him he needed. What do you think?

By Juneau Underwood on 08/18/2009 10:34 pm

Check out some symbolism in these fashion photos

Symbols of Adonis—the snakeskin half glove—also goes back to the RS snake theme

Huge oval silver belt buckle—the shield of Adonis

Chainmail vest—medieval armour

Green leather pants photo—sexy, trying-to-look-dangerous, androgynous Gangster—but the lips are way too pretty, they don't scare anybody—they do invite kisses—no change that to—"his lips in every photo invite kisses"

Red shoes—for dancing!

Black patent leather jacket—fashionisto Biker Dude

X

By xena princess warrior on 08/18/2009 6:44 pm

One Lambrit wonders how Adam can keep smiling during the Meet & Greets—he's an extrovert getting all the attention in the room!!!! He can't help himself, he loves it, it's his milieu. This is why I doubt it's his idea to stop the post-show M&Gs. Wait a minute, I'm sitting here smiling—what's going on? You Glambertinas keep me smiling and laughing.

Love, X

By xena princess warrior on 08/18/2009 5:44 pm

Another treasure. Glorious, you are tireless on our behalf. Thank you! I loved the comment by the husband of her friend, I believe, about there being something in Adam's voice that resonates in a hypnotic way. I do think there is something physiological about how we are so drawn to his voice. Truly a siren sound. . . . Her question about his singing all British songs was one that I had been wondering too. Adam seems to have an affinity for non-American music (U.K.—Muse, Goldfrapp, Bowie; German—Tokio Hotel).

By Juneau Underwood on 08/18/2009 11:04 pm

That's an interesting hypothesis, E., and in character for Adam. In a way, it's a win-win for him to excuse himself from the meet and greets. He can avoid the nightly embarrassment of eclipsing his fellow AI singers and conserve his energies. His schedule would kill ordinary mortals. That said, I'm wondering if he appears for the after parties, since those are more controlled . . . I'm seriously thinking about shaking down some friends for a pass, but what if Adam doesn't go to those either. . . ?

By Juneau Underwood on 08/18/2009 11:32 pm

My husband does wear cologne, but I haven't found Homme in Canada yet. Birthday's in Nov. E., what if you buy some and give it to another man to wear? Could be spicy and exciting.

By xena princess warrior on 08/19/2009 1:31 am

[*Gloria Beth reports that her Top Ten post was deleted from the AdamOfficial web site*]

I am so envious, it gives me something to work toward "get censored and kicked off a weblog." The only censoring I have ever experienced is when I've been tough on politicians, but it was done reluctantly.

X ***By xena princess warrior on 08/19/2009 10:45 am***

Well Xena, if we had posted our fantasies and many of our other ruminations on Adam Official, I'm sure we would have kept the censors very busy! ***By Juneau Underwood on 08/19/2009 12:28 pm***

And probably sent to detention after school—to sit with the naughty boys with the black "emo" hair, too-tight jeans and leather jackets and rhinestone covered leather work boots. For punishment, we would have to tutor them in French, English, biology, physics, art and history, health, eyeliner and nail polish, eye contact and smiling. Detention will probably take until the next day and all day Saturday.

Xena ***By xena princess warrior on 08/19/2009 10:39 pm***

We would have to be whipped too, with red leather alternating with blue feather boas. Life is rough for us truth tellers.

By Juneau Underwood on 08/20/2009 12:11 am

Do those people not get his messages? They need to do more observation and analysis. In describing his music, he talked about inspiring people to "feel love and make love." What more do they need? Have they watched him on stage? What are the demographics over there?

X ***By xena princess warrior on 08/19/2009 11:11 am***

This is why we love and need this site!! We're grown-ups here, with license to explore every nook and cranny of our Adam experience, and the maturity not to take offense even when we see something we don't agree with. Anyway, that's hilarious that they did that on Adam Official. And I agree it's one of the best Top Ten lists ever!!

By Juneau Underwood on 08/19/2009 12:26 pm

Dear Glambertinas—this is a response to an earlier thread—speculating on Adam's "dance music" on his forthcoming album.

No Worries

About Adam's Music

Can't recall Adam's exact words, but an earlier description of his album put it this way: It will make you want to love, make love, be happy, sad and get up and dance. Recently he used the term "anthems," like some of Queen's music to further specify. Why the concern over "dance" music? Whole Lotta Love, Slow Ride, Fame & Just Dance are all dance music. Do you mean something else?

Why is anyone nervous? Is there anything about his concert performances, media interviews or anything else that has caused people to lose confidence in his ability to accomplish what he wants—which includes making his fans love his music so much—we buy millions of copies and sell-out his concerts? Ultimately, we glean from his words, this is the process by which he will achieve what he wants—to love and be loved, to be settled in a home, to have the means to share his wealth with his family and friends, to pay for dinner, to give them nice things. He is the boy-next-door with eyeliner and nail polish and he said so.

While unconventional strategically—a risk taker where others are cautious, so open when others keep secrets—our radar went wild with worry that his honesty would diminish his popularity, that he would be censored on stage, that parents would write letters, that they would picket him in the Bible Belt, that the media would crucify him, that he would make powerful enemies, that he would go "Hollywood" and lose himself, that he might lose his boyfriend, that he would become overexposed, overwhelmed in the media by MJ's death, that he's too fat, too thin, hair up? or hair down?—that he would be misunderstood, hurt and unsuccessful. He might become closed and isolated, overly controlled, overly produced or contrived. And how could we forget "too theatrical" as a liability?

Instead, he is more loved, his popularity is growing exponentially, he is sure-footed and confident, as open as ever, so excited about his life, his art—he just can't stop smiling, laughing, hugging, talking—he's creatively inspired.

Adam has lived as the understudy for this role for a very long time—all his life, likely dreamt about this moment, night after night—finally the director said "You're on!" his cue to blast his talents out the back of the theatre—he's become the "voice heard 'round the world" with the physical and personal attributes worthy of this fame. So well rehearsed in his mind, he was fully prepared.

While most have always been confident in his ability to achieve his dreams, others have worries that his mother must have shed a long time ago—probably when the first "kissed a boy" photos emerged. He didn't care that people knew he is gay, but that the news might distract people from his music and performances—he diffused the potential dynamite with precision and taught us all a lesson. Whatever is in your past—own it, acknowledge it and move on.

Heroic terms and metaphors come easily, as he has fought so many obstacles in life to finally awaken in his vision—on the stage, waves of energy surge forward—felt but unseen in the brilliant lights—for him to take in and fuel his performance—to give it all back.

Standing almost next him, in the white-hot source of the fire, watching his flawless, exuberant performance, interaction with fellow performers, band, back-up singers, audience up front, in the middle and in "the gods" has solidified my confidence in him.

Someday—a Command Performance for HRH Queen Elizabeth II, organized by William and Harry and the headliners will be Queen with Adam Lambert in front for the event, fireworks will follow and during the presentation, Adam will bow, shake Her Majesty's hand, await her first words, smile, look her in the eyes and seize her affections as he has the rest of us. ***By xena princess warrior on 08/19/2009 11:03 am***

Ladies, the demise of Adam's career has been predicted so many times—including on the AI show—ROF. He took the good advice he needed, ignored negativity, went with his strategy and ability to read people—and now he's filling stadia and having an Oprah effect! Brian May doesn't seem worried at all.

I would love to run into Gene Simmons someday.

Please provide me with an example of a perfect, successful, brilliant, charismatic, beautiful and with a perfect voice, entertainer whose career was destroyed by the record industry. There must be someone.

Ladies, I love you and I really don't want any of you to worry about Adam's future, just enjoy—or I will write my anthropological/sociological/superstitious/religious—explanation, for the subconscious inability of some cultures to enjoy happiness and success, unequivocally.

I would rather work on my fantasy with the gorgeous Brazilian guy on a Mediterranean island.

Love & hugs

Xena

By xena princess warrior on 08/19/2009 9:15 pm

Go for the pillowcase! Or make one of your own. You know you can print out your favorite Adam photo on an iron-on transfer sheet, and then iron it onto the pillowcase. If you are clever, you can print it out as a mirror image so that it's reproduces in the correct orientation when you iron it on. They sell the iron-on paper at Staples. Or perhaps Xena will make a needlepoint version for you!

August 19/09 Times Union Center in Albany, New York

By Juneau Underwood on 08/19/2009 10:26 pm

Albany!!! You were an AMAAAAZING crowd! I had fun with you tonight! 7:46 **PM Aug 19th** from web

Hey when did I say I do needlepoint? Oh, now I remember—in my list of previous obsessions. Drove through the Rockies, Denver to Taos N. M. doing needlepoint all the way down, I think I missed the Grand Canyon. Wouldn't be surprised to see an Adam kit someday. I am not writing a fantasy about needlepoint!

By xena princess warrior on 08/19/2009 11:08 pm

There IS an Adam needlepoint kit. I saw it on eBay!

By Juneau Underwood on 08/20/2009 12:10 am

Ever since posting the Finishing School course on Opera, I've been fantasizing about hearing Adam sing something from the classical repertory, and that thought segued into gifting him with a love aria. My selection: "V'adoro pupille" from Handel's Giulio Cesare. The words are so fitting (trans. by R. Burstein):

August 20/09 Wachovia Center in Philadelphia, Pennsylvania

V'adoro, pupille,	I adore you, eyes,
saette d'amore,	lightning bolts of love,
le vostre faville	your sparks
son grate nel sen.	are welcome in my breast.
Pietose vi brama	My sad heart
il mesto mio core,	desires you [to be] compassionate,

ch'ogn'ora vi chiama	[my heart] which at every hour calls you
l'amato suo ben.	its dearest beloved.

This performance by Kiri Te Kenawa is a stunner—chills up my spine. Sexy beyond belief. Think of it as the opera version of Crawl Through Fire (sorry, not remotely on the same level artistically . . . but they share a common visual theme of half-clad young women caressing the youth). Imagine Adam as the beautiful young man in the video. Sigh. Going to sleep with this image emblazoned in my mind.
http://www.youtube.com/watch?v=xwXvbSGcbXM

By Juneau Underwood on 08/19/2009 11:41 pm

You are welcome. It's your moment, Cleo, when you win the love of Julius Caesar! ***By Juneau Underwood on 08/20/2009 6:49 am***

Juneau, what a lovely gift for us. I did imagine Adam as the young man, difficult not to—stunning mature woman, beautiful young man she's put on a pedestal—he changes clothes—her words express our feelings perfectly "lightning bolts of love," impossible love and begging him to be compassionate with us.

Could have been written for our situation—are we living a classic Shakespearean plot? A common narrative of art and literature?

I so want him to sing this type of music—to luxuriate in his voice, a velvet cover for the low notes—floating sheer gossamer silk for the high notes—gracing our skin as it flutters over us—so close we can feel his breath.

Wouldn't an aria in Italian be the most beautiful little gem in his album? Hmmm He wants to surprise us—this would do it.

Thanks so much J.

Xena ***By xena princess warrior on 08/20/2009 8:12 am***

An Italian Aria from Adam—mmm, what a fantasy. . . .

Did you notice that the youth in the video has a tattoo on his right wrist, which you can glimpse at the end when he reaches up to embrace Kiri? I thought about photoshopping an Eye of Horus there. And didn't the dark, glittery outfit that he puts on remind you of Adam in Beth? So many parallels. I'm sure we are just playing out a timeless narrative here. The mature woman at the height of her beauty, wisdom and power, filled with love and passion heightened by her consciousness of approaching mortality, bestowing her gift to the youth at the threshold of manhood.

By Juneau Underwood on 08/20/2009 12:37 pm

I did notice the tattoo!! the outfit, the beautiful woman—how on earth did this come to your mind? the mentor with the protégé of love—even the lighting, the set, her demeanour, so many parallels, we are living in some Greek drama, are we not? Have we not conveyed the same messages—not such evocative language, but the feelings expressed. I think you can glimpse the tattoo while he is being undressed/redressed—a little homoerotica anyone?

X

By xena princess warrior on 08/20/2009 3:35 pm

The Cosmos just aligned itself for me, I guess. I'd been humming that aria to myself for the last couple of days while drifting about in the waters off Martha's Vineyard. It's one of the most ravishing love songs, and it just arose in my consciousness, and the words in the English translation—"eyes like starlight" and "feel your heart's fire"—connected up with images of Adam. I then wanted to find a great performance and started searching on YouTube. There are quite a few of them, but something drew me to Dame Kiri, and when I saw the video, I just couldn't believe how many elements lined up with what we've been conversing about here. Incidentally, in this aria, Cleopatra is disguised, and Caesar does not know her true identity. She sings to win his love, and what's fabulous in this video is that she is singing not directly to Caesar but to this beautiful youth, who embodies passion, Eros, and she thereby awakens Caesar's desire for her. Nice resonance with my fantasy, no?

Wouldn't it be fun to watch it with Adam?

Juneau

By Juneau Underwood on 08/20/2009 8:57 pm

I hadn't even thought about Handel's homosexuality, but maybe that's why he writes such transcendent music about longing. I was just reading today about passion versus obsession. Obsession is passion unrequited. This suggests there is only one cure . . . does not bode well! :)

By Juneau Underwood on 08/20/2009 8:58 pm

And that's why we are "obsessed"—sounds like this will end badly for us, but the ride is worth it!!

Handel's homosexuality—he couldn't have described the male attendants in S&M outfits, with black nail polish, could he? But he would have liked it.

Adam has yet to sing a truly exalted love song, he only sings about unrequited love, lost love, WLL—"love" = sex, distant love. I hope he records a "happy in love" or "passionate love," "can't live without you" love, "swept off our feet" love, "tender" love song

X

By xena princess warrior on 08/20/2009 11:48 pm

[*On more Robert Sebree photos of Adam*]

Ostrich feathers!—leather!—silk ruff!—top hat! and that lower lip—"pouty" or maybe "putti"? Such timing—it enhances the opera imagery perfectly and my Shakespearean plot theory—I have to go to a huge business lunch in this condition??? what will I wear? How can I look at anyone with a straight face with this image before me? Now I'm skeeeerrrred. . . .

Bouquets of love to you Adam's Eye XOXOXO

Xena

By xena princess warrior on 08/20/2009 8:23 am

To me he looks like a fashionable, unruffled medieval knight who has returned from the crusades—a favourite of the Queen, she summons him to her chamber immediately. In spite of his fatigue, he dutifully complies with the Queen's orders, but he's not happy about it, so he is sullen and pouty—he'd rather be with the other knights.

Xena

By xena princess warrior on 08/20/2009 2:51 pm

And he's sulky because she made him wear that ridiculous hat, but he will soon put those feathers to better use.

By Juneau Underwood on 08/20/2009 7:20 pm

Yes, toss the hat and take the feathers to the clubhouse.

By xena princess warrior on 08/20/2009 8:12 pm

I have now caught up—I think. Any news, anybody out there??

Well, I have one. Yesterday I met a woman in the oddest place, who ultimately qualified to become at least an honourary Glambertina. She has a colour photo of Adam on her desk at work, located where only she can see it, but did show it to me, as a member of the Adam sisterhood.

She was at the Hamilton concert in the seat directly opposite to mine on the North Side (she's visible in the video Gloria posted with the delightful dancing Priscilla).

We finally have an actual witness to the attack missile thrown at Adam. The young couple behind her showed her what they had—a "toy" vibrator, with a soft pull cord to make it work. Within a couple of minutes of Adam starting WLL, it whizzed by her head and hit Adam in the leg, as you have seen in the videos, he kicked it ferociously back to the source—hurtling by this fan's ear, barely missing her head. Ultimately, no one was hurt—not in the audience anyway—Adam was hit.

Now here's a truly qualified Glambertina. She said that if she had been able to, she would have shielded Adam with her body, and taken the hit!!!

Is this not a Glambertina of the highest order?

Xena **By xena princess warrior on 08/20/2009 9:22 pm**

[*Re: Joke image posted on Adam Official of a dildo piercing a skull, the result of Adam kicking the flying object back into the audience. The image was removed and replaced with a more innocuous one.*]

Wow, re-writing history here! Talk about a cover-up. Where is Deep Throat when we need him? **By Juneau Underwood on 08/20/2009 11:20 pm**

▪
Good morning Philly! Www. donorschoose.org/ adamlambert Support this charity! 9:35 AM **Aug 20th** from Echofon

[*BD wonders if Adam could have had a nose job.*]

This is a pest-free zone BD, so it is impossible that you could be one—we welcome any challenges. My question for you is "why ask?" and the explanation I have for the appearance of change to a nose, from someone who proudly wears a regal one, is that the nose grows faster than the rest of the face, and eventually grows to the proper proportions to balance all the features including eyes and mouth. Adam's are particularly well balanced and symmetrical.

Does that help?

X **By xena princess warrior on 08/23/2009 10:00 pm**

▪
August 22/09 Mellon Arena in Pittsburgh, Pennsylvania

▪
Had a wild night onstage in Pittsburgh. GREAT crowd. Thank you guys. 7:36 PM **Aug 22nd** from Echofon

I have examined many photos closely and conclude that Adam still has a regal aquiline nose, although it seems not quite as pronounced as it does in some earlier photos, but I think Xena's hypothesis that he grew into his nose is plausible. I hope he never surgically alters his nose or other features. They are splendid and unique. (I am partial to aquiline noses.)

By Juneau Underwood on 08/23/2009 10:58 pm

▪
August 23/09 Wolstein center in Cleveland, Ohio

Someone described his face as "patrician." Even his nostrils are symmetrical and perfectly formed. He has no "bad or good" side, is equally beautiful in profile, 3/4 or full face, a perfect model—and that's just his face. How about those cheek bones, the jaw line—wait, haven't we done this before? Guess we can't ruminate on Adam's visage too much, have to go check some photos again.

X

By xena princess warrior on 08/23/2009 11:11 pm

I'm swooning again, and I haven't even had breakfast yet. . . . I think the "patrician" comment was in the Rolling Stone interview. He does have a princely air, epitomized for me in his performance of Beth, when he looked like he ruled not only the stage but the world.

By Juneau Underwood on 08/24/2009 7:54 am

That was lovely E. and it's great to see you express your growing confidence with your happy obsession. That's the point isn't it—we are all happier than we were. Would they prefer an interest, obsessive or not, which made us cynical or angry, sullen or depressed? How dare anyone complain about some else's happiness and question a healthy, safe means!

With few exceptions, who have since changed their minds, I have received a great deal of support from my friends, and my family is tolerant—you know about Xena II. Why? They ask me why I look great, smiling and happy—so I tell them—I'm doing a lot of writing and it's so much fun. Now they have to know what I am writing, then how did I start writing and finally Adam's name can't be kept out of the conversation any longer. It's not a secret—and there's plenty I have written that's probably better off not exposed, but too late now.

So, don't say anything all, just smile knowingly, sardonically and they'll wonder what you are up to, they will want to take whatever you're having. Maybe hum some of Adam's music, putting a little shimmy in your walk. Put on your lipstick, make eye contact and smile—leave them wondering until they can't take it anymore.

X

By xena princess warrior on 08/23/2009 11:50 pm

p.s. to above—how could I forget the great friends I have made as a result of writing? Doesn't everyone want friends with whom they can share joy, laughs and even tears, who are inspired creatively to amuse each other. How did we find each other?—you know the answer.

By xena princess warrior on 08/23/2009 11:54 pm

▪

Gearing up Cleavland!!!! 4:36 PM **Aug 23rd** from Echofon

Hi E., I also want to give thanks for this wonderful, wonderful sistergood. And yes, for any men out there, gay or otherwise, who share our love and fascination for Adam.

I've been keeping my obsession mostly to myself, even though my family knows all about it and they slip in comments from time to time. My husband makes inquiries, and my daughters make fun of me. I keep my earbuds on. Yesterday, we all ended up driving around in my Mini Cooper because my husband's car had an electrical failure and had to be towed to the garage. I had my iPod all hooked up to the car stereo, and at some point I turned it on and started playing Goldfrapp. My husband, who is always interested in new bands, said "who's this?" So I said "oh, it's Goldfrapp. They're a U.K. band." I didn't mention Adam. After a while, I put on Muse's Starlight and Supermassive Blackhole. "This is Muse," I said. They already knew I listened to Muse because of Adam. Then I switched to "Feelin' Good." "This is Adam," I told my husband. Next thing I knew, my younger daughter was singing along, then my older daughter joined in. My husband was very surprised that they knew the song. I was secretly thrilled that my inoculation had taken! Then it was on to "Mad World." More singing along, and now my girls are asking their Dad, "Don't you know 'Mad World'?" My girls have been maybe a little bit Adamized! I struggled mightily and unsuccessfully to wipe the smile off my face. :)

My neural-happiness axis is hardwired to Adam. Every time I hear his voice, his image, his name, anything that reminds me of him, I feel waves of oxytocin washing over my system.

By Juneau Underwood on 08/24/2009 8:28 am

Hi J. sounds like a bit of a breakthrough for you—smart daughters and loyal to their mother—husband enjoyed the music—it's all good. Baiting the trail to Adam is a great idea. Didn't take much bait to get us here, but others need a little more.

"Sistergood" love it!!

One day, I discovered that my husband and daughter were listening to Adam in my van without me there—I asked them about this, since they try to change to radio when I am there. *"Well, he has a great voice."*

good enough for me

X

By xena princess warrior on 08/24/2009 9:01 am

AaaaaaaaaH I know someone who met Adam—two people!!!!

Envy vibes hurtling toward you both!

By xena princess warrior on 08/24/2009 3:09 pm

Dearest Cleo—my heart is skipping, mouth dry and eyes wet—for me, the penultimate Adam experience is your meeting with him. The ultimate of course would include me. I am so happy for you and the Cleo babe, Cleo II and Cleo Mater, I am doing cartwheels to shake out the vibrations you set off in my body.

Can't speak for the others, but your perfect description of the two meetings should be enough for us, we shouldn't need concert descriptions too—you have gone above and beyond your Glambertina duty. And he gave your poster the attention it deserves, your mom and daughter the compliments—you can bask in his aura for a very long time.

Do you feel warmer? How does it feel to have him actually look at you??? The closeness to him only fuels our ardour, does not diminish it.

Love, Xena

By xena princess warrior on 08/24/2009 9:55 pm

Cleo and all the Glambertinas!! Thank you so much tonight's thrilling ride! The plaintive "we need to hear from you" to the increasingly creative threats of punishment, the impatient pleas, then Cleo delivers her first salvo, resulting in collective swooning, followed by the dish-washing interlude and then the climactic moment, so vividly rendered we can practically feel the press of the crowd, the pounding hearts and heat, the approach of Adam and then the moment when time stands still . . . I'm just blown away. Cleo, you made those moments come truly alive for us. So thrilling, so much fun!

Love, Juneau

By Juneau Underwood on 08/24/2009 11:48 pm

We need a strategy for Syracuse!! I've used up my birthday gift—maybe Christmas gift? What did you two do?

Is there an important Art gallery there? It's only 4-1/2 hours from here. Do I have any relatives there? Buffalo—yes.

X & XII

By xena princess warrior on 08/25/2009 6:13 pm

August 25/09
Schottenstein Center in Columbus, Ohio

Something to cheer you all up.

Dedicated to the one who shall remain nameless—with the initials GBA

Gloria in Bali Bliss

G. B. A. are you into pomegranate martinis again? Strawberries and Chocolate? That Bali story was hysterical! Please, don't leave us hanging —what happens next?

Are you in a bungalow on the beach—a four poster bed, draped in pristine white linen? Is the bed positioned so you can watch the sunset together while sipping rum/coconut smoothies? Just a cool satin sheet slides between you?

The only colour—the sunset and his topaz blue eyes as you toast the end of day, just melting into night as the colors fade, sky darkens, light of a demi-lune picks out the outline of your bodies, the profile of his face—perfect in every way. The fringe of lashes draws you deeper into his eyes, garnished with barely a smudge of kohl, an animated eyebrow lifts, luscious lips together for a kiss. . . .

"C'mon Glorious, let's go out in the moonlight and dance the night away" he leaps to the sand below and extends his arms to catch you when you jump—oh those taut, hard muscular shoulders and arms—fifty nights of fighting the mic for dominance, fifty nights of reaching out to a frenetic audience, fifty nights of arousing scores of women to a frenzy of excitement so powerful—they levitate to the rafters, fifty nights of sinewy body moves in four dimensions—fifty nights of hip thrusts, of stomping, sashaying, tiptoeing, dancing across the stage to pierce the hearts of those who dare look into his luminous, potent eyes.

The moon casts its curved light on smooth waters as he dances toward it—with you in tow, he slows, turns, grabs you, easily lifts you as he splashes into the surf—a powerful final thrust with his thighs. . . .

Remember these are the thighs that held Xena's legs still—while smooth hands, warmed with orange blossom oil massaged her neck, shoulders, her arms, her back—through the vale and up.

Cool water rises up to meet your overheated, over stimulated bodies as you thrash about, slippery hands, upside down, right side up, soft flesh rubs against taut—your hair swirls in a blinding arc, obscures your faces—limbs flying—hard to grasp—what is that?? Ohhhhhhh. . . . Finally you get your bearings.

Apollo lies spent on the sand.

Arising from the waters—Botticelli's Blonde Venus, you feel refreshed, indeed newly born in this life, in this place, nothing came before, no memories beyond this moment—you are compelled to live this night into perpetuity. ***By xena princess warrior on 08/25/2009 9:19 pm***

Xena, Warrior of the Word, how am I going to sleep after reading that? I hear the waves outside my window . . . transported through the night air from the shores of Cape Cod to the warm sands of Bali. But lo, who is that golden creature rising from the waters next to the supine form of Apollo? Beware the jealous wrath of Juneau, supreme goddess of Olympus. . . .
By Juneau Underwood on 08/25/2009 11:02 pm

▪

Max Martin and PINK are quite a combo . . . listening to "I Don't Believe You" song gives me chills. 4:13 PM **Aug 25th** from web

Oh J. you went and spoiled something I thought of for you—Juno, or en Français Juneau, mater of all Roman gods! Xena will have to get even for that one.
By xena princess warrior on 08/25/2009 11:09 pm

▪

max martin 4:10 PM **Aug 25th** from web

OK, I forgive you golden Aphrodite, because you are so magnanimous towards me. I am experimenting with a broader conception of Love. Can I and the rest of the Glambertinas come along with you and Adam to Planet Fierce, or a secluded isle in the Aegean where he can sing to us until the end of Time?
By Juneau Underwood on 08/26/2009 7:35 am

Share Adam? That would be quite the goddess bonding experience. I think it's a starship that will take us to Planet Fierce!!
By Juneau Underwood on 08/26/2009 8:45 pm

Glorious, this story was so easy, thinking about you and our Apollo—who can seduce women with an eyebrow—who could beat that???

A pleasure for me to give you a little gift, for all you do for us here—all the research, the cataloguing—to use a Juneau term—you are an über Glambertina.

Love, Xena
By xena princess warrior on 08/25/2009 11:22 pm

So am I! Glorious—thanks for inviting us all to Planet Fierce—what a party! Where are those servant boys??? we'll need lots of them and I believe this planet is closer to the sun, so very hot—they won't need to pack much. Lots of ostrich feather fans to keep us cool and ostrich feather umbrellas to keep us shaded.

X
By xena princess warrior on 08/26/2009 9:59 am

That interview was an excellent find, Cleo. South Pacific destination? Or maybe we can tempt him to go to New Zealand. Hilarious about his blank look when the interviewer mentioned John Cage. Will have to add "History of Electronic Music" to the Finishing School curriculum.
By Juneau Underwood on 08/26/2009 7:43 am

Do you like the resort you sent to us earlier? I believe Juneau is scouting that location for a possible school location—maybe you need to show him around—or it's a private island, accessible only by water. You know he's there, but security is so high for the powerful rock god, no boats will take you across—even to sit off shore and take some photos for the Glambertinas.

So, resourceful Kiwi sisters that you are, you build a raft from the wood from an ancient shipwreck—scattered on the beach, lashed with sturdy rope you have made—braiding the pliable vines dripping from the trees.

Aaaaahhhh don't get me started already—I am getting backed up with fantasies! I need sleep! I'll be found at my desk—desiccated from dehydration—ankle chained to the leg of the desk—water a mere ten feet away, but unreachable to me.

The only clue to the cause of my death—the final words typed on this site—*"his crotch circles became ellipses, capturing more adulation, swelling with pride, he thrusts his chest, then hips tooooooooooooooooooooooooo. . . ."*

By xena princess warrior on 08/26/2009 10:23 pm

Xena, you just get funnier and funnier. My stomach hurts from laughing without making a sound (girls are lurking around).

By Juneau Underwood on 08/26/2009 11:11 pm

A tantalizing photo for the AM.
http://topidol.wordpress.com/2009/07/11/scary-idol-fan-photoshop-of-the-day-starring-adam-lambert ***By xena princess warrior on 08/26/2009 9:25 am***

You keep outdoing yourself, Princess! Love those skinny girl jeans.

By Juneau Underwood on 08/26/2009 1:21 pm

Amazing how he is so identifiable to us now—even a photo of an elbow—we would recognize as his. Dare I make this a desktop!! I have a new area of excitement—the downy, golden hair on his arms.

By xena princess warrior on 08/26/2009 4:08 pm

Love this Bowie Medley!! How am I supposed to complete an in-depth analysis of government policy when I can't stop smiling and keep hitting replay on this one??? Surely, I will lose my edge, get all soft and empathetic and only write something nice.

X ***By xena princess warrior on 08/26/2009 10:34 am***

Re: DonorsChoose competition to raise money for art in public schools

Fantastic. Our boy has his head and his heart in the right place.

Will you also email DonorsChoose to agitate for including more programs, or doing a second competition?

By Juneau Underwood on 08/26/2009 2:54 pm

Dear Glorious, Thank you for the gracious invitation. It is tempting indeed, but I'm afraid I will be immersed in getting back to work and making sure the school year gets off to a good start . . . plus I will be seriously agonizing over what to wear to the concert (I'm going on the 13th, Providence, RI). I was going to wear a Robert Cavalli black see-through mesh top with kind of a tattoo design on the front and one arm over skinny jeans or the shiny black Issey Miyake space-age pants (skinny too), but then I was shopping yesterday with the family and they talked me into buying a black sequin sheath with skinny straps. Very sexy, I have to say. What do you think?

By Juneau Underwood on 08/26/2009 4:35 pm

The dress!!! please wear the dress! Few wear dresses and few wear sparkles and sequins—this is your opportunity to pay homage to the Fashionisto of party style. Only two of us were ornamented with silver sequins in Hamilton—Adam deserves shine, sparkle and glorious glitter!

My 2cents

Xena

By xena princess warrior on 08/26/2009 4:56 pm

(If you could only choose one, which Adam would you want to spend time with on planet fierce? On-stage Rock-God Adam or sweet angelic off-stage Adam?)

Do we have to choose? I want both!

By Juneau Underwood on 08/26/2009 10:55 pm

August 26/09 Palace of Auburn Hills in Auburn Hills, Mi.

Dear Glambertinas, thank you for all the sartorial advice/support! You've convinced me to wear the dress! With the dark Swarovski crystal necklace. Adam managed to deliver it back to me. . . .

Glorious, thanks for the luscious photos. He's having Adamgasms!

My husband and I took our girls to see a drag burlesque show in Provincetown tonight. Wasn't quite sure how raunchy it would be. It was pretty out there, but it was hilarious, good-natured, and we all loved it. Fortunately for us, there were even younger kids there, two boys around 7 and 10 years old. The Mistress of Ceremonies noted their presence and called out to their mom, "hey, Worst Mother of the Year!" My husband and I just about fell on the floor laughing.

By Juneau Underwood on 08/26/2009 9:13 pm

My girls are 12 and 15.

I'll see if I can get someone to take my picture. My older daughter is getting to be a good photographer. I'm torn about not wearing the Cavalli / Issey combo. Adam is such a fashionista. He'd appreciate my choices, I think. Oh well, I may have to go to the Manchester show after all . . . or save the outfit for his first solo tour.

By Juneau Underwood on 08/26/2009 9:23 pm

We must have pictures J! You wear the dress and you will be noticed—by everyone. Looks like he does the post-show meet & greets, so make sure you have a pair of shoes comfortable to stand in for a while. BTW, I've dubbed Adam a "fashionisto"—the masculine of Fashionista.

Go to as many shows as you can—Once is Not Enough

X

By xena princess warrior on 08/26/2009 9:55 pm

Count me in [on going to the Syracuse concert]—I'll make sure the van is gassed-up and I will do the driving. We'll take Adam DVDs to watch on the trip—how many versions of WLL and Bowie medley can we watch?

X

By xena princess warrior on 08/26/2009 11:27 pm

Awesome. I love how so many reviewers are thinly disguised fans of Adam. They are having so much fun trying to come up with new extreme metaphors to capture his fabulousness.

By Juneau Underwood on 08/27/2009 8:37 am

I. R., I am ecstatic for you!! You won't regret this. I hope you'll be able to deliver our petition to Adam! And have a wonderful, wonderful time. Shower some Adam-love on your husband so he'll think this was his most brilliant idea ever.

By Juneau Underwood on 08/27/2009 8:59 pm

What a Glorious obsession!!

By Juneau Underwood on 08/27/2009 8:56 pm

Aren't you ingenious, GB! If you get Adam for dinner, I will just have to make the drive to Syracuse, even if I have to make the round trip in one evening. . . . Xena, we are counting on you to write the letter of your life!! **By Juneau Underwood on 08/27/2009 8:51 pm**

All Hail Cleo!! the Royal Highness of the sun, moon, stars and universe of Adam.

I am prostrate before you, in admiration of your exalting experience, so brilliantly rendered in colour, light, movement, heat, emotion, so vividly shared with the sistergood and the bad.

Well Cleo, I actually fainted, dropped to my knees and fell over, mumbling *"it can't be over, it can't be over, why not me Lord?, why not me? Was I not as sweet as Cleo, not so generous? What can I offer as sacrifice? I want a piece of what Cleo got"*

I weep with envy, my eyes so green, they're olives. He reaches for you, he sings *"woman"* for you, he wears his hair down for you, he teased GB even more for you and to top it off—he went outside and talked to you!

And Cleo, you deserve every minute of pleasure you received and thank you for allowing us to peek over your shoulder. You're the most dedicated Adam-mom, Adam-daughter and Adam-fan.

"Starlight is so genuine . . . so sweet . . . so beautiful . . . I feel as though I'm floating along with him when he sings this song. I reach for him as he reaches for me . . . begging for someone to hold him. He smiles and moves so fluidly. I have shivers from head to toe . . . and I shake my head to remember where I am. He is an angel"

I have shivers from head to toe.

Love and hugs

Xena **By xena princess warrior on 08/27/2009 9:56 pm**

Is it just my filthy mind, but it looks like Adam is being ravished by Tigger? **By Juneau Underwood on 08/28/2009 6:45 am**

GBA, we must be synching up in the Ether-Aura of the universe, for me to stumble onto the name of your boat! *Glorious Obsession!* Thanks for sharing your stories about your Mom and husband getting ensnared by the Lambert-magic. I'll bet you looked fabulous in your "Adam dress." Hope you danced your ass off. I stayed at the Royal York once. Seems like a lifetime ago, but now it's another connection through time-space to the sistergood.

Today is the last day of my summer vacation on the Cape. It's going to be devoted to birthday activities for my younger daughter. We'll go parasailing, dune-buggying, cruising on a schooner in Cape Cod bay, and have dinner followed by dancing and drag karaoke. I'm definitely vying for that Worst Mother of the Year title!

By Juneau Underwood on 08/28/2009 7:23 am

Good morning ladies. I am assembling a Finishing School brochure to present to Adam. Anyone who wishes to be listed as a faculty or staff member, please submit a paragraph-description of your credentials and life experience that qualifies you to impart skills and wisdom to Adam. Doesn't matter if you are actually teaching an assigned course!! Creative license encouraged. Goal is to make Adam sign up as a lifetime student!!

And here's the latest (and I hope last) course to add to the catalog. I had to add this when I found out Adam didn't know who John Cage was. Sorry to wander off into such esoterica, but I couldn't resist.

Music History—Electronic Visionaries (Prof. J. Underwood and guest). Impress music producers and smart-ass music journalists with your knowledge of the pioneers of electronic music. The great twentieth century avant gardist John Cage described music as "an affirmation of life—not an attempt to bring order out of chaos nor to suggest improvements in creation, but simply a way of waking up to the very life we're living." We will discuss whether this concept applies to any current musicians of interest. In addition to Cage, the course will study the contributions of Martenot, Stockhausen, Boulez, Machover, Kraftwerk, Eno, Bowie, Prince, Kate Bush, Peter Gabriel, etc. The technology portion will cover the evolution of the Moog synthesizer, MIDI standard and hyperinstruments. Significant class time will be devoted to mastering the legendary Theremin, an early electronic instrument comprised of a pair of erect rods that sense the air-caresses of the hands, one of which controls oscillations for frequency while the other hand controls the amplitude. Extra credit for performing Whole Lotta Love on Theremin.

By Juneau Underwood on 08/28/2009 7:15 am

▪ Thank you Milwaukee. Fans were so sweet tonight. Thank you for the support! :) 10:48 PM **Aug 28th** from web

▪ **August 28/09** Bradley Center in Milwaukee, Wisconsin–Adam is flashed by a female fan after the show

I hope he enjoys it. I'll make it a "letter" so he can read it on the bus. You need to send me a description for the faculty profiles.

By Juneau Underwood on 08/28/2009 10:15 am

"He later added, 'I love it when older women come up to me and say, "you make me feel young again,"' because it shows how powerful music is."

Hi GB, I loved that quote and it's perfect for the letter, which I will work on after I have completed an editorial I am writing. Glorious, I might have to delve into your book of diamonds to find a couple of other quotes of his to include. As you have committed all to memory, perhaps you could suggest a few?

While I'm caught up with reading everything here, I haven't had a chance to write—so much good stuff from all of you and I have to leave it to later.

I did read in one of the interviews that his new album won't have sad songs, because he's too happy to write or sing sad ones. Guess we better hang onto all the old, pre-idol, unrequited love songs—but great to hear he's too happy to do them. It is so obvious that he is himself—who he was destined to be—now. He positively radiates happiness, on stage and off.

We have all become more radiant as we bask in his aura, sparks from a fire—sizzling when they land on us—leave a little sting behind, to sooth with his mellow, seductive voice, his stillness of body, to focus fully on his eyes.

Now, back to that other reality.

Xena

By xena princess warrior on 08/28/2009 9:54 am

It's a divine madness. You have been visited by a Muse. Hold onto him as long as you can. But exercise caution. Having him as an imaginary friend is kind of like driving while texting. . . .

By Juneau Underwood on 08/28/2009 9:53 pm

Dearest D.,

I have taken my time to reply, so I could completely focus on your eloquence in expressing your sadness at the death of your dear God-daughter and, how you have found some solace in Adam's wisdom—kind of an odd expression for women like us to say "wisdom" when we talk about him, isn't it? But truly he has a childlike gift for cutting through the chatter to get to the truth—as we age, we tend to become more guarded, as if we are under attack all the time.

As with you, Adam has opened my eyes and allowed me to open up areas of myself I didn't know existed—all for the better. Love "real man" and I think Gloria should include that sentence in her book of gems vol. 2.

I hope that as you mourn your beloved Goddaughter, you might use a song of Adam's as a talisman, a little trigger to remember her and recall happy moments with her. Moments to warm your heart with your happy memories and she will always be with you, and you will cry a little. She must have been so special—special ed teachers have unique gifts, my daughter benefited from one in particular.

Over thirty years ago, I suddenly lost a young first cousin at the age of seven, so full of life, it was as if she knew we would not have her for long. All the summer before, she sang "Bye Bye Miss American Pie" and I can't hear that song without thinking of her—fondly—her happy, smiling face, husky little voice and ring of curly hair to give her an angelic look with her big round, brown eyes. And I have a little cry.

Dorothy, thank you so much for gracing our site with your warmth and intelligence.

Love, Xena

By xena princess warrior on 08/30/2009 11:35 pm

I stopped in at the Human Rights Campaign shop in the heart of Provincetown and ended up joining and buying two pendants, one for me and one to give to Adam. It's a small steel medallion with a stylized letter E and the word "equality" stamped on the reverse side. I think it would be cool if he would wear it. When I emerged from the store, my 15-year-old asked what I got, and she asked, "Is it for Adam?" I told her I've always believed in equality for gays and lesbians, and she gave me a huge hug and said "I'm going to put the picture of the two of us as my Facebook pic." Wow! I think I've become almost human in her eyes!!

By Juneau Underwood on 08/28/2009 10:39 pm

Dearest Glambertinas, I have been quiet for a couple of days and a couple of you know why. In the meantime, I am working on the "the letter"—what a challenge! During the process, I recalled something from yesterday, or I dreamt it, rather vividly. Was there an interview with Adam about his undergarments—"commando, briefs or boxers"?

Am I going crazy? I need verification—I do know how he answered.

Xena

By xena princess warrior on 08/29/2009 11:01 pm

August 29/09 Scottrade Center in St. Louis, Mo.

Oh, thanks so much AEoH, I loved it and indeed the answer is "briefs and sometimes nothing" "briefs when I'm working."

X

By xena princess warrior on 08/30/2009 12:14 am

Hi C., this is such a rich and interesting discussion to have. I have to get going this morning, but I have a few thoughts to share. One, I think our world is full of things made by humans—writing, art, music, buildings—but inspired by something we call divine. This doesn't mean the work is therefore perfect. It is all of necessity interpreted through the human mind, with all its flaws, prejudices and cultural baggage. I am convinced that the Bible is no more privileged in this regard than any other sacred work, be it the Koran, Buddhist sutras, or the Sistine Chapel. What is so compelling and moving to me is that despite the differences in epoch and culture, people were reaching for the same thing—an experience of the sacredness of our human lives and yearning to connect with something transcendent in the universe. If we could all recognize this, we would stop arguing about which belief system is "the Truth"—they are all striving towards the same truth. There are many roads to that truth. You found yours through Jesus. I found mine through science and Judaism. Unfortunately, we get distracted and blinded by the incidental details along the way. Homosexuality is one of these distractions, in my view.

You ask why God created a man and a woman. You may also ask why God created homosexuals. As I think E. and Gloria mentioned in previous posts, homosexuality is not a willful choice that some people make in defiance of God. They are born that way. There's a lot of neuroscience research now that shows how the balance of hormones that the fetus's brain is exposed to changes the way it is wired and produces different gradations of sexuality in the adult. Scientists can engineer rats to develop as homosexuals. An estimated 10% of humans are born with homosexual tendencies. It's like race. You can't help being born with it, and so it is unjust to discriminate on the basis of it.

I sometimes think race, sexual orientation, ethnicity, economic status, nationalism, and other such divisive attributes of human society are a grand test of our ability to see through the smokescreens of prejudice and tribalism and hear the Cosmic call to Love.

By Juneau Underwood on 08/30/2009 10:19 am

Juneau, you are a wonder. After years of questioning my lack of faith and ultimately coming to the conclusion that I am perfectly OK, and even happier without it, but unable to explain why, you have given the most beautiful and non judgmental treatise on truth and love. Thank you.

By E.—on 08/30/2009 10:17 pm

The Death of Xena

A Macabre Opera in One Act

"Well Cleo, I actually fainted, dropped to my knees and fell over, mumbling 'it can't be over, it can't be over, why not me Lord?, why not me? Was I not as sweet as Cleo, not so generous? What can I offer as sacrifice? I want a piece of what Cleo got.'"

My family abandoned me years earlier for failing to buy food or to cook—they chained me to my desk to write about Adam till I died. I wrote prose, I composed poetry, I made art, I gave him everything I had, but still—no meeting, no Adam in the flesh to smile, to touch, to share a berry.

I knew he saw others—those vix and vixens—their blasted smiles burning the screen of my laptop. Did they talk about me? Did they warn him that I was a sorceress? What of the others—the members of the sistergood? I bet that Cleo with her beauty, money and power got plenty of attention and whispered lies about me in his ear—it was Cleo who filled me with a jealous rage.

Still, I did not give up until . . . resources spent, lawn so overgrown with weeds from neglect, handsome, muscular CSI agents take machetes to chop the vines blocking the door. It's hot, so they have removed the tops of their uniforms, cooler in t-shirts. They are all tenors and sing like well—Adam.

"What's that smell?" "Is it orange blossom?" When they enter my room, they hear Adam singing "You Don't Call me Anymore." I am chained to my desk, water too far to reach, my body mummified when my remains are found—wretched bony fingers resting on the computer keys, dark purple polish still visible, tufts of blue hair, muted purple and puce silk pyjamas hang loosely on my bones, room piled high with Adam programmes, photos and posters, his voice on replay—two hours of singing, two hours of interviews.

The remnants of a tray of dates, figs, strawberries and chocolate on a table nearby. On the desk, an empty bottle of cognac. Like the skeleton of a long-finished party—it's a sad picture. Two glasses, only one has been used, the other pristine—for the lover who never came?

A brocade-covered, Louis XV chaise longue in the corner, sits unruffled, arms waiting, cushions in perfect array, plump—but now dusty and unappealing. Alabaster vase holds a bouquet of black and white ostrich feathers, while wax dripped from too many candles covers most surfaces. The only light—from the moon in a black sky—peeks daintily in through the drapes fluttering in the open windows.

The detectives arrive *"when will they ever learn—he's gay and he's not coming."* (The detectives sing bass and are dressed in very tight purple jeans, large silver buckles, black open neck shirts and black jackets, python skin boots.—they all have black hair, blue eyes and the remnants of eyeliner from the night before.)

"Yeah, they sacrifice everything, everyone, for a few minutes with him, but he never gets there. How many is that now?"

"I think it's seven from that one sect alone. What do you suppose the feathers are for? They show up at every scene."

"Don't know, but the victims all have the same cause of death too—broken hearts from an unrequited love. Only the other members of the sect show up for the services"

I gave it all and he never came for me—from off-stage, Dame Kiri te Kanawa sings "V'adore Pupille" from Handel's The Sorceress.

Multi-media to enhance votre petite expérience.

The Sorceress sings to a beautiful boy pupil, as he is stripped of his white costume and redressed to resemble a Prince of Darkness—blonde hair traded for black, dark cape, black leather trousers.

http://www.youtube.com/watch?v=tNufTxa4h58&feature=related

Xena

By xena princess warrior on 08/30/2009 11:43 pm

Priscilla, I bow modestly before you and thank you—but I must call Juneau to the stage, as it is she who was inspired to share the aria with us some time ago. I did some more research of the whole opera and we wanted to do something with it. Tonight when you said "it would make a wonderful aria for a tragic opera" this of course, immediately sprung to mind and it flowed. You were the inspiration—thank you.

And yes—snakes and serpents are not just symbols of the Sorceress, but they adorn her gown and her sceptre. I think I wrote an analysis on this somewhere—but truly Juneau gets the credit for making the brilliant connection. I just write words.

Juneau! please come and take a bow!

Xena

By xena princess warrior on 08/31/2009 12:10 am

Ahh Xena!! I apologize for choking with laughter over your tragic tale of death by unrequited love. Bravissimo, maestra!! I bow before your soaring talent for marrying comedy and tragedy, and taking V'Adoro Pupille and twisting it up like this. Adam would be so proud of you.

Everyone! Be sure to watch the video. The parallels are uncanny, plus it is ravishingly beautiful, and will make you appreciate Xena's genius even more.

By Juneau Underwood on 08/31/2009 12:03 am

The pleading letter delivered to Adam
Glambertinas at wowOwow.com

Adam Lambert
Rock Star
Muse
Fashionisto
Philosopher
Sexiest Man Alive
Boy Next Door with Eyeliner

Dear Adam; 29 August 2009

You very generously asked your fans to donate to DonorsChoose.org instead of sending our gifts to you—in response, we have pledged among the few of us, $1,700 in addition to individual donations, already made by members of our group. We hope our dedication and sincere interest in you as an artist and individual, will persuade you to grant us a wonderful favor in return.

This group of your fans—The Glambertinas—is small, international and dedicated. Since June 3rd, we have been posting comments on a single website http://www.wowowow.com/entertainment/allegra-huston-adam-lambert-american-idol-304646#comments. We began to write after the appearance of Allegra Huston's article "What is it About Adam Lambert?"—she attempts to understand the reaction of a mature, professional woman to your universal sex appeal—a question we were asking ourselves. We have written over 5,000 comments trying to answer that question and of course many other related topics. One is as long as 4,000 words and describes a journey to see you perform at the Idols concert in Hamilton, Ontario. We did manage to throw a highly decorated male thong onto the stage.

Adam, we are that classic—mature Baby Boomer and beyond, woman fan of Adam—and we are well-educated, professionals and literate, hence thousands of entries and tens of thousands of words. We did learn a couple of the cyber-short forms, but we congregated at this site to be able to converse in our own style—with sentences and punctuation. We have written about our responses to your performances and interviews, our emotions, analyses, a play, a symposium, very personal tributes and fantasies. We laugh, cry and swoon together as we keep up with your activities. Most importantly, you have inspired us to make positive changes in our lives and in the world. Your artistry and personal example have been literally life-changing. For that we thank you from the bottom of our hearts.

▪ St Louis: Another fantastic crowd!!! I was feelin the love!! :) Thnx 7:38 PM **Aug 29th** from Echofon

▪ **August 30/09** Sprint Centre in Kansas City, Mo.

▪ Kansas City!! We're ready to tear it up tonight! 11:38 **AM Aug 30th** from web

▪ Thank you all for the support. Love overcomes hate. Love has no color. Love has no orientation. All is love. :) 8:11 PM **Aug 30th** from Echofon

Also thanks to you, we have become a sisterhood of American, Canadian and New Zealander fans, which would take more than a letter to describe.

Several Glambertinas have now been able to see you in concert, when you were unable to do the meet & greets—a very, very fortunate one of us, met you with her daughter and mother, at a post concert meet & greet in Pittsburgh, providing us with a wonderfully descriptive narrative of the encounter—now the rest of us want to have the same experience!! This is an attempt to persuade you to make this happen for us.

Here are some comments Glambertinas posted there:

"We are obsessed with a beautiful, sexy, erotic, witty, sometimes peacock; other times robin, engrossing and unforgettable—nightingale."

"It's incredible to me how many of us have taken actions that we would never have dreamed possible even two months ago. We are feeling creative, writing insane erotic fantasies, designing jewelry, sprucing up our looks, feeling young and in love, and making wonderful friendships here. It's all GOOD!!"

"Flirt a little, make eye contact more, speak enthusiastically and listen with curiosity. Put on some eyeliner and mascara when you don't have to and polish your nails! Give out more hugs and you'll get more back. But most of all—HAVE FUN! Adam does."

"What makes so many people find a Muse in Adam Lambert? It has something to do with his approachability and humility combined with swoon-inducing beauty of voice and physique. It also has something to do with his having been lost, been in pain, his search for love. You want to create something that will amuse him, comfort him, seduce and excite him."

"Adam has taken iconic songs from our youth, and then amazingly made them even better. He affirms that what we remember from our youth was truly great—and that it's going to get even greater! It has yanked us out of passive nostalgia and engaged us in the Now."

One of our members has amassed a huge collection of bon mots both by you and about you. Here are some of our favourites from you, which we find inspiring:

"Confidence, intelligence, and self-expression," also *"talent, creativity and open-mindedness"*—are to you, attractive attributes—they are to us as well.

"If you have a dream you gotta go get it. Take risks. Take chances. Persistence is key, you know what I mean? So please, if you have something in your heart that you want to achieve, you gotta go for it . . . for me" wonderful motivational advice for adults as well as the young people you inspire.

"I'm very inspired by past music. I'm inspired by history, different periods. Obviously, I love the whole glam rock thing . . . both in the sound and in the look and in the tone and what they were talking about. I love the sociological view of history too. The late '60s, for example, was a time of the summer of love and kind of the whole hippie movement-exploration of social norm and what was normal and expected and what was rebellious and fresh and new . . . hopefully we're entering a time where we can kind of reflect that same sentiment of hope and love and peace." We have had our hearts broken; now our hopes are being re-born.

Adam we respectfully request the opportunity to take you to dinner—about eight of us—before your show in Syracuse. (Bostonite "Juneau" invites you to afternoon tea or dinner before the September 13 show in Providence.) We have some questions that are important to us, but have not been asked in interviews or during the forums in which you participate. Hmm, has anyone asked what you sleep in? NO—not that type of question, besides we can already guess—can't we? And you told us your preferences in undergarments—so we don't need to go there either.

Here are a few questions we might have:

• Tell me about how you became aware of your gayness. What did you struggle with? What was the process of acceptance for you?
• You went through an experimental phase (like many young people), trying out different looks, the hair, personae, milieux. When did it all start to come together into something that felt authentic?
• Why do you feel that falling in love has been your greatest achievement?
• Are you a dog person or cat person? Or are you possibly a snake person?
• Do you think of yourself as Jewish? In what ways? (or not?)
• How involved are you in in creating the total sound of your performances, not just the vocals but the arrangements, instrumentation, etc.?
• What do you do to prepare yourself before a performance, physically and mentally?
• How do you keep your performances fresh?

• What have you learned, what has surprised you about this tour experience?
• What most frustrates or annoys you about yourself?
• We know you are aware of the profound effect you have had on Baby Boomer women. Do you have any insights into why?
• What questions would YOU ask your Boomer women fans?
• You pronounced "accoutrements" so perfectly in French—do you know any more French?
From the Glambertinas—or should that be "Glambertinae"—with love.

I. R. Attempted to deliver our letter but Adam did not come out due to people protesting against Adam because he is gay.

We'll figure out how to handle the letter GBA.

Only those whose views are misrepresented by those who purport to speak for them, can stop the protests and it is they who should. It's a wonder that so few people can do so much damage to the reputation of so many, however silence is permission by default. First thought—perhaps a Christian (the protesters seem to be only Christian) leader could speak up and condemn such despicable actions. I don't know any, but we could probably contact one somewhere.

On the other hand, my PR/crisis management training tells me that sometimes, a response only serves to bring attention to the protesters and a longer platform. My strategy would be to adopt a wait-and-see attitude, it should just fizzle out and Adam has stated that he does not want to be a poster boy, just an entertainer. They are more interested in the media and cameras than anything else and responding to their nastiness only offers them an opportunity to be louder and more vociferous, while starving them of opportunity should diminish them. Let their saner brethren deal with them in private.

Do they picket everywhere there are gay performers??? Obviously not—or theatres and concerts everywhere would be surrounded. What about those gay people who just quietly go about their lives? I truly do not understand the point of this—except to shamelessly exploit a beautiful, honest, charismatic young man for their personal 15 minutes of fame—a clip on TV or the internet. In this case, familiarity will bring contempt. ***By xena princess warrior on 08/31/2009 8:19 am***

I think Sarver in particular has been great on this issue.

I tend to do some of my thinking "out loud," as I did on this subject and concluded that silence is golden—from my personal and professional points of view. Support from Sarver or Kris however, goes a long way.

Really? is Brad in big trouble? ***By xena princess warrior on 08/31/2009 11:56 am***

Of course Adam will do just fine, but as fans, we are the losers, these few, excited people have deprived us of the opportunity to meet him or even see him up close. Hope everyone is patient and okay with this—they were holding him hostage. Hope it's just yesterday. Their freedom of association and free speech are impinging on other's rights to congregate in public and move about unhampered. If their actions did not force Adam to change plans, it would not have mattered, but this does.

I'm not a Princess Warrior for nothing.

Love and hugs

Xena

Defender of HRH the Rock God, GBA, Sneaky and all their fans, especially Glambertinas. ***By xena princess warrior on 08/31/2009 12:27 pm***

Thank you, very nice sentiments Priscilla, but you aren't a Queen for nothing and I a mere Princess. Yours is a softer, kinder voice, camouflaging nerves of steel and a lot of chutzpah and you deploy your décolletage most effectively.

Love, Xena ***By xena princess warrior on 08/31/2009 2:28 pm***

What a terrific, richly rendered description, I.R. I feel I was there with you!

"For the rest of my life, I will never forget a bar of the intro to Whole Lotta Love. It will be with me, even if I get dementia and can't remember the names of my own children."—A memorable line if there ever was one!

By Juneau Underwood on 08/31/2009 7:43 pm

C., they didn't string sentences together, they stuttered, they stammered, Paula fell across the desk, Kara fell off her chair and he made them "happy"! I think there's a better word for that feeling, but it was the best Kara could find—family show after all. I fell over the barricade, my daughter bruised her midriff reaching to touch the smoke that touched Adam. At least Xena II got eye contact! I got sore feet standing in the same spot for three hours, riveted.

By xena princess warrior on 09/01/2009 7:52 pm

If I decide to watch any Idol again, I will miss Paula—I liked her and her boosterism. Boy, those women were funny—loose sentences, stunned faces, slippery bodies and all!

By xena princess warrior on 09/01/2009 8:34 pm

Dearest Glambertinae,

I was talking with my male friend who has read some of what I have written here and he liked it, so while I haven't given him the URL—I keep him posted on our topics and activities.

Tonight I told him about the discussions we have about spirituality, religion, philosophy, expressions of feelings and other broader and higher level topics, not to mention the fantasies and vivid descriptions—fact or fiction. We call on any exotic resource we need to express ourselves.

He said, "*men are so stupid.*" "*Why?*" I asked—*"because you don't have such interesting discussions?"*

"*Right—it's business, sports and maybe politics*." I think he's right and that's why we spend our hours here, with such thoughtful and smart women who have original thoughts, who have lived long enough to have figured out, experienced and seen—a lot, but with room to grow and boy have we grown since June!

Inspired by the strangest catalyst who quite literally "blew our minds," we have set about to fill those reservoirs with music, imagery and thought—new, different, challenging ideas which brought us together and further fill-out our already plump lives with beautiful, creative, honest and very smart women friends, with whom we share some of our most profound feelings or radical ideas.

We laugh, we cry, we hug, we kiss and we dance with joy. I don't see men having this type of deep and fulfilling discussion to arouse such passions with each other. If they do, it's when we aren't around.

The discussion is so gracious and elegant—our collective words have become a work of art, to commemorate this time when we have come together in spirit to explore a mutual conundrum—"what is it about Adam Lambert?"

More like a pleasure cruise than a dangerous expedition—we keep coming back to the buffet for more and more Adam and more of each other, with chocolate sauce, whipped cream and a cherry on top—oh, and champagne. With beautiful scenery all the way.

Wonder what they think we women, spending all this time on line are chit-chatting about—recipes, children, cleaning ladies, paper or plastic, the price of milk (?), the economy—them???

We can't possibly still be swooning like pre-teens over some singer who caught our fancy, could we?

Love

Xena *By xena princess warrior on 09/01/2009 1:20 am*

Looking for Signs of Intelligence—in all the Wrong Places

More on the Glambertina Forum

Zucchini, you are right—this is a "forum" for us to share our ideas—no matter what topic might show up, there is someone here to pick-up the thread and run with it, or at the very least, politely respond, but I sense that we are all 100% sincere or we wouldn't waste precious time and energy with each other.

Many women have said that Adam "filled a hole in their lives," i.e., they were missing something, while I said that he blasted a hole in mine.

Last night and this morning, I realized that indeed there was an empty place in my life that I had been trying to complete and that is—friendships with women like all of you. Women with whom I could have wonderful conversations and discussions, open to any and all topics.

Not looking for women specifically, but men and women with whom I could discuss shared interests, be provocative and force people to think outside their comfort zone. I attended lectures, debates, lunches, dinners, all kinds of social events—spoke with many people, but nothing clicked. I got the sense that for all of these people, their lives were so complete, they couldn't possibly cram another acquaintance or discussion into them. Or, they are afraid to just sit down for an interesting chat, perhaps by email or phone. Too much work?

Adam talks about looking for love, about putting himself out there, but no one responds—that's how I felt. An unrequited desire for communication/connection with other people who shared interests, or were courageous enough to tackle any concept, idea or fantasy that came along..

I believe that too many people live an "unexamined" life, as one of you, maybe Juneau, mentioned ages ago. They are willing to live a life that is shallow and narrow, impervious to new experiences or challenges to their ideas and beliefs, just getting on with the daily chores to sustain their corporal lives and feel secure, passively experiencing some amusement. But, that's not good enough for us—we have spiritual, emotional, inquisitive and curious lives—also needing sustenance for us to live, to breathe.

It was Socrates, who at his trial for heresy said "An unexamined life is not worth living," risking his life. In this market forum, we are all Socratic, examining our lives and challenging one another as we seek Truth and Beauty—each day and now, in almost everything we do.

Thank you all and my heart is overwhelmed with warm tears to know you as sisters, good sisters.

Love, Xena

By xena princess warrior on 09/01/2009 11:00 am

Dearest I. R., your post is sensible, we get it.

But lately, I've begun to unfurl. This hasn't been so positive for my family, and I'm not sure how it will turn out.

But our life doesn't "turn out," does it? It just keeps unfurling until the very end, and maybe it doesn't stop there.

I'm not skeerrrrrrred, I. R.—this is a perfect place to safely unfurl—what a great word—when the flag is unfurled, it waves freely and proudly, all can see the pattern clearly, and you will benefit from it, as will everyone around you.

But do you think it is dangerous? I go back and forth on this. Does it (writing here) help us disassociate from our daily reality, or does it help us face it? Or both? (Doesn't matter, I'm coming here anyway.)

I speak as one who has spent years in a black velvet tunnel, walled-in from life—in a mental sensory deprivation unit, not just keeping my eyes closed, but my mind as well. I sought safety from trauma and that is where I thought I would find it. No sight, no sound, no words, no thoughts—even the slightest opening would send me scurrying like a cockroach into the darkness.

This is when people became very concerned about me—the silence and unresponsiveness, the colour and beauty drained from me, unable to absorb or reflect some light. That began over ten years ago.

In the last few months, I seem to have emerged from the hard-shelled chrysalis and unfurled my wings again. They're brightly coloured and shimmery—silver, blue, purple, black eyeliner and red lipstick. Two things contributed to my metamorphosis—Adam—his artistry and beauty and thanks to him, all of you. Our obsession with and adoration of HRH is how we met, but it is we, ourselves who have grown, expanded and gained a courage we didn't know we had, but was there all along.

This place helps us face daily reality—it provides a perspective and a motivation to recreate what we experience here, in other parts of our lives. This is part of your reality. Use us as a laboratory to test your ideas, concepts, perhaps a strategy or tactic, you always get feedback.

When asked what happened to bring back the old, confident, irascible, colourful Xena—I tell people about all of you—the brilliant women who have become so close and have so much fun, I can't stop visiting and you make me Feel Good. I give them an idea of some of the topics we cover—sometimes Adam's name never comes up and to a person, they are envious.

Once again, I will evoke the image of the four travelers in Oz seeking the Wizard to fulfill something they thought they were missing. After unmasking the great and horrible Wizard, he had to admit there was no magic, but he revealed to each of them that they already possessed what they thought was missing. All they needed were the accoutrements to show others. You're in there somewhere and you are "out" here—is that right?

My girlfriends recently welcomed me "back" after ten years in the cocoon, as have my siblings and my parents. My husband figured out something is different too and while he is confused about the Adam part, he likes me happy. While they might not understand how my Adam Addiction did this to me, they're pleased for me and that I found a group of women who can shut me up whenever they want to, so my family doesn't have to listen to me.

Spent a collective twelve years "on the couch" examining my life and nothing worked as well as the talk of the last few months. Things I thought I learned ten years ago, turned out to be false, so I had to keep shifting the "truth." I am not going backward again—I've lived most of my life now and I intend to spend the rest of it in the here and now, not fretting about the past or fearing the future, being tentative and cautious.

Traumas and problems have not been eliminated from my life, but I am no longer overwhelmed by them. This is the place I've been trying to find for ten years, maybe longer.

This is reality I., but without the visible—flesh and blood. We have what really counts—feelings, emotions, imagination, love and a great capacity to communicate, not just with our words, but the music we all listen to, the images we all see—that's what makes us so fulfilled to be here.

You can always resort to something I had to say out loud to someone "*I am happy—don't you like me happy?—I have girlfriends who make me happy—I deserve to be happy, don't I? And it's legal.*" "*If I am happy, you will be too.*"

I. R., if as you examine your life—and that doesn't mean you have to go backward—you can begin now by being more aware of yourself, how you feel, what you think, who you are, you in relation to others in your life. If you stumble or hit a wall—we are here for you, lean on us. I doubt there's a problem one among us has not experienced—try us out.

Out of the ashes, rises a beautiful Phoenix, unfurl your wings! We want to know the unfettered I. R. in all her glory!!

Love and hugs,

Xena

By xena princess warrior on 09/01/2009 3:05 pm

September 1/09 Target Center In Minneapolis, Minnesota

Gloria, what a perfect way to describe that feeling of stepping out into the light, instead of remaining in the dark, as a blossom and a bud. Thank you,

Love

Xena

By xena princess warrior on 09/01/2009 7:22 pm

Hey! that's a Tiffany's bag on the table, with a pair of glasses shoved in—wonder what bauble someone bought at Tiff's?

X

By xena princess warrior on 09/01/2009 1:24 pm

I have a sharp eye for good bags. In my first fantasy "shopping with Adam," we are on Rodeo Drive and I step out of Tiffany's.

I hate tattoos and my one and only, pride of my life child, wants to be a tattoo artist!! Life is one test of our mettle after another. Don't like piercings either and she has those too.

My hope is that Adam is confident in his physical appeal without needing any further bodily embellishments—for me, it would mean a more highly evolved personality if he chose not to. He is realizing his dream as he is—why fool with success? I hope he's superstitious like hockey players who don't shave, get a haircut or change their underwear during the playoffs, as long as they are winning.

Apologies to any Glambertinas with piercings—beyond ears—tattoos or any other bodily decorations. I don't even have pierced ears.

X

By xena princess warrior on 09/01/2009 5:31 pm

Since Xena Jr. wants to be a tattoo artist, at least make sure she studies with the best—in Japan. That's one place where you can call tattooing truly an art form. Undoubtedly, she'll have to sweep the stairs with a toothbrush for ten years before the master will let her take up a needle. . . .

I like the idea of Adam being evolved enough. This is something you should ask him when you have dinner with him!

By Juneau Underwood on 09/01/2009 8:01 pm

I'm not big on tattoos either. Every now and then I see a nice one, but most of them are poorly integrated with the body. I was at Tassajara a year ago, a Zen retreat deep in the mountains behind Big Sur, CA (where I used to live), hanging out at the beautiful swimming hole there. There was a couple skinny dipping, and they had tattoos, and it occurred to me that once you have a tattoo, you can't ever be truly naked again. Maybe that's nutty, but that thought impressed itself on me at the time.

By Juneau Underwood on 09/01/2009 7:57 pm

Forgive me Headmistress, for being tardy with my Curriculum Vitae, but I am trying to pad it so it's as long as Prof. Northern Spirit's. If punishment is deemed necessary, may I have the whip with the strips of purple fur?

Where did that Matador story come from—I can't stop laughing. Weren't there some illustrations to go with it? Including an instructor who is dressed in perfectly fitted but well worn from all the action it has seen, matador pants, gripping the legs to midriff and reaching up to just below the nipples, shirtless and—held up with short suspenders.

Blonde, blue eyed Lars has an excellent physique, developed from years of fighting the bull, so our student will not only benefit from Lars' instruction on how to manipulate cape and sword to satisfaction, but will develop attractive upper-body musculature and strength.

Also, the student must earn the right to wear the grand Suit of Lights, so for practice he will be relegated to used trousers, worn thin, with some gaps in the fabric where it has been stretched too tightly, we only have the one pair, so if they go, well. . . . This will enforce a sense of humility and a desire to progress to the highest level. We have found this method especially effective for a fashionisto student.

Detailed before and after photos of the student's progress, as well as video of the teacher and student in action, will be provided for the student to take home to serve as a tutorial as needed.

Prof. X. P. W.

By xena princess warrior on 09/02/2009 12:00 am

GBA! you have me in hysterics! I am supposed to be winding down to get some sleep, but noooo—I see this mysterious message pop-up. *"Se."* Hmm, much as I like cryptic word puzzles, Scrabble, am a student of mythology and symbolism, it just baffled me. It's familiar, but strange at the same time.

I looked through my library of music on my computer and finally found "Se"—I knew it was here somewhere. It's you Gloria, isn't it? Didn't you say you had been to India, to an ashram, to study Hindu mysticism and sacred music? Try and deny it!
http://www.youtube.com/watch?v=nMsv3MrbDcs

By xena princess warrior on 09/01/2009 11:33 pm

That was me Xena! How did you ever find this one? In a past life, during one of my pilgrimages to Darjeeling. I remember that long ride atop the Indian train transporting me and my followers across the northern plains, the lot of us swooning under the hot sun for days (although I was fortunate to have devoted servant Brad cooling me with enormous fans of ostrich plumes and plying me with soothing sips of water scented with orange blossom). We left a cloud of dust and glitter in our wake. Then, on day three, the land became greener and train began to ascend into the foothills. The air became cooler, and as the grasslands gave way to tall forest trees, we revived and began to sing and then dance for joy. I didn't realize it at the time, but my serenader, Shiva, must have been the reversely reincarnated (preincarnation?) of the love-child of Adam and Anoop. Another Cosmic connection. . . .

By Juneau Underwood on 09/02/2009 7:29 am

I feel like the child being called to bed and answering "but I'm not sleepy! I'm not ready to go to bed. I just want to finish this drawing, then I'll go." Oops—that was me, still is.

"You have to get up for school tomorrow." I heard that!

I do need to rest up for Scott, the massage therapist—he uses holly oil and speaks to me in Latin, all those muscles, nerves, ligaments, bones—all in Latin, as he describes what he massages, what's connected to what, at least that's what I think he's saying.

If he starts to speak French—I'll get fired as a patient.

'night to all

XOXOXO

Xena

By xena princess warrior on 09/02/2009 1:05 am

It's a good thing women can hide their "feelings."

By Juneau Underwood on 09/02/2009 7:32 am

Reveries on Dior Homme

Sisters, I was at the mall earlier this week getting my daughter's laptop refurbished for school, when I happened upon a Sephora store. Some thousands of posts ago, one of the sistergood mentioned buying Dior Homme at Sephora, so with a wildly pounding heart bucking around in my ribcage, I strolled into the store, looking—I hope—nonchalant, feeling like a spy who could be wrestled to the ground at any moment by Federal marshals with muscular arms dressed in chest-hugging T-shirts.

Struggling mightily not to start rampaging through the aisles screaming *"where is it, where is the Homme?"* I cased the joint and determined that the fragrances were displayed against the walls. I examined the closest display but realized from the predominance of pastel colors and curvaceous packaging that I was in the wrong section. I clandestinely navigated to the opposite wall, where the clean lines and predominance of tans and grays signaled that I had found the men's department. Thanks to the alphabetical ordering, I quickly found my quarry. A liquid of palest gold pooled within a cube of clear glass, capped by a shiny gold cylinder the size of his fingertip. I had to know. His. Scent.

I felt even more bashful about skulking there amongst the men's fragrances than when I bought my maiden issue of Rolling Stone. I've always been quite allergic to fragrances, so it would definitely arouse suspicion if I were to tote one of those pellucid cubes home. Where could I possibly hide it? In a secret drawer with the Rolling Stone? All I wanted to do was sniff it. Checking over my shoulder to make sure no one was watching, I seized the precious vial (imagining *he* has its twin on his dresser), raised my trembling index finger to the cool gold knob, and plunged.

A tiny mist blossomed and dissolved in the air before my wondering eyes. An aroma filled my olfactory passages—my god, so sumptuous yet elusive that I could not grasp it. It made me suddenly, intensely hungry. It is a delicious scent but not sweetly cloying, like warm cookies without the calories. I became desperate to put a name to the tantalizing aromas, but my trembling neurons fired in a confused swirl, unable to rest on a name, an association. Baltic amber? Vervain? Vanilla? Cinnamon? It's sexy as hell. It's triggering a dance in my limbic brain, the emotional part, and undoubtedly also the reptilian subcortical provinces that gov-

▪

September 2/09 Allstate Arena in Rosemont, Illinois

▪

Adam announces on Twitter that his new album will come out **November 24**

▪

over **86K** raised by http://www.donorschoose.org . . . !! thank you guys so much! keep it coming! fyi my album drops Nov 24th ! **5:46 AM Sep 2nd** from web

▪

Chicago! Thank you for all the noise! Nice and rowdy! Hell yeah! **8:06 PM Sep 2nd** from Echofon ern the animal appetites. I would want to bury my nose in the armpit of any man wearing it. So this is the scent of Adam. I feel a deep sense of relief. It's not harsh, overpowering or sentimental. Impeccable taste the man has.

I aim the nozzle at my wrist and press again. The cool mist shocks my warm skin. I rub pulse points together, inhale—panic—did I overdo it? Will everyone I walk past know what I had done? There was no hiding it. I flee the store, get lost in the parking garage, eventually find my car and drive home, raising my wrist to sniff every thirty seconds. At home, I keep inhaling surreptitiously. I'm waiting for my husband to crinkle his nose and ask "what's that smell?"

It's only later, in the quiet of night, when my initial excitement has cooled to sustainable levels, that I realize this scent has not provoked the usual physiological rejection. It gives pure, unadulterated pleasure. My husband loves fragrances but had given them up because of my allergies. Perhaps I have stumbled upon a way to bring them back into our lives. Thank you Adam.

Juneau

Juneau Underwood on 09/03/2009 11:24 am

September 4/09 Alliant Energy Center in Madison, Wisconsin

(I speak) . . . the language of LOOVE" http://vodpod.com/watch/1922072-great-dish-of-salt-adam-lambert-answers-fans-questions-l-a

I've never made a sex tape . . . thank goodness. http://adamlambertsite.wordpress.com/2009/07/20/adam-lambert-noooo-i-never-made-a-sex-tape-thank-god/

Wow, that's really flattering. I'm glad I'm causing 'gasms. http://www.youtube.com/watch?v=JbhaPMiz_Xw TV Guide Part 2 Interview

Entitlement is not sexy. Twitter, adamlambert, August 9/09 9:21 PM

I've had my heart broken. I've chased after people and had it not work out. Throughout my entire 20s so far I've wanted to be in love. That's what I want. I think everybody deserves that. And, I've only been in love once, so I'm still looking. http://www.youtube.com/watch?v=JD5C9hXy0MM

I have crushes on women all the time. I find women beautiful. And to be the object of desire to a woman is a great compliment. http://www.accesshollywood.com/adam-lambert-on-coming-out-ive-never-been-in_article_19178

I'm like your boy next door who decided that he wanted to be a rebel one day. So, I'm a nice rebel. http://www.thenation.com/doc/20090615/wypijewski

I'm like a fireman and a fire starter all at the same time. http://www.rollingstone.com/rockdaily/index.php/2009/06/26/kris-allen-adam-lambert-reveal-plans-behind-american-idol-tour/

I'm not trying to preach to anybody. I'm not trying to spread any agenda. I'm just trying to get people up and dancing and feeling good. There's nothing controversial about that. http://media.www.thechaparral.com/media/storage/paper570/news/2009/05/11/Entertainment/Backstage.Pass.American.Idol.Season.8.Part.Two-3752265.shtml#2

But the fire he brought was beautiful, a jewel
Of countless facets, a spectrum infinitely broad,
An aetherial motion they never tired of looking on;
The flame was gorgeous, and they were human,
And they took that gift. . . .

("The Fire Fetched Down" by George Bradley)

Chapter 5 Avatar

Two big events yesterday, dear Glambertinas: I spoke for the first time with Xena on the phone, and I MET ADAM!!

After a summer of anticipation, I finally saw him last night at the Dunkin' Donuts Center in Providence. So much to tell . . . I'll start with my preparations. In the morning, I called Xena and we spoke for the first time. I felt I knew her so intimately from all the wowOwow postings and emails we had exchanged. We meshed instantaneously, like a pair of veteran dance partners, and launched into an energetic conversation that veered from topic to topic with ease and delight. I had to force myself to end the call so that I could get ready for the concert (and not completely neglect my girls before I rode off on my adventures).

I wore the black sequined dress that I bought in Provincetown, the one about which my husband said *"you should get it to wear to the American Idols concert,"* with the girls chorusing their support. My 12-year-old did my hair for me, ironing it into a silky mane, and approved my smoky eyes (we went shopping for new makeup at Sephora last weekend). She sternly advised me not to wear my leopard pumps, but go for the open-toed dark brown foxy sandals, which played off my brown eye shadow and mink crystal necklace. She was right (and they were more comfortable any way.) She took some photos to immortalize the moment (Mom in makeup! In a sparkly dress!). I didn't figure it out at the time, but looking back, I realized I should have found some glittery wings to strap to my shoulders, so that I could look like a dark Artemis, twin to Adam's dark Apollo when he performed with Kiss. . . . The final step in my ritual: Dior Homme applied to my pulse points.

▪

Twitter party
Not coming out tonight . . . gonna rest my throat :) Madison: you guys were amazin! Had me wailin! But I WILL do a Twitter party!!!! 8:30 PM **Sept 4th** from Echofon

RT @SheaGlambert: @ adamlambert Does the Kradam thing bother Katy and Drake? Naw. They've hung out before too! Kradam calls them **KAKE.** 9:26 PM **Sep 4th** from Echofon

RT @hasan657: @ adamlambert have you ever been to australia? Yes. Sydney was Very cool. The poeple there are frendly and so down to earth 8:44 PM **Sept 4th** from

In my bag, I packed my letter, RIFS brochure and Human Rights Campaign pendant to give to Adam, and a letter and Human Rights Campaign bracelet to give to Michael Sarver, to thank him for saying that Adam was the person who had influenced him the most. I also at the last minute decided to print out one of the Robert Sebree photos for Adam to sign. My daughter helped me with that too, although she opined that the photo made Adam look scary. "Why don't you pick one where he's smiling?" she asked, but I said I prefer the sultry, contemplative look.

While my daughter and I were fussing over my hair and makeup in the bathroom, I said "you must think I'm nuts." And she said, in her so-grown-up voice, "Mom, if he makes you feel young again, that's cool." She's my precious little sage. I want to laugh and hug her to pieces. Later, as I was driving her to her friends' house, and I was all giddy, she remarked "Adam Lambert has completely changed you." I laughed and said, "Well, maybe he's changed me back to what I was like when I was young." And I told her about Xena, how Adam had pulled her out of a ten-year depression and how her friends and family were saying she was like she used to be. My little one became very thoughtful and said "I want to be like Adam Lambert when I grow up." I hope what she meant by this was, she wants to be someone who makes other people so happy (and if she could do it by singing and being a star, all the better!).

On the hour drive to Providence, I got on the phone with Xena again. We have so much to say to each other! Our chatter burned through the minutes and too soon, I had to hang up so I could find a place to park. The stars aligned for me; found a free spot on the street half a block from the arena. Then I called her again and we talked some more until my dinner dates arrived. And that's a BIG part of my story too. N, almost alone among my friends in being an American Idol watcher, and her daughter drove down from Boston to meet me. And that morning I called my Providence friend MC, who had said previously that she was going to be in Korea. I thought perhaps she hadn't gone, and I rarely get to see her, so why not? It turned out she had just arrived from Korea that morning. She was exhausted, but said she would try to meet for dinner, but would probably pass on the concert. But a few minutes after I hung up, she called me back and told me that her girlfriend had told her she couldn't miss this. Turns out the girlfriend is a fan! MC was astounded, because "she doesn't even know who Brad Pitt is." I will have to find out whether we have another Glambertina in our midst! I showed MC the RIFS brochure.

▪

September 5/09 Conseco Fieldhouse in Indianapolis, Indiana

▪

Indianapolis! I was born here! Left 26 yrs ago. Good to be back. :) 1:14 PM **Sep 5th** from

▪

Indianapolis was a great crowd! Oh and #signanoopdesai !!! 8:14 PM **Sep 5th** from Echofon

▪

September 6/09 Van Andel Arena in Grand Rapids, Michigan

▪

So please dear readers, why don't you tell **ME** what u think it means. :) 2:58 PM **Sep 6th** Echofon

▪

Happy Labor Day!!!! Take it easy everyone! :) 2:41 PM **Sep 7th** from Echofon

▪

September 8/09 Sovereign Center in Reading Pennsylvania

The Providence crowd was on fire. The arena was sold out, and the audience warmly cheered every performer. Maybe the Idols say "you guys are the best audience we've had" at every venue, but this night it felt true. I won't go into details on everyone's performances. You've all heard it, and it's pretty accurate. Matt G. was a standout. Alison could have been better. She has pipes, but she doesn't yet own the stage. There was an enthusiastic Danny Gokey contingent there, and it was hard to believe that the crowd could get any more worked up than it did during his set, but incredibly, as the stage went dark for the long, pregnant pause before Adam's set, the mounting tension and excitement in the crowd was palpable. And with the first blitz of strobe lights and thunder claps, the entire arena rose as one to its feet with a collective roar. The only people who remained sitting were the ones in wheelchairs (and I almost expected some of them to leap to their feet too). And yes, I felt the temperature rise, a tide of heat fueled by adrenalin and hormones surging through every living body in that arena.

I've had so much information about Adam's performance that it's difficult to describe the experience without feeling like I'm recycling or filtering through other people's accounts. Having watched so many videos and read all the wowOwow accounts, I knew what to expect, what to look for. Adam's voice and dance moves are forever etched in my memory thanks to the wonder of YouTube. It's strange and more than a little disturbing how exposure to media alters our experience of reality.

I decided NOT to bring any recording equipment because I wanted to be truly present. Even so, I found my perceptions and consciousness kept shattering into fragments, as though I had some extreme form of ADD. My left brain was noting that Adam's voice sounded higher than I expected from listening to him on iTunes. And it didn't quite fill up the hall in the way that some had described. That may have been the fault of the sound engineering. And I loathed the echo effect. I wanted to hear his pure voice.

My right brain was hyperventilating, trying to take it all in and finding it impossible. I was about 100 feet from the stage, far enough so I couldn't really see his face. His hair was down over his eyes, like a black stallion's mane. But I didn't want to watch the jumbotrons for close-ups either . . . that felt too much like watching TV. I couldn't bear to do that when the flesh-and-blood Adam was there in front of me. And as everyone who has gone before me has said, as hard as we try to hang on to and savor the moment, it all goes by too fast. As his voice

▪ **September 9/09** Title "Time for Miracles" is revealed

▪ Wachovia Arena in Wilkes-Barre, Pennsylvania

▪ **September 10/09** Arena @ Harbor yard in Bridgeport, Connecticut—Kris does not perform and Adam has a fever

▪ Yuck. Everyones sick. Including me. :(singing's no fun when u feel crappy, but imma do my best tonight Bridgeport. 9:50 **AM Sep 10th** from Echofon

▪ Thanks Bridgeport. Fun show tonight. Fever started after I got offstage. :(I guess I got over-heated. Haha. 2m is get better day. 8:15 **PM Sep 10th** from Echofon

▪ **September 12/09** Cumberland County Civic Center in Portland, Maine soars with the last notes in Let's Dance *(That's OUR song, from our night on the beach Adam)* he sinks through the floor. Is he Persephone being reclaimed by Hades? Or Orpheus bravely descending to bring back his love? The crowd has mind-melded into a seething ocean of unrequited longing, begging him, *Come back!! Come back!!*

MC was my narrator, perfect in the role, completely bowled over by Adam, saying he is like Elvis but better, and that the world of rock has not had someone so talented and with such sex appeal in a long time. She said she had missed out on being able to do the crazy fan stuff when the Beatles were big, so this was a chance to experience it for the first time in her life. Any fatigue she was feeling left her (helped by the fact that she made the wise decision to call in sick the next day), and she insisted on joining me at the barricades in hopes of securing Adam's autograph. We bought a program so I could ask every Idol to sign it (it seemed impolite to not have something for everyone to sign). We left before the finale and secured a front-row spot right at the beginning of the line.

While standing there, I was anxiously juggling my packages, trying not to drop things (I did a couple of times any way), and then remembered that I had a mirror compact in my purse, so I took that out and tucked it into the bodice of my dress. I decided I would ask for Adam's lip print. (Sorry to steal my own idea back from I think it was Priscilla.)

After about 30 minutes, Alison came out (so petite and sweet, wearing huge false eyelashes), then Anoop (he had some stubble—trying a new look?).

Not long after, I felt more than heard the crowd stir, almost as though the earth had shifted, and then there he was: Adam, not more than 15 feet away. He was wearing his baseball cap and a dark gray denim jacket with shredded patches. He still had his stage make-up on, with very dark shadow and liner ringing his eyes. With his heavy foundation, his face looked like a mask—an unearthly, beautiful mask. He didn't speak, to preserve his voice. He worked his silent way down the line, as hundreds of arms thrust their petitions towards him, communicating through gestures and facial movements, like a celestial Mime.

People who asked for photographs or for their shirts to be signed, were politely but gently refused with a shake of the head. Again, my senses were saturated. I tried to soak him in with my gaze, but I was also trying to make sure he got my letter (delivered right into his hands!! Woo hoo!!), signed my photo, and then I handed him the compact and asked for his lip print. He looked at it quizzically, and I said "kiss it!"

Twitter Party

@traceyzat Will there be any ballads/love songs on your album? Of course! 8:57 PM **Sep 12th** from web in reply to traceyzat

@AwesomeGal1967 WHO IS YOUR FAV NFL TEAM? LOL You actually think i watch football? not so much. . . . 8:53 PM **Sep 12th** from web in reply to AwesomeGal1967

@theglamkimmy what r ur thoughts on the tour coming to an end? I'll def miss the rest of the idols. they've become like family. 8:47 PM **Sep 12th** from web in reply to theglamkimmy

@tracie312 What will happen to Skingraft jacket after the tour? Thinkin bout auctioning it off for charity. Should I have it cleaned 1st? :) 8:01 PM **Sep 12th** from web

@shilohsrock: Have you ever thought of doing your make-up more dramatically? umm is that even possible? ha. Its pretty overthetop as it is. 7:55 PM **Sep 12th** from web

@danyglambertgal: whats your fave scented candle? Red Currant by Votivo. The sexiest smell!!!! 7:44 PM **Sep 12th** from web in reply to danyglambertgal

which after a pause (Was he thinking this was totally weird? Was he amused?) he did. I have an indelible memory of his holding the mirror in both hands, looking at it, then glancing up, locking eyes with me, and then kissing it and handing it back. I tried to suppress my squeals of joy, unsuccessfully. I closed the compact and tucked it back into the bodice of my dress, over my heart.

I stayed to wait for the other Idols, asking each to sign the program. The one I was looking for, Michael Sarver, came out last. I gave him his letter. Kris and Lil did not come out. We watched chief of security "Ray" go around making sure everyone was on board, and the first of the tour buses rumbled to life and started to roll out of the parking lot. MC and I walked back to my car, and I dropped her off at her truck and headed for Rte. 95 to take me home. I fired up Goldfrapp's SuperNature on my iPod, blasting over my car speakers, and was soon cruising at 80 mph, hoping to catch up to a bus before it forked off towards Syracuse. I was so high, the hour drive home passed quickly, and despite the late hour, I felt not even a trace of fatigue.

▪

September 13/09 Dunkin Donuts Center in Providence, Rhode Island

▪

September 14/09 War Memorial @ Oncenter in Syracuse, New York

▪

Syracuse: thanks for bein a great audience!! Wish my voice would come back all the way! That flu ran off w my goods.. One more chance!! 7:28 **PM Sep 14th** from Echofon

When I arrived home, I peeked again at the mirror, and hid it in my desk drawer thinking I couldn't possibly tell anyone about it. But this morning, after my husband and the girls had examined the program and photo, I couldn't resist, and I showed them the mirror. There was the mark of Adam's lips embossed on the glass. My girls looked aghast, and DH was shaking his head. My fifteen-year-old announced: "I am now officially embarrassed!" I've been chuckling over that all day!!

Later, I examined the lip print more closely. A pale pucker, like a tattered ghostly blossom with crinkled petals, and in the middle, the distinct mark of two incisors. And also there in the residue from his lips (his lips!), his DNA.

Xena says she is going to ask him to kiss a mirror tonight. And if he balks, she will tell him "You did it for Juneau! You have to do it for me!" Will he be amused or creeped out to realize there exists this secret global society of fans who are communicating like a spy network, following his every move and scheming to make off with bits of his DNA?

Coda: MC wrote to me today: "Adam is amazing. He reminds me (except he's better) of a whole bunch of people: Elvis Presley, Boy George, Freddy Mercury, Elton John. . . . We're seeing the birth of a star."

Earth to Adam, we are afloat in an ocean of love and gratitude.

By Juneau Underwood on 09/15/2009 12:23 am

Thanks Clare! I'm still afloat in an Adam-induced cloud of euphoria (reinforced by the enthusiasm on this site). I don't know if I spent as much time as I would have liked to hone this, but I can feel Xena breathing down my back. She will be posting her Syracuse experience soon, I'm sure, in 4D, full sound and lighting effects!!

By Juneau Underwood on 09/15/2009 7:37 am

I've also just posted on this album a photo of my mirror that Adam kissed. You can see his DNA on it (albeit a little out of focus). I'm convening a conference call with Francis Collins, James Watson and Harold Varmus to look into the feasibility of cloning. They are very excited about the possibility of creating a small army of Adams. This should raise the nation's support level for scientific research. Top secret though. 19 Entertainment would be very unhappy if they found out.

By Juneau Underwood on 09/15/2009 1:23 pm

If we can clone Adam, perhaps we can bottle his essence and solve the aging problem. ***By Juneau Underwood on 09/15/2009 4:54 pm***

Dear Sistergood,

How can a person get any work done with all this chatter!! Setting a poor example for RIFS!! We are SERIOUS women!

Niamh Cat: "You described the experience of listening to him so well, wanting to be fully in the moment but another part of your mind slightly adrift in time; past, present, and future clashing in a whirl."

It was truly an out of body experience.

E.: "Well, Adam has compelled you to be forever 'glammed.'"

Yes, I will need to create a new line item in the household budget for eye makeup primer (never even heard of the stuff before), eyeliner (Urban Decay cream eyeliner), eye shadow (more Urban decay), mascara, eyebrow gloss (never heard of that before either, but I suspect Adam uses it), bronzing powder, concealer—items I never owned before in my life, but my daughters are teaching me. Haven't glued on rhinestones yet, but that's probably somewhere in my future.

"In this digital age we are acutely aware of the rareness of the 'real' thing and the blurring of the lines between the virtual and real world. Hmmm, topic of in-depth future study, I think."

Perhaps technology only makes us more aware of what was always true, that blurring of lines between raw perception and the reality that our minds construct. In fact, there is no such thing as a raw perception of objective reality, except possibly in a newborn. Everything we experience and think is shaped by previous experiences and memory. So what is Real?

"How many times have you taken that treasure out? Don't lie, I bet dozens of times!"

"OMG—thank you for the "KISS " I can almost see the freckles!! Too much to bear in the middle of the afternoon—swoon."

Ki: "To have his lip prints tucked away forever beside your beating heart!!! AND TO HAVE ACTUALLY WATCHED THOSE LIPS DO THEIR SAINTLY WORK!!"

OK, after reading you ladies, I need another fix . . . whew! I realized I need to take a new photo, orienting it in the proper direction. I am so tempted to kiss it . . . if you are swooning from seeing it on the web, imagine what I'm going through having the mirror sitting RIGHT HERE on my desk!! It's sheer torture—in a good way.

I keep seeing him lift the mirror to his lips with something like reverence and planting his kiss there. Those darkened eyes, the hair tumbling over his forehead . . . it's looping in my brain. Now I am going to faint.

BD: "I bet Adam would have rather kissed you than your mirror!!!!!!!"

BD, he's gay!! Oh but I wish . . . I comfort myself thinking he restrained himself because he had a cold and didn't want to give it to me. So considerate. I should have said "Let me share the burdens of your virus. When your throat aches, mine will burn. When you feel a fever coming on, I will spontaneously combust. When your body hurts, I will throw mine under the (tour) bus!!" OK, enough.

E.: "WE MUST do a giant get-together with all the North East Glambertinas before the album comes out . . . keep the good feelings going!"

How about a CD coming out party in NYC over Thanksgiving weekend, to be broadcast on YouTube? Maybe Adam will see it! Maybe he'll come to NY to sing on Saturday Night Live or Letterman.

By Juneau Underwood on 09/15/2009 6:03 pm

I just posted a new photo of THE KISS on Photobucket. Scroll to the leftmost image in the album. This one was a bitch to compose. It's hard to photograph a mirror. A bit too much flash on the photo, but I hope you appreciate the arrangement of objects.

By Juneau Underwood on 09/15/2009 7:04 pm

Thanks Kim! I love the idea of a barely visible kiss tattoo.

By Juneau Underwood on 09/15/2009 9:38 pm

Welcome back my Uber Queen!! I can't wait to hear all about your epic journey to Syracuse. I heard about the handsome men. We will want FULL DETAILS. As for Adam Jurassic Park, am working on it with a brain trust of Nobel laureates. Question: should we tweak the gay gene?

By Juneau Underwood on 09/15/2009 8:45 pm

This is the final night for the American Idols tour.

I'm getting emotional! It's the end of the beginning . . . let's hope Fortune smiles on Adam. The ride is going to be wild, and we'll be there with him. ***By Juneau Underwood on 09/15/2009 9:34 pm***

As G. so profoundly said . . . this really was the "Summer of Love 09"

I remember the summer of 69, I was 22, had just met my "to be" husband, was head over heels in love, life was wonderful, full of possibilities and promise, music filled my every waking hour—from the Beatles

"Abbey Road" to Janis Joplin, CSNY, Joni Mitchell and Jimi Hendrix. It was a heady time and I was excited about my newly realized future

Now, 40 years later . . . lots of water has run under this bridge, in a metaphorical sort of way, and I had another Summer of Love! Who would have ever freaking guessed?? All at the hands of a 27 year old wunderkind! He jumped into my heart somewhere around March and took me for a roller coaster ride I could have NEVER imagined. As Juneau has so beautifully said, he has made me feel young again. I am sitting here literally with tears streaming down my cheeks because I can't find the words to explain what this whole experience has meant. I had such a full heart already, how in the world did Adam Lambert find the room to jump in and make it even bigger?? What was it about HIM? I've watched that damn show every year, ho hum, move on. Why him, why now, in 2009, exactly 40 years later? I can't even remember my life before him can any of you? He is just a cute boy who sings, right, but damn, the joy he has brought to me is like something I said about 300 pages ago. . . . A Phoenix rising from the ashes . . . truly remarkable!!!

I am feeling such a melancholy tonight with these concerts ending, I've had a terrible two weeks but I knew I could just come here and my spirits would be lifted and Adam would just be a YouTube click away. We've had him at our beck'n call for 3 months now and I am spoiled, I don't want to stop.

. . . and you amazing ladies, what are the chances that we would have EVER met in the "real" world!!! Thank you all for this Summer of Love . . . my "fangirl summer," my "giggly girlfriend" summer. What was my life before you, can anyone remember?

Our American Idol Adam is gone, breaking out of the chrysalis, the constraints of the tour bus, ready to open his wings and fly. It's his world to explore now and we wish him well, but I fear we will lose a bit of him. I am thinking of Juneau's kiss imprint . . . like a little son kissing Mommy goodbye as he goes off to school, "I'm a big boy now, watch me run"

. . . and off he goes. Treat him well world, we'll be watching!!

I'll wipe my tears and smile, with pride and love.

By E.—on 09/16/2009 12:09 am

September 15/09 Verizon Wireless Arena in Manchester, New Hampshire

Idols Live tour has officially ended. Thanks to my fellow idols and all the fans for making this summer such an adventure. 4:52 PM **Sep 16th** from Echofon

Dearest E.,

Your words bring tears to my eyes. Adam has taken us on an intoxicating magic carpet ride, and it is wrenching to see it end. I've been thinking about you and the grief you have been working through with the tragic loss of your friend. What an impossible mix of emotions to try to contain in one soul. It's almost too much, and yet isn't it at times like this that we feel most alive? This is what it feels like to watch your child graduate from college or walk down the aisle to get married . . . letting go of your most precious treasure, setting it adrift upon the ocean of the world with your most fervent prayers for fair winds and favorable currents.

"I am sitting here literally with tears streaming down my cheeks because I can't find the words to explain what this whole experience has meant. I had such a full heart already, how in the world did Adam Lambert find the room to jump in and make it even bigger ?? What was it about HIM?"

Why is it that this one young man has stirred up such powerful feelings in us, women of the Baby Boom era? I'm a decade younger than you, so I didn't experience the Summer of Love directly, but its afterglow certainly had a profound effect on my generation. What I said to Xena the other day is that perhaps we feel this way because Adam is the fruition of the hopes and dreams of our youth. The rock stars of our youth were unevolved, mired in male chauvinism and easily corruptible by the lure of drugs, sexual overindulgence and new wealth. And we see this carried to ever greater excess in the Pop mainstream of today. When that kind of excess is combined with mediocrity, it's intolerable. We tuned out.

But then out of this Babylon emerges this wonderful human being, so gifted and yet so normal, decent, and approachable. He connects Earth to the Heavens, and invites us to climb that ladder with him. This is the transformative magic of Art. (And not even High Art, but nonetheless exceptional on its own terms.) But E., Adam is just the catalyst. We are the chemicals, harboring in our Selves the molecular potential to undergo this transformation. We just weren't expecting someone to appear at this moment and drop a match. As I wrote some 6,500 posts back, this is about us. We have lived, matured, learned how to love in ways we couldn't have when we were young and fair. Many of us have navigated the complicated, evolving love inside a marriage and experienced the intense, confusing love for a child, and now these multihued rays of love have converged as though through a reverse prism upon this being, Adam Lambert.

"Our American Idol Adam is gone, breaking out of the chrysalis, the constraints of the tour bus, ready to open his wings and fly. It's his world to explore now and we wish him well, but I fear we will lose a bit of him."

NAH, I DON'T THINK SO!! I believe our community will go on for quite some time, and Adam is going to keep stirring things up, with the help of the canny publicity machine of 19 Entertainment. We have the movie soundtrack and the CD coming. The gossip mills will report Adam-sightings. We will hear and dissect every detail of his love life, his public appearances, his new home (I hope Mommy Lambert and Drake have everything ready for him; he's sick and needs to get better!!), his car, his favorite bands, his fashion sense, his line of cosmetics . . . he will be an industry.

The big question for us is, are we ready to stretch our own wings and fly farther than we have gone before? I surely feel new sources of energy that I didn't know I had, and a desire to satisfy a need that has been buried "way down inside" until Adam came along and gave us every inch of his love. Glambertinas, can we join together in a cause we can all believe in? Should we break out of this cyber chrysalis that we have been enjoying this summer of our love, and launch ourselves into the real world to effect change? How about forming Adam's Army for the Arts and fight to keep the arts in our schools? There are so many worthy causes in the world that need our energy and passion.

Above all, I want to re-envigorate my life with those I love and care most deeply about: my husband, my daughters, the rest of my family, friends and collaborators. If this whole experience means I have come to understand myself better, to be more creative, and to share new facets of myself with those around me, this truly will have been a Summer of Love.

L'Shana Tova (Happy New Year), with all of my love,

Juneau *By Juneau Underwood on 09/16/2009 8:41 am*

Xena Plots Revenge—Adam Talks Her Out of It

"Well Cleo, I actually fainted, dropped to my knees and fell over, mumbling "it can't be over, it can't be over, why not me Lord?, why not me? Was I not as sweet as Cleo, not so generous? What can I offer as sacrifice? I want a piece of what Cleo got"

First Hamilton, then the letter, now Syracuse—Cleo's had three encounters of the closest kind—Xena's had zero—and perhaps the unkindest cut of all Juneau! She's one-for-one.

I had been plotting my revenge—looking for the perpetrator who blocked my access to Adam and someone would have to pay.

Again, the now unbearable rejection by my Magnificent Obsession—for the third and final time. For two nights now, I have cried in my pillow—mascara running—puffy eyes.

This time, someone might have to get hurt and it won't be you Dearest Priscilla—you are the only one who understands, I know, sharing a bed, leaving the maid to find our tear-drenched pillows in the morning. Gloria watched porn, we sobbed. Must be all that chocolate she eats—or maybe it's something about blondes—but how would we know?

This must be Juneau's fault—AGAIN!!—she, the size 2 brown-eyed minx, reeking of Homme, dressed to thrill, all bare legs and shoulders. All she needed was Adam's lips for a split-second, *"just kiss it!"* she said and Adam obeyed.

She gets the kiss, I get the germs. She gets the party, I get the hangover.

When Xena is hugely disappointed, she doesn't get mad, she gets even, so I am polishing my sword and my breastplate. I hope I'm not forced to use them, but if any more people keep him away from me. . . .

Xena did not survive the Persians, the Barbarians, the Huns, the Carpathians, go-go boots, Tiny Tim and foot-wide shoulder pads to die at these barricades—armed police protecting Adam, GBA, Sneaky et sons magnifique lèvres rose. Undignified to die like this.

I have met business leaders, government leaders, military generals, ambassadors, rock stars and royalty, yet this young man, whom I have schemed and travelled distances to meet, has evaded me again! *"Am I not as human as all the others you met outside the wall? If you prick me, do I not bleed?"*

After the show, Adam's personal attaché Raymond des Cheveux Longues, a brilliant Ambassador, emerged from the building to address the Glambertinae in person, sotto voce, to break the news of Adam's serious infirmity—guards at the ready, hands on holsters—should Xena unsheathe her sword, they were armed and dangerous.

Already prepared for battle in her shiny silver breast protector, her eyes—emerald lasers—the look that stopped Napoleon's army on the Russian front—hand on the ornately carved titanium hilt of her sword.

Unintimidated, the brave and diplomatic Ambassador Ray—who had earlier graciously accepted and delivered our gifts—precious as gold, diamonds and sapphires—approached and looked at each of us with such empathy, I broke down—had my well of tears spilled over, he surely would have offered his shirt.

What of Rob, the beautiful sweet boy who came to stand next to me? He said he was one of the "weird kids" who identifies with Adam, with his copy of Rolling Stone at the ready for the signature to save as an amulet, a memento of his brush with a blazing star who cares about this Rob, and all the other Robs.

What did I have to complain about? I stood with four wonderful Glambertinas, with ready arms, tea and sympathy. Rob's friend, a girl, had earlier departed and left him alone to wait—he had no one to console him—I hugged him and I gave him my wishes for a happy life and suggested he drop that unsupportive friend.

This is the Adam effect—is it not? All of us, all sexes and weird kids, no black or white, no young or old, just beauty and light, love and a passion for life. I savoured the moment with my arms around the young man, and he hugged back—perhaps this is the hug I intended for Adam but instead I gave it to the one in the crowd who truly needed it.

I won't forget him, he looked like Adam at the first audition.

High on testosterone from the one man hormone dispenser and just a single warm, sweet and slightly stinging snifter of cognac and Grand Marnier, not in Baccarat, just glass—a silent toast to the Adam I just soaked up and now radiated, just enough to dry my tears for a smidgeon of hedonistic fun.

In the corner, the Wizard has polished his glass ball to show me why Adam had not shown up in Hamilton, but then lured me insistently to Syracuse, to this place, not to take something home, not to get an autograph, a handshake, maybe a photo—but to leave something behind, a hug and a few understanding words for Rob—to amuse and entertain some strangers in a bar, to plant a smack of Stiletto Red lipstick on the cheek of some bemused young man we involved in crazy Glambertina games and, to do a bad imitation of Adam's crotch circles in the bar.

This proved to be just the bait to attract a few bar patrons who then followed us—well not all of us, just the Blonde Bombshell—out the door. The elevator in the Syracuse Renaissance Hotel now sports some graffiti:

"for a good time, call 1-GLA-MBE-RTNA"

From that magical glass ball, Adam spoke to me, his voice now even huskier than when he sang, almost a whisper—while the video played:

"Princess, you have spent another day with some of the finest women you know, you wanted love and friendship, you got it, lots of it. Does it get any better than a day with Glorious, Priscilla, my love Cleo and her friend A?

"I did get the chicken soup you sent, thank you—I shared it with everyone else, they needed it more. I told them my fans sent it and they said to tell you thank you. Especially Gokey who said "you have the best fans Adam." Did you hear him? He sounded gooood.

"Last night, my voice was not in the best shape, so I put everything I had into performing for you on the stage Princess—I saw you on your feet, dancing, smiling, laughing, cheering, waving, singing—some special new moves just for you—and you spotted them! You know the choreography too well Princess. Had to twist up the old steps to keep you on your pedicured toes, with neon cuffs at your wrists. I gave you that extra ooooff!

"You and your girlfriends—the Glambertinas, sorry, Glambertinae—Gloria and Priscilla—made me laugh so hard, I couldn't stop smiling during Starlight! Did you see when I tripped after I spotted it? Who had the idea for the cape? Made my day—please say thanks from the bottom of my heart.

"My loyal, royal love—Cleo—radiant in the front—I blew her a kiss and her friend—a new Glambertina? How many are you now? Are you all friends, like family? Where do you all come from? I know Canada. New Zealand?? I have always wanted to go there.

"And Princess, thanks for looking after Rob—did he look familiar? My young friend needed you more than you needed me that night. Did he hug you back?—I hope so, that was from me.

"How's Scott working out for you? Is he soothing your aches and pains, physically? mentally? Great hands. Thought you'd get along. Does he look familiar? Tall, dark hair, blue eyes? Not my type.

"Princess, please stop crying—I'm only an entertainer, isn't that enough? Besides, entitlement is not sexy."

No, neither is mascara running down the cheek.

—

Trying to console ourselves with cheesecake and retail therapy, Thelma, Louise and I stop at a mall, but it doesn't work very well. I arrive to find the other two seated at a plush, curved banquette, wood topped with mirrors, marble table and in a room reminiscent of a Minoan or Samoan? castle—where are the ostrich feathers?

Oh, no! Lots of great things can happen on a banquette—a leg massage, a break from the dance floor to adjust a dress, champagne, a little handholding and intimate chat in a dark corner where no one can see who is kissing whom. The marble table—it's cooling when you get hot, it holds the strawberries, warm chocolate, whipped cream and candles.

Well, it's too late to change now, so we just have to force ourselves to sit at that table—with our Adam imaginings in our minds. Gloria only adds to my torture, by laying her travelling "outdoor" Adam on each table, wherever we go.

Cheesecake—a staple of the women's comfort food menu and like the cup the knights shared to bond before battle, we order one piece with three forks. But Gloria has a little scheme—she has ordered a Chocolate Silk Tuxedo—and instructions on "how" to eat this. Gloria—the woman never sleeps—I know because I left her watching porn when I fell asleep and when I awoke, she had just returned from the gym!!

So, a *chocolate silk tuxedo*—sounds like men's apparel—do we smear it on our bodies? No, we take our fork and with the tines at a perpendicular angle to the plate, slide it down, stripping off a sliver with four layers and a froth of whipped cream on top. Whipped cream end first, the long, narrow pièce de résistance is inserted into the mouth, leave a little behind on the lips to lick up later, tongue protruding to catch each crumb and convey the sweet, smooth morsel as far as it can go and close your lips around it. It seems to expand to a satisfying fill from cheek to cheek, hold it gently in place to melt, liquefy and trickle down the throat. Repeat until the entire piece has been consumed. The three of us were sliding off the banquette by then.

This mall was a bad choice—first store—leather jackets—black and a red one—reminded me of the one Adam bought me on Rodeo Drive—my shoulders droop in sadness and I hustle out the back door and into a jewelry shop—dripping with silver chains, silver medallions, rhinestone bangles—now I'm screaming! All these reminders of him—this is not helping me!

I'm blindly wandering aimlessly and trip into another store—what's that smell? I'm in Sephora and there's a display of Homme two feet away from me. I turn to the left, black eyeliner and shimmery shadow—to the right—hair products—there's no escape. In a self-defense maneuver, I spray Homme into the air and back out of the store.

Find the others, we escape to the chariot, whip the horses into a frenzy of hooves and feathers and take off for home.

I awoke this morning, Adam's voice singing Whole Lotta Love, vestiges of his performance remain from my dream, wonder what the Glambertinas are talking about on line—do I want to know yet? Too soon to watch the videos from the last performance. I have survived the heartbreak, thanks to that crystal ball, but I'm not quite ready to face anyone yet.

Crystal Ball Adam is too modest—he's more than "just an entertainer" and wish I could still say this—*"a ton of ink has been spilled"* on this site explaining in how many ways, he is more than an entertainer. This is what Glambertinas do—we listen, we watch, we think, we feel, analyze, write and share our thoughts, respond to each other, thoughtfully, sincerely. Sometimes tears, most often laughter so powerful, we are developing our abs into six packs. In my case, a one pack.

More than a rock star;
He's a sex therapist
He's a family counselor
He's a mentor
He's a role model
He's a cheerleader
He's a lover,
He's a big brother
He's a philanthropist
He's a good friend
And he is my Muse—that's enough for me.

—

Almost four months have I spent getting to know him and what have I to show for it?

A happy DH, Xena II, closer to me than ever—posted my concert photo on her Facebook and her friends nominated me "coolest mom," a renewed appreciation for the arts, found my voice to write in ways I never thought possible and while intrinsically satisfying itself, the real benefit is all the friends that I have made through words, all of you. And to anyone who's in the doorway, you too.

Perhaps best of all—"old Xena" is back after a ten-year hiatus. Thank you Adam—I don't need an autograph now—I have happiness back, it's not a stranger anymore. I can laugh till it hurts, chokes and tears me up and at the other end, I can feel melancholy and sadness without fear of falling down the black hole when I do. I feel attractive enough to smile and expect one in return—how great is that!

I can't wait to see the next incarnation of Adam—solo rock star, recording artist, live entertainer, media darling—how will my Muse inspire me when next we meet?

With so much love
Xena
XOXOXOX

By xena princess warrior on 09/17/2009 2:38 am

My love, Xena, you make me laugh and cry harder than any friend I've ever known.

I was afraid you were going to finish me off forever. My family would have wandered into the bathroom to discover my bloodless body half slumped out of the tub, like the Death of Marat, my "Adam and Lips" photo still clenched in my hand, your highly polished and lethal sword blade plunged into my size 2* breast. But by the grace of Adam, your anger and despair turned to compassion, your frustrated lust diverted to those lucky men who didn't know what hit them, your pent-up rage and energy burned off with pelvic gyrations and a generous helping of chocolate.

". . . perhaps this is the hug I intended for Adam but instead I gave it to the one in the crowd who truly needed it."

Now you're going to make me cry, noble Xena!! Wasn't Rob lucky to have met you in his moment of distress? He looked like Adam at the first audition? You should have invited him along to your pajama party . . . especially since his friend ditched him.

"Adam's personal attaché Raymond des Cheveux Longues, a brilliant Ambassador."

Brilliant! I really wish I had gotten his attention in Providence. I wonder if RDCL will be deployed to protect Adam when he embarks on his world tour? You will then be able to use your diplomatic wiles to negotiate a secret audience with the glittering Prince. Indeed, our gallant Raymond is not a bad-looking man, and I wager he is not immune to the substantial charms and persuasive powers of Glambertinas. Let your tears well over next time, and perhaps he will offer more than a shirt to dry them on. There will be a next time!!

Add to the list of what Adam is: He's a Matchmaker.

Look how he brought us all together. How did he know we would fall in love with one another?

I love you with all my heart, Glambertinas,
Juneau

*Size 4, actually. Let's not exaggerate.

By Juneau Underwood on 09/17/2009 10.40 pm

ROCK ICON FINISHING SCHOOL (RIFS) BROCHURE

Founded in 2009 by a concerned community of scholars, the RIFS provides a unique post-graduate education for individuals who have had to sacrifice formal schooling in order to develop their preternatural talents and meteoric careers. Previous experiences of getting no satisfaction will be redressed by our distinguished faculty, noted for its depth and breadth of learning, instructional skills, talent, enthusiasm, attractiveness, confidence and hedonism. A RIFS education will blow open your world and, as a secondary benefit, prepare you to impress the world leaders, business tycoons and Nobel laureates with whom you will soon be mingling at places like Davos and the TED Conference. We accept applicants who demonstrate high intelligence, curiosity, talent and a desire to be sent back for schoolin'.

Our Campus—Paradise and the World
RIFS is headquartered on the breathtaking, secluded north coast of New Zealand. Our facilities are equipped with luxurious guest rooms, a world-class spa, state-of-the-art recording studio, healthful and delicious meals, and a championship golf course. Maximum privacy and security guaranteed. While our campus provides a restful refuge, our curriculum is highly portable. The faculty is available to travel and help students complete their coursework in tandem with a world concert tour.

Academic Course Offerings

▲ ***Architecture*** (Prof. X. P. Warrior). A comprehensive survey of world architecture, including ancient Egyptian, Greek and Roman, medieval to modern European, Indian, southeast Asian, east Asian, and concluding with contemporary masterpieces of Latin American, Oceania and Japan. The unifying theme of this survey will be the Tower: its practical and symbolic significance through the ages. You must commit to extensive field investigation and dramatic impersonations of architectural landmarks.

👁 ***Art History*** (Prof. X. P. Warrior). This year, our celebrated instructor in art history will explore her favourite topic: Eros in Art—A Global Perspective. She takes "around the world" to a new level. This course will include tactile exploration of classical Greek sculpture and very close visual examination of Grecian urns, Mughal and Chinese miniatures, Japanese woodblock prints, and 20th-century masters including Schiele, Picasso and Koons, among others. Silk scarves, gloves and magnifying glasses will be supplied. Please notify professor if you are allergic to latex. Requires field investigation; recommended pairing with Prof. Warrior's survey of architecture course. Work-study opportunity.

Astronomy (Prof. J. Underwood and special guest). Why astronomy kicks astrology's butt. This cosmic survey begins with questions about our own planetary system ("Is there life on Mars?)," Milky Way galaxy and the space-time singularity in which we currently find ourselves. The second half of the course will probe the harmonics of Supermassive Black Holes, the ultraviolet frequencies of Starlight and whether Stardust glitters. We will visit ancient astrological sites (Stonehenge, Teotihuacan, Machu Picchu, Vezelay) and ascend to high elevations (Mauna Kea, Andes, Himalayas) to obtain crystal-clear, varied perspectives on the night sky. Air mattresses and down-filled silk quilts will be provided for optimal prone viewing positions, but participants must supply their own heat. During our stop in England, Prof. Brian May will lecture on interplanetary dust and astronomical themes in British rock music. Travel will be coordinated with Architecture and Art History.

Biology (Prof. J. Underwood and Prof. N. Cat). The science of Life—what could be more profound or beautiful? This course will review the fundamentals of molecular and cell biology—DNA, protein synthesis, intracellular signaling and all that—and move up to systems, organisms and evolution. We will explore the Origin of Symmetry in life forms and species characteristics driven by sexual selection (butterflies, the peacock's tail, exotic male genitalia in the insect world). Significant class time will be devoted to the evolution of homosexuality, a seeming paradox if one considers evolution only in the context of the selfish gene, but which makes perfect sense if one considers Richard Dawkins' concept of the meme, a unit of culture that, like a gene, evolves through selection pressure to give rise to self-propagating systems. We will debate the hypothesis that homosexuals, being free of the burdens of physical procreation, are able to invest resources in creating and propagating memes (e.g., in medicine, science, arts, literature), which have contributed to the overall survival and well being of our species. Extra credit for writing a thesis on why women adore gay men.

Calculus (Profs. C. Lambert and Glorious B.). Calculus is the study of Change. It may refer to any method or system of calculation guided by the symbolic manipulation of expressions. Ability to express and manipulate are prerequisites for this course. Newton used the methods of calculus to solve the problem of planetary motion, the shape of the surface of a rotating fluid, and the motion of a weight sliding on a cycloid. In this class, calculus will be applied to solve the trajectory of a spaceship attempting to dock with a Venutian space station, and whether an extra-dry martini should be stirred or shaken. Extra credit will be given to students who propose and solve an original problem related to the motion of a weight sliding on a cycloid. Double credit for a demonstration of limits in calculus. Is there any penalty for going past the limit? Whips, anyone?

Chemistry (Prof. S.S. Hill). Chemistry is the investigation of the properties of matter, especially changes that occur in a chemical reaction. Professor Hill will focus on the chemistry of love, specifically of pheromones. Emitted by nubile creatures, these mobile molecules waft through space and deeply penetrate their intended receptors, the perfect fit setting off waves of chemical excitement that fire up the brain in a paroxysm of desire. Pheromones are important to a variety of behaviors including mate attraction, territoriality, trail marking, danger alarms, and social recognition and regulation. Laboratory experiments will collect data on Student's response to pheromones. Extra credit: Apply liquid chromatography to the chemical analysis of Dior Homme.

French Poetry (All faculty). Mostly because it would be so awesomely sexy to hear our Student speak French. The syllabus includes the works of Apollinaire, Baudelaire, Breton, Cocteau, Genet, Rimbaud. Class field trip to Le Père Lachaise Cemetery in Paris, with a wine-tasting celebration at the tomb of Jim Morrison. Detours to sex clubs in nearby Pigalle will cost extra. Students must supply own accoutrements (e.g., whips and handcuffs). Entrance fees may be waived if you wear a bejeweled leather jock strap.

Geometry (Prof. C. Lambert and P. Q. O. Desert). A mathematical discipline concerned with questions of size, shape, and relative position of figures and with properties of space. The practical aspects of this relating to the now infamous trio—Adam, GB and Sneaky—are . . . enormous. (Please consult the professor if you need assistance deciphering terminology.)

The Art of Food Selection & Preparation (Prof. EKA). Esthetics and nature come together in the selection and preparation of food to derive the most pleasing and suggestive smell, taste and touch. The humble Avocado (from Aztec "ahuacatl", meaning testicle tree), a fruit that is firm, yet soft and pliable to the touch when at the perfect stage of ripeness. The Asparagus—that thick, woody stalk, tapering towards the tip, a bulbous head, cooked to perfection, warm and yet retaining it's firmness, dripping in the best organic butter. And the ripened Fig, an Italian delicacy engorged with nature's juice, sliced open to reveal. . . . Oh , we will save that for class. The correct opening and eating of the Oyster, sliding its slippery goodness into the mouth of your associé gastronomique. Extra credit class in the application and enjoyment of chocolate body paint, using or course, the finest dark Chuao chocolate with a hint of lavender and dusted with gold glitter.

Food and Physique—Advanced (Profs. EKA and J. Underwood assisted by all faculty). Science and esthetics come together in the art of healthy cuisine and maintaining a gorgeous, love-ready bod. In this course, students will be challenged to take a set of raw ingredients and transform them into a sensuous feast capable of seducing the most hesitant of lovers. Past challenges have included meals comprised entirely of zucchini, another restricted to foods with negative calories, and a meal comprised of gonads. *La pièce de résistance:* Rocky Mountain Oysters Flambé, or "Your Sex Is on Fire." Not for the faint of heart. Biology is a prerequisite. Each class ends with a session of 200 stomach crunches and 100 push-ups, assisted by the professor. Final project: "Fruits avec Chocolat Chaud sur Crème Frappé" dessert or breakfast in bed or midnight snack. Strawberries, raspberries, blueberries and pineapple dipped in luscious warm chocolate and then finished with a gob of whipped cream. Extra credit: Use methods of molecular gastronomy to transubstantiate the above dessert into a form that will float in warm, scented bathwater (no Jacuzzi).

Geology (Prof. N. Spirit). The first half of the course will explore, in intimate detail, the nature and catastrophic effect of Plinian eruptions, characterized by the massive and continuous spewing of large amounts of ejecta into the stratosphere. The second half of the course will focus on plate tectonics, the shifting and grinding of crustal plates and the volcanoes that form along the world's greatest subduction zone, the Pacific's Ring of Fire. Students will master the self-exciting dynamo hypothesis of terrestrial magnetism, which explains the wanderings and occasional reversals of the magnetic poles. Extra credit: Hands-on exploration of caves and other secret passages. Bonus points for finding the magnetic pole.

Health II—Oral Hygiene (Prof. Glorious Beth). In this course, the mouth receives the respect and affection that is its due. We will appreciate the paradox of the lips, sculpted like marble yet yieldingly soft as a breast. We will master the delicate art of parting those lips with fingers, gently and firmly, coaxing them wider apart until we have an unobstructed view of those admirable incisors, cuspids, bi- and otherwise, and molars, forming strong arches to frame that acrobatic muscle, the tongue. We will learn the importance of the salivary glands, conduct a vocal cord health check, test for control of the gag reflex, and learn the correct technique for palpating the Adam's apple. Extra credit for evening seminars devoted to candlelit bouts of oral poetry, including "I crave your mouth, your voice, your hair" (Pablo Neruda), "My mouth hovers across your breasts in the short grey winter afternoon in this bed we are delicate and touch so hot with joy we amaze ourselves to. . . ." (Adrienne Rich), and "I have a fire for you in my mouth, but I have a hundred seals on my tongue" (Rumi).

✡ ***Hebrew, the Language of Love*** (Guest Prof. A. Lambert). The Finishing School espouses the view that students learn by teaching. Hence, in this class, instruction will be in the hands of our student, who has capably proven his ability to seduce audiences in sung Hebrew. Whether he understands what he's saying, who cares? It's enough to make any Jewish mom proud. Professors auditing this course are required to closely study all of Adam's YouTube videos in which he sings in Hebrew. Remember: *L'fum tzara agra* (according to the effort is the reward)!

Calligraphic Arts (Prof. EKA). Starting with Egyptian hieroglyphics and the Eye of Horus, we will broaden your knowledge of symbols. We will trace the evolution of the written word through the Etruscans, Hebrews and Romans. We will hold your hand steady as you learn the stiff, angular lines of the Roman capitol, then introduce the Insular scripts with the curved, rounded lines of Uncial and Carolingian. Next, the world of Black Letter, the fifteenth century's architectural alphabet, may require a visit to the dark scriptorium of a medieval monastery where we will revel in all things Gothic. Here we will explore the proper preparation of the quill pen, the gathering and cutting of the perfect plume to obtain the staff that is hard but pliable. Once we have reached the climax of our task we will finish with a bit of fun applying illumination, gold leaf and rhinestones to our masterpiece.

Manifestation (Professor Glorious Beth A.). In this course for Old Souls, methods of bringing forth goals and dreams will be explored. "If you believe it, then you will see it" is the basic premise explored. What are your dreams and what are you willing to give up to achieve them? Experimentation with visualization, positive energy and energy healing will complement the readings. Required books include Find Your Courage, The Magic of Thinking Big and How to Win Friends and Influence People. Students who have shown practical knowledge of the principles may be exempt from reading, while courageous students go to the head of the class (and sit on the professor's lap). Manifestation of "being in love" and owning a home in LA with hookah den is guaranteed. Advanced standing given to students who express their thanks to the Universe for alignment.

Music—Advanced Opera (Profs. Warrior and EKA, with assistance of student body). This course is restricted to students who have demonstrated extraordinary mastery not only of vocal technique but also of stage movement. Ability to provoke eruptions of Eros an absolute must. Student(s) will observe and comment on Dame Kiri Te Kanawa's ravishing performance of V'Adoro Pupille from Handel's Giulio Cesare. Final project: produce and perform an Aquarian Age adaptation of Bizet's opera, Carmen. The role of the wild gypsy seductress will be performed by the student who satisfies the above-stated prerequisites, without regard to gender. Professors will take turns in the role of the hapless Don José and the bullfighter Escamillo. Taking the Oral Hygiene course concurrently will be beneficial.

♑ ***Music History—Electronic Visionaries*** (Prof. J. Underwood and guest). Impress music producers and smart-ass music journalists with your amazing knowledge of the pioneers of electronic music. The great twentieth-century avant gardist John Cage described music as "an affirmation of life—not an attempt to bring order out of chaos nor to suggest improvements in creation, but simply a way of waking up to the very life we're living." We will discuss whether this concept applies to any current musicians of interest. In addition to Cage, the course will study the contributions of Martenot, Stockhausen, Boulez, Machover, Kraftwerk, Eno, Bowie, Prince, Kate Bush, Peter Gabriel, and others. The technology portion will cover the evolution of the Moog synthesizer, MIDI standard and hyperinstruments. Students will attempt to master the legendary Theremin, an early electronic instrument comprised of a pair of erect rods that sense the air-caresses of the hands, one of which controls oscillations for frequency while the other hand controls the amplitude. Extra credit for performing Whole Lotta Love on Theremin.

♒ ***Physics*** (Prof. J. Underwood). The crown jewel of human scientific achievement (I'm not showing any bias am I?), physics is the analysis of nature in order to understand how the Universe aligns. This course will introduce Maxwell's Demon, from James Clerk Maxwell's *Theory of Heat.* We will cover the fundamental theorem of Emmy Noether, math dominatrix of her day, who proved that the Origin of Symmetry rests in the laws of conservation (of energy, linear momentum and angular momentum). We will debate the possibility of traveling via wormhole among Parallel Universes. We will also devote special evening sessions to pulling the plug on G-String Theory and calculating the mass and angular momentum of an extraterrestrial object sighted recently on YouTube known as the "Glam-Bulge." The class will make a field trip to the Large Hardon (*pardon,* Hadron) Collider, which occupies a vast tunnel excavated beneath the Franco-Swiss border. Mandatory laboratory experiments on vibrations, oscillations, excitations and energy transfer.

Spanish Culture: The Art of Fighting Bull (Prof. Lars Olsen). Successful graduates earn the right to wear an authentic suit of lights—customized, heavily studded, embroidered and embellished, glittery, shiny and rich—and to wield a red silk cape and a sword to threaten, cajole, and capture the rage of a snorting, galloping ton of bull. But first, a careful sharpening, then hand-polishing of the blade, beginning with long, smooth, caressing strokes with rosemary oil and finely finishing with short, tight hand strokes, to bring a lustrous shine to the entire shaft, right to the ornate handle erupting at the top, where the weapon will be grasped for a triumphal wave to a cheering, gasping, swooning throng, throwing flowers, hankies, stockings into the ring. *Olé*. To reach this level of orgasmic perfection takes training. Acolytes will be relegated to used trousers, worn thin, with some gaps in the fabric where it has been stretched too tightly. We only have one pair, so if they go, well. . . . This will enforce a sense of humility and a desire to progress rapidly to the highest level. We have found this method especially effective for a fashionisto student. Detailed before-and-after photos of the student's progress, as well as video of the teacher and student in action, will be provided for the student to take home as a tutorial.

Torah for the 21st Century (Prof. J. Underwood). A historical, literary and spiritual exploration of the Five Books. In Genesis, we will debate the pictorial subtext of a certain Rolling Stone magazine cover with regard to the relationship between Adam, the serpent and the Fruit of the Tree of Knowledge. Other topics for discussion include: Children of Abraham: Can mutual love of a rock star pave the way for peace in the Middle East? The Tower of Babel and the Temptations of Hollywood. Exodus: The Quest for Spiritual Liberation in the Desert. King David: The First Rock Star. Extra credit: Create and celebrate your own Bar Mitzvah service. C'mon, amaze your mom (again).

First Aid (Prof. Isabel R). Cardiopulmonary resuscitation; mandatory class participation. Hours of practice will be devoted to the art of mouth-to-mouth resuscitation and manual stimulation of the cardiac muscle. Students will be instructed in the proper bandaging of minor cuts and bruises, application of salve to whip lashes and first-degree burns, and treating accidental overdoses of testosterone. Extra credit: Develop standard operating procedure in the event that recipient of mouth-to-mouth suffers cardiac arrest as a result.

Physical Culture—Golf (Prof. X. P. Warrior). Our Mistress of Golf instructs: Slow, smooth practice stroke, maybe another, then loosen the shoulders, feet still and supporting, easy grip on the shaft as hands slide to find the sweet spot, draw it back, eye on the ball, then release, move the club head through ball smoothly, cleanly—to roll toward its destiny—follow through, lift head for the final—there it is! The satisfying spiral of the ball as it slides down the sides and mercifully lands on the bottom. This happens eighteen times on the course before we return to the club-house for a post-game analysis of swing, stroke, stance, exploding sand shots, followed by herbal massage, sauna, shower, cocktails on the terrace, and seafood dinner in a private beach-side gazebo lit by a glowing sunset of hot colours.

Our Distinguished Faculty

Headmistress and Founder of RIFS Juneau Underwood is a writer, biomedical entrepreneur, Web innovator, globe-trotting adventuress, Zen/Torah mistress, garden designer, gastronome extraordinaire and former gay club diva. Professor Underwood infuses her instructing with the three S's—Science, Sensuality and Spirituality. A descendant of samurai, Prof. Underwood was reared in upstate New York and schooled in Switzerland, Tokyo, and Harvard, where she concentrated in physics and disco dancing. She has authored a renowned guidebook to Japan, written for national magazines and documentary films, and is a member of the Brain Trust. Favorite pastimes include sword-play, the Japanese tea ceremony, jamming with her band and riding stallions. Prof. Underwood regularly commutes to a Parallel Universe as suburban wife and mother.

Dr. Glorious Beth A., AKA the blonde bombshell, brings 25 years of experience in the field of oral health and dentistry to her professorship. Due to her extraordinary skills, compassion and success she has been able to limit her practice to the treatment of young adults with perfect smiles who were raised by dental hygienists and/or dentists. Occasional rants with the Universe have brought forth happiness, a world class Rock Star/Sex God and a supportive sistergood. Her love of Calculus and especially "no limits" have earned her associate status in the Calculus course taught in conjunction with Prof. Christine Lambert. This pairing assures very powerful three-ways with an appropriate student. Sexy is sexy and so is Math!! She volunteers her time in the area of crisis and grief counseling and is well versed in helping to navigate the pitfalls of sudden fame and wealth. Glorious Beth holds no grudges even when accused of being an imposter or of not sharing the Rock God.

Professor Niamh S. Cat is uniquely suited for the teaching of biology, being both a small black domestic feline and a tall human female with a background in biology and psychology. Her dual nature gives her a unique perspective in understanding the natural world and our connections to it. Prof. Cat is a gifted jewelry designer who draws her inspiration from the forms of nature.

Professor EKA—E. Kate Adam, Master of the Quill. Bachelor of Education, Bachelor & Masters of Art, specializing in charcoal & pastel portraits of young handsome androgynous singers & musicians. Master Calligrapher and teacher of Lettering Arts and Design. Amateur Astronomer and Stargazer. Chef specializing in the locavore, back-to-the-farm movement and follower of Michael Pollan. Book diva and moderator of a 28-year Literature & Libation Club, Jazz aficionado and firm believer in the total sensuous moment combining the right food, drink, music, atmosphere, and design.

Professor SweetSue Hill has a graduate degree in Chemistry and has been involved for many years in developing drugs to treat various eye diseases. Her interest in the chemistry of pheromones has led to her becoming a highly sought-after consultant to the global fragrance industry. Although this cannot be confirmed officially, it is rumored that Professor Hill was involved in cracking the code for the formulations for Coca Cola and Dior Homme.

Professor Christine Lambert is perfectly suited to her position at the Rock Icon Finishing School. As Professor of Calculus, she has a Bachelor of Science with a major in Mathematics, and a Diploma in Teaching. She has taught both at High School and University level. Currently she teaches internal and extramural students, so is able to conduct her teaching from New Zealand if necessary. She also has MUCH experience teaching one on one, which is by far her most preferred position! She has also recently gained her Professorship in Cryptography, having no formal training in this field but rather an innate ability to understand puzzles and codes of all descriptions.

Professor Lars Olsen, master matador. Blond, blue-eyed Lars has an excellent physique, developed from years of fighting the bull, so our student will not only benefit from Lars' instruction on how to manipulate cape and sword to satisfaction, but will also will be able to develop attractive upper-body musculature and strength. Lars is fully certified in CPR and Minor Surgery, and is internationally renowned for his skill in hand-sewing the famous Suit of Lights. He enjoys romantic poetry, molecular cuisine, and occasionally steps in to assist the Advanced Opera class in the role of Escamillo. He is also an enthusiastic participant in the gastronomic courses, volunteering the use of his firm abdominals as a serving platter for bivalves and hot dripping wax.

Professor Northern Spirit hails from northern latitudes where she obtained two degrees in the geological sciences. She has extensive hands-on experience teaching undergraduate laboratory classes and has participated in numerous field trips to volcanic hotspots along the Pacific's Ring of Fire, transform fault zones in California, overthrust regions in Canada's Rocky Mountains, and other exotic locales in the world. Her most popular field trips are those related to the study of terroir in Napa and Sonoma valleys. Away from the classroom Professor Spirit spends quiet time exploring the wonders and intricacies of origami architecture, gently coaxing delicate and hidden forms from Japanese paper. But it is billiards that most captures the fascination of Professor Spirit, allowing her to apply her fine knowledge of Newtonian physics to the interaction of hard spherical bodies on a frictional surface. Endless hours are spent studying the effects of a striking cue shaft against the cue ball and the interplay of the squirt angle with the amount of juice.

Professor Priscilla Queen of the Desert is qualified to teach Business, Accounting, Computer Science, Mathematics, and Nail Art. She attended schools in South America, Europe, and North America and speaks Spanish, Italian, and French fluently. Her passion for numbers and patterns led her to study Computer Science at MIT where she also mastered several computer languages. She pursued a successful career in the computer industry before going into education. Her previous Professorship was at "Hogwarts School of Witchcraft and Wizardry," where she taught Arithmacy to many unruly students. Professor Desert provides across-the-board support to faculty and students on all matters related to laptops, operating systems, filters (or lack thereof), hacker counterattacks, information security, identity theft and telekinesis. Prof. Desert's love of music, food, and laughter together with her multilingual abilities make her a perfect fit at RIFS.

Professor Xena Princess Warrior, a descendant of ancient Macedonian fighters, was a student of Socrates, her philosophical mentor and teacher, the original rational thinker, the father of logic. Two important lessons from the Great Philosopher: *True wisdom comes to each of us when we realize how little we understand about life, ourselves, and the world around us* and *An honest man is always a child.* The Professor considers herself a "seeker of truth and beauty" in all aspects of life and culture. During the twentieth century, Prof. Warrior completed a Bachelor of Fine Arts degree and her studies included Ancient Egyptian, Greek, Roman, Mediaeval and Renaissance art and architecture, African and Modern Art, photography, film, political science, sociology and anthropology, for which she wrote a landmark paper on Macedonian Witchcraft and Magic.

Xena Princess Warrior and Juneau Underwood are pseudonyms, and are not to be confused with any person or character, living or dead, animated, anime, chibi, shouju, shoujen, mythological, real or not.

ISBN: 978-0-615-33169-0

Photographic credits
Cover: photograph by Cleopatra of Egypt
Page 2: photograph by Juneau Underwood; background photograph
by Robert Sebree
Page 62: photograph by Xena II
All others by Cleopatra of Egypt

Designed by Jeff Wincapaw
Typeset by Brynn Warriner
Published by BadBoys Garage, Seattle
www.adamlambertbook.com
Printed and bound in Michigan by Thomson-Shore, Inc.